Prime Minister Priti ...

... and other things that never happened

PRIME MINISTER PRITI ...

... AND OTHER THINGS THAT NEVER HAPPENED

edited by
DUNCAN BRACK
and
IAIN DALE

Biteback Publishing

First published in Great Britain in 2021 by
Biteback Publishing Ltd, London

Selection and editorial apparatus copyright © Duncan Brack and Iain Dale 2021.
Copyright in the individual essays resides with the named authors.

Duncan Brack and Iain Dale have asserted their rights under the Copyright, Designs and
Patents Act 1988 to be identified as the editors of this work.

ISBN 978-1-78590-676-3

10 9 8 7 6 5 4 3 2 1

A CIP catalogue record for this book is available from the British Library.

Set in Bembo and Optima

Printed and bound in Great Britain by
CPI Group (UK) Ltd, Croydon CR0 4YY

MIX
Paper from
responsible sources
FSC® C020471

Contents

Introduction

Duncan Brack and Iain Dale

Here in this book, you will find twenty-three examinations of things that never happened, from Randolph Churchill not dying in 1895 to Franklin D. Roosevelt succumbing to polio in 1921, to Ireland joining the Allies in the Second World War, to Margaret Thatcher winning the Conservative leadership election in 1990, to Tony Blair introducing proportional representation, to no fewer than four different outcomes of the Brexit process. And you will also find one chapter on something that hasn't happened yet…

This is the fifth in the series of books of political counterfactuals one or both of us has produced, the others being *Prime Minister Portillo and Other Things That Never Happened* (2003), *President Gore and Other Things That Never Happened* (2007), *Prime Minister Boris and Other Things That Never Happened* (2011) and *Prime Minister Corbyn and Other Things That Never Happened* (2016). As we have observed before, 'serious' historians have tended to look down their noses at the study of counterfactuals; E. H. Carr, for example, dismissed them as an idle 'parlour game'. Nevertheless, they have a distinguished record. Winston Churchill contributed a chapter (on what if Robert E. Lee had won the battle of Gettysburg) to a 1931 collection called *If It Had Happened Otherwise*, and other counterfactual analyses have been published by historians and sociologists such as Robert Fogel, Geoffrey Hawthorn and Niall Ferguson. Indeed, counterfactual history has become increasingly popular, featuring in many books, novels, documentaries and films in recent years.

We believe that counterfactual history has value in the study of the past in several different sets of circumstances. It can reinforce the analysis of what actually happened by identifying the points at which things could have happened differently and the relevance at each of these key points of both individual choices and broader political and socio-economic forces. It can help in analysing the causes underlying particular events; arguably, as Fogel pointed out, in making claims for causes of any kind, historians are always implicitly considering and discarding potential counterfactuals.

To succeed in these aims, the counterfactuals must be plausible. Start to change one decision or happening or event in history, and it can be difficult to justify not changing others; there have to be boundaries, and the more rigorously these are policed, the more convincing – and the more analytically useful – the results become. So, the chapters in this book are limited to occasions when very little needed to have happened differently for the ultimate outcome to have been very different – and, mostly, limited to changed individual choices or actions, or changes in the individuals concerned, set against unchanged economic and social backgrounds.

Accordingly, no fewer than five chapters consider what would have happened had key figures in history died before their time – hardly a strain on the imagination. In reality, Clement Attlee was seriously injured in the First World War; had he not survived, would his most likely replacement, Herbert Morrison, have proved as effective – or perhaps more effective – in bringing the Labour Party to power in 1945? Franklin D. Roosevelt almost died of polio in 1921; with a less interventionist and less internationalist President in the White House in the 1930s and '40s, there could have been no New Deal and no hope of US support for Britain in wartime. And if Donald Trump had died of Covid-19, as he possibly almost did, Mike Pence could easily have proved a far more effective candidate in the 2020 election; it would have been difficult, after all, for him to have been worse.

Two chapters deal with counterfactuals in Irish history. If Éamon de Valera had died in a car crash in 1942, would his successors have been so determined to keep Ireland out of the war? Then if the country had joined the Allies and benefited from US support after 1945, it could have had a profound impact not only on the development of the Irish economy but also on the politics of the entire island. And looking further back, if the British authorities had not treated the losers in the Easter Rising so harshly, could Ireland have avoided the deaths and bitterness of the war of independence and the civil war?

Two chapters consider what could have happened had individuals lived rather than died. If Randolph Churchill had not died in 1895, it is reasonable to assume that he could have fulfilled his early promise as a successful and popular Conservative politician, with potentially profound consequences for the political career – or absence of one – of his neglected son Winston. And imagine what could have happened had John Lennon survived his shooting in 1980; could he have decided to use his global fame to press for gun control and eventually to enter British politics?

Other chapters deal with the consequences of key decisions taken differently. If Tony Blair had decided to implement the report of the commission on voting systems that he had himself established, it would have had profound consequences for British politics, not least in making it far more likely for parties to split on key questions of policy – something that could easily have happened in the years that followed. If the Liberal-supporting *News Chronicle* had not shut in 1960, it could have helped sustain the Liberal Party and ensured that its successive waves of revival in the 1960s, '70s and '80s did not eventually run into the sand. One of our favourite chapters traces how different the recent history of the Labour Party and the EU referendum campaign could have been if only Eric Joyce MP had decided not to have one more drink on the night of 22 February 2012...

This being a book of political counterfactuals, of course some chapters look at different outcomes of elections – though we have covered so many of them in the earlier books that we include only a couple here. One considers what would have happened had the independent candidate, Ross Perot, withdrawn from the 1992 US presidential election; in reality, he did, then he changed his mind and re-entered, eventually winning 19 per cent of the popular vote – a record for a third-party candidate. The other looks at what might have happened had Boris Johnson won the 2019 election with only a small majority; how would he then have coped with the divisions within his party over his handling of the pandemic?

Given that party leadership elections now seem to occur with ever-increasing frequency, several chapters consider what could have happened had different leaders been in place at particular times. So, one chapter has Nick Clegg resigning as Liberal Democrat leader and Deputy Prime Minister in 2014, after his party's disastrous showing in the Euro elections; could Vince Cable, his obvious successor, have rescued the Lib Dems from catastrophe in 2015? Another has John McDonnell, instead of Jeremy Corbyn, fighting and winning the Labour leadership election in 2015 and then proving to be a far more effective leader than Corbyn (no great leap of faith required there), with profound consequences for the course of British politics over the following six years.

The authors of other chapters are less convinced that a party changing its leader would have led to very different outcomes – which helps to underline the value of counterfactuals, pointing us to broader underlying factors that did make a difference. While it seems wholly plausible that Margaret Thatcher, given a more effective campaign manager, could have won the 1990 Conservative leadership election, would it have stopped the disintegration of the Tory government that followed in reality? And if Jeremy Corbyn had stood down in late 2017, it is difficult to see how Labour could have done anything else but lose in 2019.

Two chapters look ahead to the implications of different leaders in the future. How would Rebecca Long-Bailey, our chapter's winner of the Labour leadership contest in April 2020, have fared in the 2023 election? And what is Priti Patel's election-winning strategy as the successor to Boris Johnson?

Given recent history, naturally several chapters look at different outcomes of referendums. Not just Brexit; one chapter considers what would have happened if Scotland had voted 'Yes' to an assembly in 1979 – as the Scots did, only to be foiled by the '40 per cent rule'. Of course, most of our chapters on this theme look at Brexit; hardly surprising, given the narrowness of the vote and the many possibilities that were to be considered and discarded over the following three years – after all, very few people in 2015 would have predicted the situation we now find ourselves in. Some of the chapters mentioned above discuss the possible consequences of different Labour leaders for the outcomes of the referendum, while one further chapter looks at what would have happened if Britain had voted Remain in 2016. It seems unlikely that this would have ended the debate over Britain's relationship with the EU. No fewer than three chapters consider the possibility of Theresa May finally getting her Brexit deal through Parliament, though each under different circumstances and with very different outcomes, not just for the UK and the EU but for the government's handling of the coronavirus pandemic – where, let's face it, there are so many possible different choices the government could have made that one could write a book just on that.

All of these counterfactual scenarios are, to different degrees, plausible. As in the previous four books, the authors have adopted a variety of approaches, including scholarly analyses of the possibilities and causalities of different outcomes, and fictional accounts of alternate political histories – and sometimes both. And quite apart from their analytical value, helping us to think about political history and what determines how politicians act, these chapters have great entertainment value; at some of them, you will laugh out loud.

If any reader has ideas for topics, or authors, for a potential further volume, we would be very pleased to hear them; send us your ideas via email at dbrack@dbrack.org.uk and/or iain@iaindale.com.

We hope you are stimulated, provoked and entertained by *Prime Minister Priti and Other Things That Never Happened* – but could have.

~

Acknowledgements
Our warmest thanks go to John Barnes, Richard Briand, Philip Cowley, Mark Egan, Peter Golds, Tim Gordon, Dianne Hayter, Tony Little, Tony McNulty, York Membery, Christian Moon, Ted Morris, Mark Pack, Greg Rosen, Neil Stockley, Stuart Thomson and Christian Walker for reviewing draft chapters; to James Stephens and Lucy Stewardson, of Biteback, for their constant encouragement and support; and, above all, to all the chapter authors, for producing high-quality work to a demanding timetable.

DUNCAN BRACK AND IAIN DALE
June 2021

Authors

Josh Bartholomew is a politics student with a passion for political history from Gladstone to Johnson.

David Bean returns to the series following his entry in 2011's *Prime Minister Boris*, which considered a Hillary Clinton victory in the 2008 Democratic Party primaries. He has spent most of the intervening years with the Policy Research Unit at the House of Commons.

Francis Beckett is a journalist, author and playwright. His nineteen books include *Clem Attlee – Labour's Great Reformer* and *Jeremy Corbyn and the Strange Rebirth of Labour England*. His play about Clement Attlee, *A Modest Little Man*, played to packed houses at two London theatres.

David Boyle is a former parliamentary candidate and editor of the weekly *Liberal Democrat News*. He is co-director of the think tank New Weather and policy director of Radix UK. He is the author of a number of books, most recently *Tickbox* and the *Caractacus* trilogy of novels.

Duncan Brack has co-edited all four previous volumes of political counterfactuals published by Politico's and Biteback. He is editor of the *Journal of Liberal History*, a Liberal Democrat activist and a former special adviser to Chris Huhne in the coalition government. Despite his appearance in Chapter 13 of this book, he was not one of its authors.

Richard Brooks and **Amanda Chetwynd-Cowieson** co-founded the youth and student wing of the People's Vote campaign, 'For our Future's Sake', together in 2018. They share many things in common: an unexplainable love of the areas they are from (Dover and Cornwall, respectively), an enduring membership of the Labour Party and now a chapter in this book.

Tom Chidwick is a freelance writer and contemporary historian who writes a fortnightly column for *Scottish Review*. Before the Covid-19 pandemic, he divided his time between London and Edinburgh and is currently writing a history of the 1979 referendum on the creation of a Scottish Assembly.

David Cobley has held senior leadership positions in insurance companies and regulators around Europe. This is his first published counterfactual, combining his professional skills in understanding different scenarios with his long-standing interest in politics. Born in Wiltshire, David lives in Belgium with his partner, Viviane, and his son, Joshua.

Philip Cowley is professor of politics at Queen Mary University of London. When he pitched the idea for his chapter, he thought it was a what-if that would have made a material difference to what happened subsequently; then he wrote it and realised he was wrong, and that it probably wouldn't have done.

Iain Dale is the presenter of the *Evening* show on LBC Radio. He also presents six podcasts, including *For the Many* and *Iain Dale All Talk*. He is the author of *Why Can't We All Just Get Along: Shout Less, Listen More* and the editor of *The Prime Ministers*. He lives in Tunbridge Wells and Norfolk.

Dr Julian Huppert was MP for Cambridge and now runs an interdisciplinary centre at Jesus College, Cambridge. He is deputy chair of NHS Cambridgeshire and Peterborough CCG and a director of the Joseph Rowntree Reform Trust and advises tech companies on ethics. He is an aspiring mountaineer.

Noah Keate is a politics student at the University of Warwick. He has written for an extensive number of student publications, including *The Boar*, *Perspectives*, *Cobalt* magazine, The Meridian Magazine and Backbench. Originally from Cambridge, he enjoys reading, writing, drinking tea, exploring cities, watching films and listening to *The Archers*.

Tom King is a political writer and consultant, at present advising investors on how governments shape markets. In 2020, he published *The Generous Society*, a new liberal vision. He likes many things but especially music, wine and food that's too good to cook at home.

Graham Kirby has written for *Independent Voices*, *The Advocate* and *Vice*, among others. His fiction has appeared in *Storgy* and Bandit Fiction. He has also worked with the Iris Project to adapt Greek drama for state-school audiences. Most prestigiously, this is his third contribution to Biteback's what-if series.

Simon Marks is the president and chief correspondent of broadcast news agency Feature Story News. An Emmy award-winning Washington correspondent, he reports events across the USA for broadcast networks worldwide. In the UK, you can hear his coverage every day on LBC and Classic FM.

Ben Monro–Davies is an executive producer with Sky News, having previously worked in senior positions at the BBC and ITN. He's also the host of the *Big Ben History Podcast*, where you can hear interviews with all the people who were in the Cabinet room when Margaret Thatcher resigned as Prime Minister in 1990.

Nathan Morley lives in Derby and is a keen student of British politics. He works in a family holiday rentals business, having previously lived in Lanzarote in the Canary Islands.

Michael Mowlem grew up in Finchley, north London, with an early interest in both music and politics. A first cousin presented a US radio show about the Beatles in 1978; the recording he sent over to London became Michael's first introduction to the band. The sitting MP in Finchley was Margaret Thatcher, inspiring in Michael a passion for politics. He has had a 32-year career in finance, principally in private equity investing, and he lives in London with his wife and two daughters.

Jason O'Mahony lives in Dublin and has been a columnist for MarketWatch, *The Times* (Ireland edition), *Sunday Business Post* and *The Dubliner*. He currently writes for the *Irish Independent*. He was at one time a Progressive Democrat candidate and has campaigned in various Irish elections and referendums, occasionally on the winning side. He works in the Irish construction industry for a leading builders' providers chain. He tweets at @jasonomahony.

Paul Richards is a writer. He has written many political books, articles and pamphlets, including *How to Be a Spin Doctor* and *Tony Blair In His Own Words*. He has contributed to two previous collections of counterfactual essays: *Prime Minister Portillo* and *Prime Minister Corbyn*. He is a former chair of the Fabian Society, and he served as a special adviser under the Labour government. Paul was a Labour candidate at the 1997 and 2001 general elections.

Teddy Robertson is an amateur historian and political analyst.

Andrew Stone is head of history at Saint Francis Xavier Sixth Form College and secretary of Wandsworth National Education Union. He has contributed to a range of publications, including Politics Review Online, rs21 and *Critique*. In his spare time, he likes to bemoan his lack of spare time on social media.

Dr Robert Waller is a former fellow and lecturer at Magdalen, Trinity and Wadham Colleges, Oxford. He is currently a teacher of history and politics and the author of eight editions of *The Almanac of British Politics* and of the Ramsay MacDonald chapter in Iain Dale's *The Prime Ministers*.

David Walsh is a solicitor working in the London insurance market. He has a keen interest in British political history.

Chapter 1

What if Randolph Churchill had not died in 1895?

David Walsh

'What brings men to the front is much more opportunity than character.'

Randolph Churchill, 5 November 1889[1]

A carriage swept up the Mall towards Buckingham Palace, leaving a welcome breeze in its wake. The passengers, a man in his early fifties and his attractive younger wife, were in high spirits despite the oppressive heat. For him, this July day marked a moment of triumph after a turbulent career; for her, there was the quiet satisfaction of knowing that she had been right to admonish her husband's lack of ambition when, nearly thirty years earlier, she had written to her then fiancé to say: 'I would like you to be as ambitious as you are clever, and I am sure you would accomplish great things.'[2] Now, as the carriage pulled into the courtyard within the Palace, he, Lord Randolph Churchill, was moments away from accepting from the King his appointment as Prime Minister.

Had they the time to pause for thought, it would surely not have escaped their attention just how ludicrous the situation was. Randolph was about to kiss hands with King Edward VII, a man whom he had once tried unsuccessfully to blackmail over a scandal involving Randolph's elder brother, the Marquess of Blandford, some compromising love letters and a married former mistress of the then Prince of Wales.

Randolph's wife's past indiscretions were no less embarrassing. Jennie Churchill, daughter of a New York entrepreneur and one of the beauties of her time, had once been Edward's mistress. Churchill's son, Winston, aged just twenty-seven but already an MP and whom Jennie had very deliberately not invited to the Palace, had asked her that morning: 'Will he [the King] continue to be friendly to you?' Fortunately, the King was an amiable man, and he and Randolph had been on good terms for some years (the latter remaining apparently unaware of his cuckold status). It helped Randolph's case in the King's eyes that the late Queen Victoria, with whom her son had rarely agreed, had thought Randolph a 'catastrophe'.[3]

With the formalities complete, Randolph and Jennie returned to their carriage for the short journey down Birdcage Walk, up Horse Guards Road and into Downing Street. There, staff worked frantically to remove the last possessions of Randolph's predecessor, Lord Salisbury. Officials ran hither and thither, and young men (and some old ones) with hopes of advancement loitered in the corridors. Arthur Balfour, nephew of Lord Salisbury and Randolph's erstwhile rival for the premiership, was nowhere to be seen.

Winston waited in the doorway to No. 10, smiling as he savoured the moment of his father's triumph. However, his joy was short-lived. 'I see you continue to lead an idle, useless and unprofitable life, as ever,' Randolph said as he walked past Winston into the cool shade within the building. Looking for some support from his mother, Winston found none. 'You really mustn't upset your father so, Winston. I simply don't have time for this right now.'[4]

~

Some of the above is true. Randolph Churchill really did try to blackmail the future King Edward VII, and Jennie Churchill did have an affair with Edward. She even had a discreet lift installed in her London apartment to take her obese lover from street level to her bedroom (although this was after Randolph had died). It is also well documented that Randolph and Jennie's parenting of Winston was anything but warm and nurturing. In fact, during Winston's school days, he wrote to his parents seventy-six times; they to him only six times, and their letters were littered with remonstrations. It did not stop him trying to win his parents' affection for the rest of their lives.

What is not true is Randolph Churchill's ascendancy to Prime Minister in 1902. It was in fact Arthur Balfour, nephew of Lord [Robert] Salisbury, who acceded to the premiership in that year, hence the idiom for nepotism 'Bob's your uncle' – though singling out Salisbury for a charge of nepotism seems somewhat harsh; of the nineteen Prime Ministers who preceded Balfour, only two did not pave the way for at least one younger brother, son, stepson or nephew to enter the House of Commons. William Grenville and Pitt the Younger were the two exceptions, and they were both the sons of Prime Ministers themselves.

Randolph's rise was, to his credit, largely the product of his own efforts (although being the second son of the 7th Duke of Marlborough no doubt helped). His attainment of the premiership was a realistic possibility had the uncertain malady which afflicted him not manifested itself in 1885 and killed him a decade later.

What would have happened to both Randolph and Winston if the former had lived a longer, healthier life? Could he have risen to be Prime Minister as his supporters (and even some of his detractors) thought possible? If he had become Prime Minister, how would his premiership have differed from the leader he would have supplanted? And, perhaps most significantly for the future of the United Kingdom, what would the impact have been on a young Winston Churchill in the nascent stages of his political career?

~

In 1886, Randolph's star was in the ascendant. In Salisbury's first administration he had been India Secretary, and by August of '86, he was Leader of the House of Commons. At thirty-seven, he was to be the youngest Chancellor of the Exchequer in over eighty years. A dazzling politician, he was pragmatic to the point of opportunism, an electrifying speaker both inside and outside the Commons and a manipulator of the media *par excellence*. Contemporaries said of him that if only he could constrain his erratic behaviour and tendency towards recklessness, the keys to 10 Downing Street were his for the taking.

In many ways, Randolph was the typical scion of the nineteenth-century English aristocracy. His background was ducal but, relative to other members of his class, impoverished. He attended Eton but appears to have left his teachers with little faith in his academic potential. Fox-hunting rather than studying occupied his time at Oxford. Appalling rudeness, aggression and rebelliousness were the character traits that marked him out; in 1870 he was fined for verbally abusing and physically assaulting a policeman. Against the better judgement of the university and his father, he tried (unsuccessfully) to sue the policeman for perjury.

After a year of travelling in Europe (about which little is known – perhaps for the best), he returned to Blenheim Palace, his ancestral home. In 1874, he married Jennie Jerome, the twenty-year-old daughter of a prominent but impecunious New York entrepreneur. That same year, he entered the House of Commons as MP for Woodstock, effectively his family's borough.

His early years in Westminster were unremarkable; he was an ultra-Tory, a reactionary, and showed none of the (relatively) reforming credentials that became apparent later in his career. Even Disraeli, perhaps the greatest Conservative Prime Minister of the second half of the nineteenth century and someone whom Randolph would later lionise, was denounced as insufficiently conservative for 'wishing to toady to the radicals'. By the early 1880s, however, Randolph's outlook had changed. In part, this can be explained by a period of serious ill health in 1882, after which there was a marked change in tempo: an escalation in activity and a growing impatience with life on the back benches.

Randolph had also fallen under the influence of two mentors. The first was Sir Charles Dilke, a rising radical star and someone whose career would burn nearly as brightly – and burn out nearly as quickly – as Randolph's own. The latter had described Dilke to his wife as 'a horrible extreme radical', but they would later form a lasting friendship.[5] Crucially, Dilke was an independently minded politician capable of criticising both the Liberal and Conservative front benches. Randolph would develop an affinity for independent political company like him.

The second influence over Randolph at this time was Gerald FitzGibbon, a Dubliner and long-standing Lord Justice of the Court of Appeal in Ireland. Randolph had travelled with his father to Dublin after the 7th Duke was appointed Lord Lieutenant of Ireland in 1876. There, Randolph fell in with a group of Dublin professionals, the most prominent of whom was FitzGibbon. These men were undeniably Unionists who were committed to the Protestant interest in Ireland, but they were also flexible and realistic in their willingness to work for the benefit of Irish Catholics. By 1877, Randolph was making speeches which attacked the government's policy of neglect towards Ireland. He believed that conciliatory legislation would make sense of the Act of Union and avoid the need for Irish Home Rule. To that end, Randolph supported measures for the expansion of Catholic intermediate and tertiary education. Too often he would find himself up against the 'dead weight of unimaginative Tories',[6] but he nevertheless used his experience in Ireland to establish a reputation in Westminster as an 'Irish expert'.

In the wake of the Conservatives' 1880 general election defeat, Randolph became allies with a small cadre of like-minded MPs who were discontented with the ailing leadership of Lord Beaconsfield (the title Disraeli had taken in 1876). They would become known as the Fourth Party: an opposition within the opposition. While the Fourth Party's numbers were few, their persistent attacks on Sir Stafford Northcote (at that time the Conservative Party's leader in the House of Commons and the embodiment of the 'Old Gang', whose flaccid and socially exclusive leadership Randolph despised) gave the Fourth Party an outsized reputation.

What really set Randolph apart from his contemporaries (and what will resonate with the modern reader) was his almost Trumpian powers of self-promotion. He can rightfully claim to have been a pioneer in political public relations at a time when the mass consumption of newspapers was if not in its infancy then at least in its adolescence. The editors of the *Morning Post* and *Vanity Fair* were two relationships he successfully cultivated. In later days, he could count on *The Times* and even the *New York Tribune* for regular column inches. He was a master of the unofficial press leak and an early subscriber to the theory that any publicity is good publicity. The humour, and sometimes the vulgarity, of his speeches (he once described Northcote as having the effect of 'sewer gas upon the human system; sickening, enfeebling, enervating and emasculating') guaranteed that his words would be printed verbatim in the newspapers. He was not averse either to a healthy dose of empty sloganeering. 'Tory Democracy' was the tag Randolph applied to his growing movement; when asked to explain what that meant he would reply, only half-jokingly, 'I believe it to be principally opportunism.'

Lord Salisbury's minority government of 1885 gave Randolph his first Cabinet experience. He was offered the role of Secretary of State for India but, in a sign of his power at this time, he refused the position unless his nemesis in the Commons, Northcote, was despatched to the Lords. Salisbury agreed. Save for the annexation of Upper Burma, Randolph's seven months as India Secretary included little that is worthy of remark. It was cut short in January 1886 by Gladstone's brief return to Downing Street, but with the collapse of that ministry, which followed the Irish Home Rule crisis in the same year, Randolph returned as Chancellor of the Exchequer and Leader of the House of Commons. With Salisbury sitting in the upper chamber, Randolph conducted the government's business in the Commons. This put him first in the line of succession as Prime Minister.

~

In the real world, Randolph's prospects of successfully navigating his way to No. 10 had been fatally undermined even before he became Chancellor. The illness which first afflicted him in 1882 – and seems to have turned him into a 'young man in a hurry' – returned in 1885. By 1886, he was already partly deaf, and over the following years he began to experience episodes of severe confusion, acute high blood pressure and speaking difficulties. He stopped attending the House of Commons altogether from May 1890 to the summer of 1892, and even when he returned in 1893, his speeches lacked coherence and were sometimes scarcely intelligible.[7] Two years later, aged just forty-five, he was dead.

Randolph's early demise was a topic of much morbid fascination. Rumours abounded that he had contracted syphilis from a French mistress,[8] a maid at Blenheim Palace[9] or an 'old hag' at a student party.[10] The truth is probably less salacious; a brain tumour seems the most likely cause of death. The impact of that tumour on his health waxed and waned from 1882 onwards but appears to have pushed him into a terminal decline from 1885 onwards.

Randolph's death meant that he had departed the political stage by the time Lord Salisbury resigned in 1902, and Arthur Balfour succeeded him unopposed. Balfour's premiership was underwhelming. He inherited the leadership of a Unionist Party – the name given to the Conservative and Liberal Unionist coalition – which held one of the largest majorities for generations and included political stars of the future like Winston Churchill. In a little over three years, Balfour's mismanagement of the Unionists had driven Winston and others from the fold and led to his government's resignation and devastating election defeat in 1906, with the loss of 246 seats.

~

Is there a course through which, if Randolph had had more time before his illness entered the terminal phase, he could have navigated successfully all the way to No. 10? The first thing to note is that even if Randolph had been a healthy man, his personality and politics were such that his career was always going to be something of a roller coaster. His five-month tenure as Chancellor in 1886 is a case in point. He was regarded by civil servants as a good minister, but that view was not shared by his Cabinet colleagues, many of whom were of the 'Old Gang' and harboured resentments after having been on the receiving end of Randolph's insults.

Personalities aside, Randolph's politics were also something of a square peg in the round hole that was Salisbury's 1885 and 1886 ministries. If Tory Democracy meant anything, it was the cultivation of new areas of Conservative support through popular legislation. By 1886, however, Randolph was complaining to Salisbury that 'it is an idle schoolboy's dream to suppose that Tories can legislate' for the benefit of the masses. Salisbury's position – that the harnessing of popular forces was a danger to the stability of the country – was a repudiation of Randolph's strategy and principal talent, and it contributed to Randolph's repeated resignation threats.

As Chancellor, Randolph advocated financial retrenchment, particularly for the Admiralty and War Office budgets, to facilitate a populist policy of reducing income tax. This was Gladstonian economic orthodoxy (which perhaps explains why Randolph was so popular with Treasury officials), but it put Randolph at odds with the ministers for those offices. Aware that the rest of the Cabinet sided against him, Randolph tried to force the issue, but instead of merely threatening resignation as he had done previously, this time he actually offered to step down. The move backfired spectacularly, as Salisbury accepted the resignation without hesitation. Randolph's ill health probably did play a part in his abrupt departure from government – it certainly made him more irascible – but there was almost an inevitability that Randolph's time in Salisbury's second ministry would be short-lived. Personally and politically, he was a poor fit.

This is not to say that, in the absence of his growing ill health from 1885 onwards, Randolph could not have made a comeback to front-line politics at a later date. In 1890, negotiations for Randolph's return to government were opened, and, as his biographer R. F. Foster noted, rumours of his readmission became so prevalent that it was reported in diplomatic despatches, and several of Randolph's correspondents wrote to him with (premature) congratulations.[11] His mother, the Duchess of Marlborough, was drafted in to make the case for her son's return. In a meeting with Lord Salisbury, she recorded the latter's insistence that Randolph's time would come, and that Salisbury was himself nearly played out.

In 1891, William Henry Smith, the bookseller and newsagent of the family firm W. H. Smith and also Leader of the House of Commons, died at his official residence in Kent. This prompted a Cabinet reshuffle, but precisely at the moment at which Randolph could have returned to government, ill health intervened, causing him to seek recuperation abroad, and the opportunity was lost.

In a scenario in which the tumour that afflicted Randolph had remained relatively benign after 1885, it is entirely possible that he would have benefited from the 1891 reshuffle. Salisbury would, no doubt, still have had his reservations, but Randolph now had some allies in Cabinet, including the Home Secretary, Henry Matthews, and the president of the Board of Trade, Sir Michael Hicks Beach. Most importantly, Arthur Balfour, who had succeeded Smith as Leader of the House of Commons, approved of Randolph's return. By 1891, Salisbury's government also had a more reforming nature than had characterised his ministries in 1885 and 1886. Legislation such as the 1890 Housing of the Working Classes Act (which promoted slum clearance and the construction of working-class housing) and the 1891 Elementary Education Act (which effectively introduced free elementary education for all) led one informed commentator to say that the measures being passed by Salisbury's government at this time were 'really Liberal measures with a smack of radicalism about them'.[12] This was the type of government legislation on which Randolph and Salisbury saw eye to eye and for which Randolph could be a useful and effective advocate.

~

Chief Secretary for Ireland, made vacant by Balfour's promotion to Leader of the House of Commons, was the obvious position to give to Randolph; it flattered the self-proclaimed 'Irish expert'. Serving briefly from November 1891 until Salisbury's government made way for the fourth and final Gladstone administration in August 1892, and again from 1895, Randolph reaped the benefits of Balfour's labours. The latter had embraced coercion to reduce unrest among the Irish peasantry. By 1891, this strategy, together with the fall of Parnell (Irish nationalism's most dangerous advocate),[13] brought about a relative calm in Ireland and took the wind out of the sails of the Irish Home Rule movement.

Randolph, whose job was made easier by Balfour's success, was not one to give praise even where it was due; he pressed the idea that 'Balfourism is played out and the time is come for a "generous policy"'.[14]

While Randolph was a staunch Unionist (he had come close to charges of insurrection when, in 1886, he said that 'Ulster will fight and Ulster will be right'),[15] he was prepared 'to go a long way' to legislate for the interests of all the Irish people. This 'long way' involved amendments to the 1890 Local Taxation Act, so as to provide funds for Irish national education, the provision of £100 million to facilitate tenant land purchase and, most importantly, the Local Government (Ireland) Act 1898, which established a two-tier system of local government in Ireland [in the real world, these were all ideas which Randolph developed in the late 1880s]. The latter involved local government similar to that already created for England, Wales and Scotland, but, crucially, it also established two provincial councils, one in Dublin and another in Belfast. Randolph's Conservative colleagues had misgivings about the councils, but he had the support of Joseph Chamberlain and Lord Hartington of the Liberal Unionists (with whom the Conservatives were, from 1895, partners in the Unionist coalition) and the Conservative peer Lord Carnarvon. [Again, in the real world, this really was an idea that had the support of Randolph, Hartington and Carnarvon – provincial councils were not discussed with Chamberlain, but he favoured a generous policy towards the Irish at this time.] Ultimately, Salisbury and the majority of Tories were persuaded to support the legislation by Randolph's pragmatic abandonment of some of the most controversial aspects of the Bill (Salisbury, whose prejudices as regards the Irish were well known, was implacably opposed to the councils having control of the police and the magistrates) and by Randolph's exhortation that by giving the Irish some degree of representative local government, the political energy in Ireland would be dissipated by redirecting it towards local institutions. The policy was an undoubted success: those provincial councils would survive for almost exactly 100 years until the devolutionary settlements with Scotland, Wales, Northern Ireland and Southern Ireland in the late 1990s.

With success in Ireland, Randolph expected promotion, and the

Second Boer War (1899–1902) provided the opportunity. The unpreparedness of the British Army during the early stages of the war brought
calls for the Secretary of State for War, Lord Lansdowne, to resign. The
handling of the war effort tested Randolph's capacity for collective
ministerial responsibility to the limit, and he was widely thought to be
the anonymous author of a number of newspaper articles which attacked
Lansdowne. In 1900, Lansdowne was reshuffled out of the war ministry,
and Randolph was appointed in his place. As with Ireland, the timing of
Randolph's appointment as War Minister was fortuitous; by the end of
1900, the British were nominally back in control of Boer territory, and
Randolph took (unjustified) credit for that in the September–October
1900 general election campaign. The fact that a guerrilla war continued
for a further two years did little to dent his reputation, although he had
to call upon all his rhetorical skills when defending the use of concentration camps in Parliament.

By 1902, thoughts turned to the question of who would succeed
Salisbury as Prime Minister. The death of his wife in November 1899
was a grievous loss, and his health weakened. He also caused unrest in the
ranks with the promotion of three of his family circle – too many not to
be resented. There were two obvious candidates to succeed him: Balfour,
who, as Leader of the House of Commons and Salisbury's nephew, was in
pole position; and Randolph, whose success in the Irish and War Offices
had gone a long way to address the concerns that many had had about
him earlier in his career. Two factors allowed Randolph to edge past
Balfour. The first was that, compared to Balfour, Randolph was more
in tune with politics in the early twentieth century. Where Balfour had
had little participation in the 1900 general election campaign, Randolph
had enthused massive audiences around the country. The 1900 Unionist
victory became known as 'Randolph's election'. Perhaps crucially,
Randolph also had a fondness for Chamberlain, which was strong and
reciprocated. Chamberlain was too much of a 'political bogey' among
the Tories to have leadership ambitions of his own, but his following
among the Liberal Unionists, which was crucial to the stability of
the Unionist alliance, meant he could act as kingmaker. He was well

aware of Balfour's cynicism for reform; always at odds with the more progressive direction of the Unionist alliance, Balfour had remarked in 1898 that 'all that was really worth reforming had been reformed'.[16] By contrast, Randolph shared Chamberlain's commitment to reform, so it was on Randolph's head that Chamberlain placed the crown.

~

We return now to that hot July day in Downing Street. Winston waited in the anteroom outside his father's office as the great and good of the Unionist alliance flowed in and out. Randolph had turned quickly to the formation of a new Cabinet, and the expectant faces of those who entered his office gave way to relief or disappointment, depending on the outcome of each interview. Winston waited in hope, daydreaming about a seat in Cabinet at his father's side. Eventually, as the evening shadows fell across London, Winston summoned the courage to speak to Randolph. 'Might there be a role for me in Cabinet?' he asked. Randolph's response froze Winston to stone. 'You know that I have discerned nothing remarkable, nothing of singular promise, in you.' Before Winston could open his mouth to defend himself (he had, after all, graduated from Sandhurst with honours, ranked eighth out of 150 cadets – at least this is what Churchill claimed; in fact, he had graduated twentieth out of 130)[17] his father continued: 'Perhaps some more time on the back benches will do you some good, but – make this position indelibly impressed on your mind – if your conduct and action is similar to what it has been so far in your life, my responsibility for you will be over.'

Winston was devastated. Violet Bonham Carter, Winston's long-time friend, was of the opinion that 'he worshipped at the altar of his father', but this latest setback tested Winston's admiration. He could not help but wonder what might have been if, instead of becoming his father's private secretary upon graduating from Sandhurst in 1896, he had pursued his dream of seeking military action in fields as far-flung as Cuba, India or the Sudan. Perhaps he would have made a name for himself, proved his mettle under fire and (most pressingly) made some money.

While Winston sat on the back benches, with his 'black dog' moments

– the name he gave to his episodic depression – becoming all too frequent, Randolph's ministry laid the foundations of the welfare state. The Education Act of 1902 was the platform upon which a national education system would be built by subsequent governments. This was an early test of Randolph's management of the Unionist alliance. The Education Bill, among other things that were unpopular with the Nonconformists and Radicals on whose support the Liberal Unionists relied, granted ratepayers' money to voluntary Church of England schools. Randolph worked with Chamberlain to agree a major concession: local authorities would be given discretion over the issue of rate aid to voluntary schools. [In the real world, the tin-eared Balfour forced through the legislation without any concessions, alienating his Liberal Unionist allies and contributing to the fall of his government in 1905.] Other legislation was less controversial; for instance, the Unemployed Workmen Act of 1903 established distress committees that gave out single grants to businesses or local authorities to allow them to hire more workers to reduce the number of people out of work. These were important reforms but paled in comparison with Randolph's 1905 Old-Age Pensions Act.

The idea of old-age pension legislation was first mooted by Chamberlain in the early 1890s and was adopted as a policy by Salisbury's government later in the decade. A committee of experts was appointed, chaired by Lord Rothschild, head of the eponymous banking house, who had been a close friend of Randolph for many years. The committee recommended a pension of five shillings a week, but interest in the scheme fell away once the Boer War began, and the costs of a three-year conflict meant there was little appetite for diverting the taxation needed to finance the pensions. By 1905, however, Randolph wanted to put the pensions question back on the table.

Randolph had a genuine strain of radicalism in his political thinking; he had long been a reader, and an admirer, of social reformers like Sidney Webb who had campaigned for an old-age pension. Moreover, he had an acute sense of the flow of public opinion; he would have been aware of the extreme popularity of the National Committee of Organised Labour for Promoting Old Age Pensions for All, which from 1902 to

1905 campaigned throughout the country for this social welfare reform. Eager as ever to ensure the Liberals did not monopolise progressive policies, Randolph encouraged Rothschild's committee to reconvene. [In the real world, Randolph had left the political stage before the idea of an old-age pension took root in the Conservative Party, but it is precisely the sort of social reform that Randolph would have favoured had he attained the premiership.]

Increasing direct taxes to pay for pensions remained out of the question, but Randolph had a fiscal ace up his sleeve. Tariff reform, which involved the protection of British industry by imposing duties on overseas imports, had been an issue that the Conservatives had been flirting with for some time. Randolph's position on the subject was characteristically ambiguous and opportunistic. In 1881, he had come out strongly in favour of 'Fair Trade', a system of commercial protection. He would later remark privately: 'Within these walls, I am a Fair Trader; outside, I don't know anything about Fair Trade; when the masses shout for Fair Trade, then I shall be willing to take up and champion the cause.' Protectionism was popular with the Tory base, and Joseph Chamberlain was a powerful advocate for it, even if many of his Liberal Unionist colleagues were dyed-in-the-wool free traders. [In reality, Balfour's failure to reconcile the free traders with the protectionists in the Unionist alliance led to Chamberlain's departure from government in 1903; Winston's crossing of the floor to the Liberals in 1904; and the devastating election defeat for Balfour's government in 1906.]

By contrast, Randolph sided decisively with the protectionists and imposed tariffs on industrial imports. Better attuned to public opinion than most, he refused to put tariffs on agricultural imports, because he anticipated how unpopular the resulting rise in food prices would be with the working man. While this was welcomed by the majority of Tories (and Chamberlain), Randolph ensured that he continued to enjoy the support of most free-trader Conservatives and Liberal Unionists by earmarking the revenue from the tariffs to pay for the very popular old-age pension. This neat triangulation ensured that Randolph had sufficient support to introduce both tariff reform and the Old-Age Pension Act in 1905 without irreparably damaging the Unionist alliance.

By 1907, Randolph's government had run its course. He was still held in high regard for the progressive measures he had implemented. However, the public had grown weary of Tory-led governments, which had held the reins of power for all but nine of the preceding thirty-three years. The 1907 general election was a narrow victory for the Liberal Party under Sir Henry Campbell-Bannerman. Randolph managed to hold on to his Paddington South constituency, which he had held since 1885 when his family seat of Woodstock had been abolished. When, shortly after the election, it was suggested that he might take a seat in the House of Lords, he was happy to relinquish control of the Conservative Party as the weight of more than three decades in politics began to take its toll, and the ill health that he had experienced in 1882 began to return.

Winston was not so lucky. His time in Parliament had been unremarkable, and his father's animosity towards him meant he had not achieved Cabinet rank. Instinctively a free trader, he did not agree with Randolph's tariff reform, although he favoured the old-age pension. Filial loyalty meant he did not follow the small number of his erstwhile colleagues who, in opposition to tariff reform, crossed the floor to join the Liberals (one of whom even became Home Secretary). In the 1907 general election, his Oldham seat was captured by the Liberal Party, and he left the Commons for the final time without having made a name for himself. He had always said, 'It is a fine game to play – the game of politics – and it is well worth waiting for a good hand before really plunging.' He had been dealt a good hand in having his father as Prime Minister, but nothing had come of it. Winston could only hope that when his father finally passed away, he would succeed in his place to the House of Lords. For the time being, as storm clouds gathered across Europe, he had only one career to fall back on: a return to the army.

Postscript
The idea of Randolph Churchill, had he lived, becoming Prime Minister is far from preposterous. Far more of a progressive than Balfour, it is likely that he would have pushed harder for social reform and Irish conciliation. He might even have won an election in 1907, although

Randolph's susceptibility to ill health meant that, after five years leading the country, he would likely have been too exhausted to lead the
Unionist alliance to a third consecutive victory.

As regards Winston, for some readers, the concept of him ending his
political career in relative obscurity is difficult to swallow. His colossal
status leads one to assume that his rise to greatness was inevitable, but
that assumption gives too much weight to nature over nurture. Winston
was indelibly shaped by his experiences before and after entering
Parliament. He appears to have believed that his father died of syphilis
– he would later tell his private secretary, Anthony Montague Browne,
that 'my father died of Locomotor ataxia, the child of syphilis' – and that
his father's early death foreshadowed his own: in 1899 he asserted: 'My
father died too young. I must try to accomplish whatever I can by the
time I am forty.'[18] With that motivation, and away from the shadow of
his father, he was free to pursue many of the adventures (in Cuba, Sudan,
India and South Africa) that would make his fame and fortune and help
him to acquire connections that would shape his character. For example,
had he not travelled to Cuba via New York in 1895, he would not have
met the New York Congressman Bourke Cockran, who was to teach the
young Winston about the power of oratory. On a personal level, had he
not crossed the floor to the Liberal Party in 1903, it is highly unlikely
that, the following year, he would have been invited to a party at the
home of the Liberal grandee the Earl of Crewe, where he was to meet his
future wife, and rock during unsettled times, Clementine Hozier. Had
his father lived longer, these formative experiences probably would not
have happened, and Winston's course would have been very different.
Instead of an illustrious political career that would see him appointed
as Prime Minister in 1940, Winston, having lost his Oldham seat and in
need of an income, would most likely have returned to the army, peril-
ously close to the eve of the Great War.

For any reader who is still sceptical that Winston could have been
diverted from a path to political glory, consider that, as Andrew Roberts
has written, if Randolph had lived just six months longer, to retire after
the 1895 general election, he would almost certainly have been offered a

peerage (as many grandees of the Conservative Party were). This would have been inherited by Winston, who would then not have had the career that he did in the Commons. In those circumstances, he would have had a vanishingly small chance of becoming Prime Minister in 1940.[19]

Notes

1   R. F. Foster, *Lord Randolph Churchill: A Political Life* (Oxford: Oxford University Press, 1988), p. 381.
2   Ibid., p. 18.
3   Ibid., p. 362.
4   See Andrew Roberts, 'A Famous Name: November 1874–January 1895' in *Churchill: Walking with Destiny* (London: Penguin, 2019) for examples of the constant remonstrations Winston received from his parents.
5   Foster, *Lord Randolph Churchill*, p. 29.
6   Ibid., p. 55.
7   Ibid., pp. 368, 377.
8   Anita Leslie, *Jennie: The Life of Lady Randolph Churchill* (London: Hutchinson & Co., 1969), p. 108.
9   Shane Leslie, 'Randolph Churchill 1849–1895' in *Men Were Different* (London: Michael Joseph, 1937), pp. 68–75.
10 Frank Harris, *My Life and Loves* (London: Frank Harris Publishing Co., 1925), pp. 482–85.
11 Foster, *Lord Randolph Churchill*, p. 367.
12 David Steele, *Lord Salisbury* (London: UCL Press, 1999), p. 227.
13 Like Randolph Churchill, the Irish Nationalist politician and MP Charles Stewart Parnell would also die aged forty-five. His career had been brought to an untimely end by a much-publicised affair and divorce proceedings.
14 Foster, *Lord Randolph Churchill*, p. 353.
15 See Randolph Churchill's speech at Ulster Hall, Belfast, 23 February 1886.
16 Steele, *Lord Salisbury*, p. 306.
17 Roberts, *Churchill*, p. 29.
18 J. B. Atkins, *Incidents and Reflections* (London: Christopher's, 1947), p. 125.
19 Roberts, *Churchill*, p. 30.

Chapter 2

What if Clement Attlee had died during the First World War?

Andrew Stone[1]

It was 5 April 1916 in Mesopotamia, and Captain Clement Attlee was about to receive a very painful – yet very lucky – break. He had already survived the Gallipoli campaign, the brainchild of the First Lord of the Admiralty, Winston Churchill, though he had suffered a nasty bout of dysentery for his troubles. Now he was part of the force tasked with relieving the city of Kut-al-Amara, which was besieged by the Ottoman Army. The prize, as would become so familiar in what would soon be renamed Iraq, was control of plentiful oil reserves.

In the pre-dawn murk, he clasped the red flag of the South Lancashire Regiment, braving heavy fire and leading his men in storming an enemy trench. Suddenly, a shell exploded, and shrapnel scattered his battalion. He was blasted across the battlefield, and when he regained consciousness, he was covered in blood, with wounds to his groin, buttocks and knee joint. He was treated and evacuated, and while a fleeting victory was achieved against Turkish forces, it was at the cost of 1,300 casualties in just a few hours.[2]

Labour's boom and bust

Imagine that Captain Clement Attlee had paused momentarily before that trench, that the shrapnel had struck a few centimetres higher and fatally severed an artery. Or, conversely, that this misdirected 'friendly fire' had missed him completely; Attlee could then have remained part of the assault, only to die prematurely as part of the subsequent fateful attack.

Biographers and historians have argued at length over Attlee's impact on history. While the Labour government that he led from 1945 to 1951 undoubtedly defined the post-war consensus of the mixed economy and welfare state, Attlee's personal centrality to these developments is more in dispute. Was he, as in the famous damning epitaph attributed (probably falsely) to Churchill, 'a modest little man with much to be modest about'? How might the Labour Party – and the nation – have fared without his steadying influence?

A privately educated Oxford graduate, conservative in early outlook, Attlee was not an obvious fit for the young Labour Party, let alone as its likely future leader. Yet by 1907, he found his way to parliamentary social-ism via volunteering in poverty-stricken east London, which convinced him of the inadequacy of philanthropy. The First World War was the making of him. Prior to that, he stood unsuccessfully for election to the Independent Labour Party's (ILP) National Administrative Council, Stepney Borough Council and the Limehouse Board of Guardians.[3] In 1914, he rejected the anti-war arguments of his comrades, and despite being a year over the upper age limit of thirty, he lobbied to be enlisted, eventually gaining a commission as a second lieutenant, and later as captain and major. His distinguished war service became a huge asset when the conflict ended and his political career resumed. Despite once again suffer-ing electoral defeat in March 1919 in the Limehouse division of the London County Council (LCC), Attlee was trusted to manage Labour's November push for the local borough councils. His reward for its convincing victory (taking forty-three out of sixty seats, where it had held none before) was to be appointed, at thirty-six, as Stepney's youngest ever mayor.[4]

Efficient as his management of the campaign undoubtedly was, Labour would probably have established a dominant position in the area regardless. In the immediate aftermath of the war, the East End working class was more confident and militant than before.[5] It had recognised its economic contribution to wartime production and increasingly looked to the Labour Party – its constitution effectively reorganised by moder-ates Sidney Webb and Arthur Henderson[6] – to assert its claim to political rewards for its sacrifices.

However, there is no guarantee that whoever had replaced Attlee as Limehouse's Labour candidate in the 1922 general election would have been victorious. Attlee won by only 1,899 votes over the Liberal incumbent William Pearce, requiring an impressive swing of 23 per cent. A more controversial or less competent candidate might have failed to make the breakthrough, which could have made ripples in east London, where Labour politics was particularly fractious. It is hard, though, to see it retarding the decline of the Liberals nationally, who were already noticeably squeezed by the two-party system in an age of mass enfranchisement.

Attlee's time as Undersecretary of State for War in Labour's minority government of 1924 was unremarkable, and probably would have remained so for most substitutes. Ramsay MacDonald's administration was determined to prove Labour responsible managers of capitalism, and this was nowhere more evident than in its foreign policy. On his first day in the Colonial Office, J. H. Thomas declared to his assembled civil servants: 'I am here to make sure there is no mucking about with the British Empire.'[7]

Not that Labour was rewarded for its moderation, with the forged Zinoviev letter[8] used to support a red scare unjustified by the party's actions in office. Labour, like Attlee, also adopted an equivocal attitude to the 1926 General Strike, contributing to the lack of leadership that ensured its defeat. Attlee's main intervention was to chair the Stepney electricity committee, negotiating with TUC representatives to ensure a minimum supply to hospitals while non-essential supplies were cut. When a local engineering firm refused to co-operate, strikers took matters into their own hands. Attlee was sued, and damages of £300 awarded, setting a precedent that could have bankrupted him. He was saved by an unlikely source – Malcolm MacNaughton, a KC and Ulster Unionist MP, who appealed against the judgment.[9] They had been friends in chambers during Attlee's short-lived legal career; a stroke of fortune that would have eluded less well-connected Labour politicians.

Absent for much of the preceding parliament, in India as part of the Simon Commission, Attlee was initially passed over for a ministerial post in Labour's second government of 1929–31, later becoming Chancellor of the Duchy of Lancaster and then Postmaster General. Though his latter tenure lasted just five months, he set in train several policies that would make the Post Office a more efficient, market-orientated business.[10] Still, his involvement in the Cabinet was low-key, and if this had been his last experience of government, history would hardly have blinked at his absence.

The replacement of the Labour administration with the Conservative-dominated National Government led by MacDonald left Attlee as one of only three of the rump of forty-six Labour MPs (or fifty-two including independents) elected with frontbench experience. The others were George Lansbury, the veteran socialist who gained the leadership, and Sir Stafford Cripps, the former Solicitor General.[11] It is of course possible that whoever had filled Attlee's stead in government would have followed his path to Deputy Leader of the Opposition; the other possibility is that Cripps, the aristocratic lawyer turned radical firebrand, would have stepped up.

Swing to the left

Before becoming the skeletal face of post-war austerity as Chancellor, Cripps had spent much of the 1930s trying to pull Labour to the left through a mixture of policy initiatives, alliances and extra-parliamentary action. A month after the ILP voted to disaffiliate from Labour at its July 1932 conference, he filled the vacuum by creating and bankrolling the Socialist League – 'Part think tank, part grassroots activist network, part left pressure group.'[12] It included most of the leading lights of the Labour left of its generation, including Harold Laski, Nye Bevan, Barbara Betts (later Castle) and Ellen Wilkinson.

The fact that Attlee, as deputy leader, contributed to pamphlets and lectures for the league suggests that Cripps could also have combined participation as Lansbury's second in command. Although the trade union bureaucracy was suspicious of aristocratic socialist intellectuals like Cripps and Laski, it too was disorientated by the events of 1931, when the Labour government split under the strains of coping with the

Great Depression, and the party then went down to catastrophic election defeat. This compounded its disillusionment with the preceding two years of Labour in power. Hampered by economic orthodoxy, in the face of recession its Chancellor, Philip Snowden, had favoured palliatives over major economic stimulus and capitulated when a committee of inquiry called for by the Conservative opposition demanded swingeing cuts to unemployment benefits.[13] In contrast, Cripps, despite his background, was a natural rebel. An eloquent speaker such as he, with (albeit limited) experience of government, might have been acceptable as deputy, at least as a stopgap before the 'big guns', such as Arthur Greenwood (who returned to Parliament in 1932) and Herbert Morrison (1935), could be re-elected. Perhaps, the party establishment might have considered, leadership could tame Cripps, as it would later with figures from the left such as Wilson and Kinnock.

In this scenario, deputising for the like-minded Lansbury, Cripps might not have considered a ginger group such as the Socialist League as necessary to his ambitions. However, there may still have been an organisation expressing the grassroots Labour swing to the left. Perhaps a less well-funded alternative might have emerged, similar to how Momentum would later provide ballast to Jeremy Corbyn. Meanwhile, the ageing Lansbury's waning health would have given Cripps, as it did Attlee, ample scope to prove his potential as a parliamentary leader.

Whatever his oratorical skills, however, Cripps's commitment to economic transformation and pacifistic internationalism was always likely to lead to conflict with the big beasts of the Labour right, such as the Old Etonian economist Hugh Dalton, the plain-talking trade unionist Ernest Bevin and Herbert Morrison, the former conscientious objector who became head of the LCC and unified London Transport. While the League of Nations Union's Peace Ballot of autumn/winter 1934–35, a grassroots plebiscite of over 11.5 million people, showed widespread support for collective security based on multilateral disarmament,[14] the Socialist League's unilateralism at the 1934 Labour Party conference went a step further.[15] As the international situation darkened with Nazi rearmament in Germany and the Italian invasion of Abyssinia, a pacifistic policy became increasingly difficult to defend. In our reality, Bevin launched a merciless attack on Lansbury at the subsequent conference, accusing him of 'hawking your conscience round from body to body asking to be told what you ought to do with it'. Dalton gloated in his diary that Bevin 'hammered Lansbury to death', and the anti-war position was overwhelmingly crushed, prompting Lansbury's resignation.[16]

Arthur Greenwood: Leader of the Opposition

In October 1935, with the dissolution of Parliament and a general election imminent, how might Cripps have responded to this setback? He would have been under pressure to join Lansbury in stepping down, probably in favour of Arthur Greenwood. But there was also a case for continuity; a caretaker to rally Labour at the polls before an enlarged Parliamentary Labour Party (PLP) could take a longer-term view. This cohort, which would probably have approached the 154 elected under Attlee, would have included Morrison, whose ambition for the top job was barely concealed. Backed by the intelligentsia, the press and Hugh Dalton, his big handicaps were the enmity of MPs sponsored by trade unions or from the north, and Bevin.[17] In reality, in December 1935, Attlee won a three-way contest against Morrison and Greenwood, with all but four of Greenwood's nominees backing Attlee in the second round.

Like the protagonist of Robert Tressell's socialist classic *The Ragged Trousered Philanthropists*, Arthur Greenwood's father was a painter and decorator, and his son's embrace of education in becoming a teacher and then an economics lecturer recommended him well to a movement that appreciated self-improvement allied to the collective good. After serving as an adviser to Lloyd George's wartime coalition and first being elected to Parliament in 1922, he became head of Labour's research department in 1927. This role attested to a confident grasp of detail, and as Minister for Health in the second Labour government, he steered through important legislation on pensions and housing.[18]

There was little love lost between Morrison and Greenwood, with Morrison believing that the latter exploited freemason contacts to further his career. So, while they were politically closer to each other than either was to Cripps, a Blair–Brown-style deal would have been unlikely. Fortunately for them, Cripps's support in the PLP was far weaker than in the wider movement, so while he might have gained thirty or so votes from left allies, Morrison and Greenwood could each have expected to double that. Knocked out of the second round, Cripps would then have become kingmaker. Despite their policy differences, Morrison had smoothed Cripps's way into Parliament in 1929,[19] so could reasonably have expected some reciprocation. However, Cripps's endorsement might well have been counter-productive, reaffirming suspicions that Morrison held more skills in backroom deals than in sticking to his principles. Greenwood, known for his cordiality, could have narrowly pipped him.

Greenwood's leadership would have faced major difficulties, for three reasons. First, even if Morrison was offered (and accepted) the deputy leadership, the appeasement of his ambitions would only have been temporary, and Dalton, Wilkinson and others could be expected to advocate his promotion behind the scenes. Second, while the economy was beginning to improve – and potentially therefore taking the wind out of the sails of Labour's critique – the international situation continued to darken, posing difficult issues of principle and tactics. How far, for example, should the party challenge the government's policy of non-intervention in the Spanish Civil War, especially when Léon Blum's Popular Front in France was outwardly in favour? Third, while well-liked and skilled in policy detail, Greenwood had his own personal demon – alcoholism – which could only be expected to worsen with the pressure of leadership and the attendant manoeuvring against him.

Cripps would now have been free to throw his weight behind a push for a united front of the left, formalised in the Unity Manifesto of January 1937, which was backed by the ILP, the Communist Party and the Socialist League, and advocated by the newly launched *Tribune* magazine, which Cripps bankrolled.[20] Labour's National Executive rapidly disaffiliated from the Socialist League in our world, and Greenwood would have likely approved this course too. But Cripps continued to be a nuisance, swinging behind a Popular Front policy two years later, which this time saw the left advocating a cross-class, anti-fascist alliance. Attlee had the *sangfroid* to ridicule Cripps's contortions with scurrilous verse and hold out for his expulsion alongside his allies Aneurin Bevan and the veteran Charles Trevelyan.[21] But when faced with pressure from both the Labour left and right, it is quite possible that Greenwood would have buckled. Perhaps a major speech at conference or in Parliament would have been cancelled or, even worse, delivered while clearly under the influence of alcohol. Westminster and Fleet Street were discreet about such things at the time, but there were limits. Maybe the euphemism 'tired and emotional' would have been coined much earlier; party notables would have encouraged a resignation on the grounds of ill health; and Morrison would have seized the opportunity to take the leadership.

Peace and war

Inheriting the party in early 1939, Morrison could have used his negotiating skills to reach out to the left, overcoming his frustration with Cripps and using his intimate relationship with Wilkinson to ensure that Bevan, Betts and other leading leftists were at the forefront of an anti-appeasement offensive co-ordinated with Eden, Churchill and other Tory rebels.[22] It is conceivable that this strategy could have hastened Chamberlain's resignation after the outbreak of war, though only if it sufficiently emboldened his party critics – a lack of tenacity was not one of his faults. In the real world, it was Morrison who posed the vote of censure that ultimately did for Chamberlain, and though it is possible that he, unlike Attlee and Greenwood, might have accepted a place in coalition under Chamberlain, it seems very unlikely.[23] Morrison had the malleability of the ambitious pragmatist, but on this issue he and the Labour Party were fixed. As Greenwood reportedly told the outgoing Prime Minister: 'The Labour Party did not just dislike [Chamberlain], but saw him "as something evil".'[24] Even the electoral truce with Chamberlain, which Labour observed during the period of 'phoney war', has been estimated to have cost the party a quarter of its membership.[25]

Churchill may not have formed as effective a partnership with

Morrison as he did in reality with Attlee, as their personal contrasts (the bipolar rhetorician alongside the scheming bureaucrat) were less complementary. The personable Dalton, Morrison's most likely deputy in the War Cabinet, might have been called upon to calm stormy waters. But the big test that faced them between 26 and 28 May 1940, when the defeated French Prime Minister Paul Reynaud relayed the possibility of negotiating a 'grand bargain' with Hitler,[26] would probably have united all concerned. With British troops encircled at Dunkirk, the situation was certainly bleak, but defeatism would have been anathema to most of the Labour membership, as well as to the wider public. The last gasp of appeasement expressed by Halifax and Chamberlain in entertaining this approach could surely only have been sustainable as a 'palace coup' – perhaps literally, with the recall of the Nazi-sympathising Edward VIII.

With Morrison as Lord Privy Seal and (de facto and later officially) Deputy Prime Minister, Dalton would probably have been a floating Minister Without Portfolio, and Cripps could have been rehabilitated as Minister of Economic Warfare. Bevin would still have been a natural choice as Minister of Labour and National Service, as he was in reality. The man who famously responded to Morrison's lament that he was his own worst enemy by quipping, 'not while I'm alive he ain't'[27] was liked by Churchill, and his authoritarian approach was all the more effective from years of training as a trade union official.

Attlee certainly contributed to the direction of the war, but it is hard to pinpoint any turning moments in its course in which he was indispensable. He was more significant in quietly nudging Churchill towards post-war reconstruction plans, most notably (with Greenwood's help) the Beveridge Report. There was impatience from the Bevanites at the slow pace of advance, understandable after the betrayed promises of the First World War. The growing evidence of socialist feeling, such as the warm public reception of Beveridge's plans displayed in Mass Observation reports, found an outlet in by-election successes for left-wing independents and Common Wealth Party candidates. At the 1942 Labour conference, Bevan narrowly lost a vote to end the by-election truce with the other coalition parties, though when Attlee put the case the following year the margin was more convincing.[28] Morrison might have been more assertive in voicing Labour's frustrations within the Cabinet and tipping the wink to his party that he was doing so, but he had been adept at playing the long game at the LCC and would surely have maintained the coalition at least while the outcome of the war remained uncertain.

The biggest obstacle to this would have been Morrison's antipathy towards Bevan, who once called him 'a third-rate Tammany boss'.[29] Assuming that Morrison had averted or reversed Bevan's real-life expulsion for supporting the Popular Front in 1939, and that the latter still challenged the truce in 1942, with less tactful management the vote maintaining the by-election agreement could easily have been lost. This would have made Labour's continued participation in Churchill's coalition very awkward. However, the PLP might not have considered itself beholden to this vote, and though ignoring a key decision by the supposedly sovereign conference would have been hugely divisive, it would not necessarily have been fatal – as Hugh Gaitskell's resistance to the 1960 party conference motion on unilateralism would later prove.[30]

The Morrison administration

Like Attlee, Morrison would have faced growing calls from the left to leave the coalition during 1944. In reality he, Attlee and Bevin were caricatured as 'Three Blind Mice' by *Tribune* for not realising that the Tories were stringing them along.[31] Should an election have been forced before the victory in Europe, though, it seems doubtful that Labour would have achieved the landslide it did the following year; Churchill would have been able play his trump card as the man needed to win the war.

So, we will assume that the schedule for the election in July 1945 was substantially unchanged, and that Labour's manifesto, 'Let Us Face the Future', which Morrison co-authored, was recognisably similar. Morrison would thus enter office with a large majority and a mandate for change. Who might he have chosen to help him to deliver it?

Unlike Attlee, he might have overridden King George VI's appeal not to appoint Dalton to the Foreign Ministry, caused by what Dalton considered to be a matter of personal spite.[32] However, in Morrison's account it was he, rather than the monarch, who had persuaded Attlee to keep the temperamental Dalton away from diplomacy.[33] Bevin might be thought unlikely to find promotion under his rival's premiership, but the only contenders of similar stature – Cripps, Laski and Bevan – would have been deemed too pro-Moscow, so we will assume that Bevin and Dalton remained as Foreign Secretary and Chancellor respectively by default. Cripps at the Board of Trade and Bevan at the Ministry of Labour would be consolation prizes for a left that Morrison wished to restrict to only essential positions.

Though sexist prejudice would probably have prevented her consideration as Home or Foreign Secretary, Wilkinson could have been deployed at the Ministry of Health, where indeed Attlee had originally planned to appoint her in our universe.[34] James Chuter Ede, former teacher and undersecretary to Rab Butler, would have been a natural replacement for Wilkinson as Minister for Education.[35] Emanuel Shinwell, one of the few established figures with whom Morrison was on good terms, would have been a possible Home Secretary in Chuter Ede's stead.

In January 1947, Wilkinson caught pneumonia, which proved fatal after she overdosed on her medication. Given that she caught it undertaking ministerial duties – opening the exposed Old Vic Theatre School[36] – it is possible that a posting at the Ministry of Health would have saved her. However, considering the appalling weather of the winter of 1946–47, as well as her chronic asthma and history of bronchitis, influenza and lung infections, it is still likely that she would have fallen ill. If so, Morrison would have needed to find a safe pair of hands to complete the creation of the NHS. Given the chain of candidates eliminated from contention by this counterfactual, the young Hugh Gaitskell would have been a credible left-field (but not left-wing) choice. Instead of facing down Bevan in 1951 to impose prescription charges as Chancellor, Gaitskell may well have implemented them as Health Minister, supported by the like-minded Evan Durbin, and succeeding (after a more junior ministerial apprenticeship) his exhausted mentor Hugh Dalton as Chancellor at the end of Labour's first term. Morrison's autobiography claims that he favoured refusing Dalton's resignation after his lapse in leaking aspects of his Budget prior to presenting it to the House in 1947.[37] Today, in an age of almost routine pre-publicity for ministerial statements, Dalton's rectitude certainly appears quaint, though it probably also reflected his growing anxiety about the country's balance of payments.

Why no Cripps as Chancellor? Partly because, if Dalton had stayed on until 1950, Cripps's health would have already been in serious decline. There is also the matter of his penchant for intrigue. It is easy to see Cripps using Morrison's own bout of pneumonia in 1947 as a pretext for advancing one of Morrison's rivals for the leadership, much as he attempted to do against Attlee. Unlike Attlee, Morrison would hardly have rewarded this slight with an effective promotion, and Cripps may have found himself on the back benches for the remainder of his career.

If the name Evan Durbin is unfamiliar, it is because in reality he died in September 1948, heroically attempting to save children, including his daughter, from drowning while on holiday in Cornwall. He was a junior minister at the Ministry of Works but was widely tipped for future success, including by both Dalton and Attlee.[38] An alternate deployment could have changed these holiday plans and ensured his survival. This would have been a mixed blessing for Morrison, who would have appreciated Durbin's concern for social psychology and moderate social democracy and have benefited from access to his skill and intelligence, but also would have been challenged by his centralising managerial instincts.

Domestic policy

Beyond fantasy reshuffles, how might policy have evolved in a Morrison administration? As in our world, the context would be a widely felt desire for a welfare state and economic intervention to ensure prosperity, social insurance and full employment. The Beveridge Report would have remained the road map, though some detours might have occurred. Morrison was less vocally enthusiastic about nationalisation in general, and specifically regarding iron and steel.[39] Dalton, who wished to expedite it faster than in fact occurred, could have been expected to clash with Morrison over this, but if Morrison got his way with a 'hybrid scheme', it could have saved Labour considerable political grief in 1949, when they eventually legislated in the face of significant resistance. Fuel and power, transport, the Bank of England and civil aviation would all most likely still have been nationalised in some form, as promised in Labour's 1945 manifesto.

Dalton would no doubt have remained committed to 'cheap money' – low interest rates to promote investment – along broadly Keynesian lines, and Bevin to a pro-America policy, despite the tensions over the terms of the Anglo-American bailout loan agreed in 1946 and secrecy over atomic developments. Morrison might have been more prompt in countering the 'manpower gap' identified by Dalton,[40] cutting foreign military deployments more rapidly to deliver an industrial stimulus. Both Dalton and Cripps, though, were less enthusiastic about promoting immigration to fill those jobs.[41] The British Nationality Act of 1948 excited little attention at the time, though its comparatively liberal provisions would become more contested later. An expanding economy in the early 1950s would ensure that Commonwealth immigrants could not be credibly scapegoated for unemployment, and a Morrison administration, informed by the experience of the LCC, might have been more supportive of local authorities' attempts to assist integration. But with housing supply still under pressure, he would be unlikely to address the main problem facing new immigrants – the five-year residency requirement for council housing – which pushed many into the hands of slum landlords.

Morrison could have been expected to prescribe a more municipal version of the National Health Service under Wilkinson before her death – no doubt the recalcitrant doctors and dentists would still have needed to be bought off, perhaps alongside the retention of voluntary hospitals within an NHS run through local government. General Practitioners might even have retained independent status as private contractors, diluting somewhat the NHS's principles. He could also have insisted on a greater priority for housing, perhaps giving it a separate ministry – reflecting the importance given to the issue by electors, which, as a long-time inner-London MP, Morrison might have been expected to appreciate. But Bevan's emphasis on good-quality council-built housing might have been sacrificed for quantity, with a greater proportion coming from private-sector housing associations. In the short term, this would have weakened the Conservative critique of missed building targets but with a legacy of smaller units with more ongoing maintenance problems.

One casualty of Wilkinson's absence at Education may have been the raising of the school leaving age to fifteen. Although Chuter Ede would have been in favour, it took all of Red Ellen's tenacity to protect this measure in the face of manpower shortages and austerity pressures. It is hard to imagine Chuter Ede issuing, as Wilkinson did, an ultimatum to campaign outside Parliament if the policy was deferred or rejected,[42] or it having the same weight even if he had. The many prefabricated huts that supplemented school buildings for the next two generations might have been missing from our landscape entirely. More importantly, the education of millions of children would have been curtailed as a result. Her cognisance of the importance of nutrition would also have been lost; it was her experience of subsidising milk in her own constituency[43] that encouraged her to extend the measure to all schoolchildren after the war. Without Wilkinson, Education Secretary Margaret Thatcher would have been spared the 'milk snatcher' epithet, as there would have been no free milk to withdraw, but the ills of childhood malnutrition would have endured longer through the years of austerity.

Such compromises might have eroded the electorate's enthusiasm for Labour sooner and weakened the electoral arithmetic that would otherwise have seemed to benefit Morrison. A consensus would still have prevailed with the Conservatives, just one marginally more to the right than under Attlee around issues of governmental intervention.

Averting crises

More respected than liked, there is the possibility that Morrison's colleagues would have sought to remove him when he contracted pneumonia in January 1947. However, there was much greater tolerance for illness among leaders at the time, with both Attlee and Churchill weathering extended periods of convalescence. In any case, the impact of the winter fuel crisis was only just beginning to be felt, and further strains such as the switch to dollar convertibility would only come into effect later in the year. The ultimate devaluation of sterling in 1949 reflected an objective weakness of the economy that went beyond individual leaders. However, what one historian has called the 'slow, painful and at times muddled'[44] way in which devaluation was handled was not inevitable, exacerbated as it was by the sickly Chancellor Cripps's long recuperation in a Swiss sanatorium. A present Dalton would surely have acted more promptly.

In general, Morrison would have been a more decisive, and therefore a more divisive, leader than Attlee. If his memoirs are to be believed, he would have favoured a strengthening of working-class representation over what he considered middle-class intellectuals (he probably had Dalton's protégés, such as Gaitskell and Durbin, in mind). Despite his clashes with the man himself, Bevin-style no-nonsense pragmatists would apparently have found favour. This might have been achieved through amending conference procedures – for example reversing the 1937 reforms that had given Constituency Labour Parties greater say at the expense of trade union affiliates – or through promotions. He would have wrapped himself more in the union flag than the red, viewing nationalisation as a matter of ensuring economic efficiency rather than of fulfilling socialist principles. He would have allowed Clause IV, the totemic commitment to wholesale nationalisation, to remain a dead letter in the constitution – as he wrote in his memoirs, 'An effort to strike it out might well mean more trouble within the Labour Party than the attempt would be worth.'[45]

While Attlee allowed a redrawing of constituency boundaries (overseen by Chuter Ede) to exaggerate the Conservative recovery at the 1950 election, costing Labour thirty-five seats according to Churchill's estimate,[46] Morrison was alert to the danger and would have been keen for his Home Secretary, Shinwell, to avert it. Even quite minor amendments could have seen Labour achieve the relatively secure majority of twenty to thirty predicted by Attlee, rather than the six which in fact left them prone to rebellions and defeats. The margin might have been even more comfortable if Morrison's instinct had proven correct that a later polling date – e.g. in May rather than frigid February – would have boosted the Labour turnout.[47] And Dalton as Chancellor, egged on by Morrison, might have been more willing than the austere Cripps to sanction a giveaway Budget in the interim. Barring a disastrous string of defections or by-election defeats, this could have enabled Labour to serve for a full second term, rather than an abbreviated one concluding with defeat in 1951. Even if an earlier election had been deemed necessary, it is hard to imagine Morrison observing the scrupulous propriety of Attlee arranging it around the King's (ultimately abandoned) overseas schedule rather than party interest.[48]

Foreign policy and denouement

Though, remarkably, Morrison was not included in Attlee's private decision to develop nuclear weapons, there is no reason to doubt that he would have favoured a comparable policy. Yet among the section of Labour MPs that saw the creation of Israel as a heroic venture – rather than the 'nakba' (catastrophe) described by the expelled Palestinians – he commented approvingly that 'the Jews have proved to be first-class colonisers, to have real good, old empire qualities, to be really first-class colonial pioneers'.[49] He would probably therefore have pressured an unwilling Bevin to take a more immediately pro-Israeli policy in the Middle East. However, it is hard to imagine a scenario in which the overwhelmed British mandate, under pressure from the US, would not have contributed to a damaging and unequal partition comparable to that which continues to mire the region in conflict today.

Similarly, Attlee's belief that Indian independence was a success is hard to square with the estimated 1 million fatalities of the process, though generations of divide and rule made a peaceful secession unlikely. Attlee's own insights – from the provocative Simon Commission, which was widely resented for excluding Indian participation, and in directing repression against the Quit India movement during the Second World

War[50] – would have been lost to Morrison, who was not renowned for his grasp of foreign policy. But this exponent of 'the jolly old empire', who described talk of self-government for many colonies as 'ignorant dangerous nonsense ... It would be like giving a child of ten a latch-key, a bank account and a shotgun,'[51] would also have faced the intractable problem of financing and policing the continued occupation of a country in near-permanent revolt. For similar reasons, during the 1951 Abadan Crisis, Morrison's favoured policy of 'sharp and forceful action' against the Iranian nationalisation of their oil wells[52] may well have been restrained by a Cabinet (and a Foreign Minister, perhaps a young talent like Denis Healey, replacing the recently deceased Bevin) more attuned to Britain's declining imperial status.

Growing affluence might have allowed Morrison to survive internal critics well into the 1950s. A third term would even have been possible, perhaps based on a 'Butlinist' managerialist consensus of Chancellor Durbin and his shadow, Rab Butler. But while calls for a more red-blooded socialism might have found a limited audience, foreign policy was likely to remain contentious. Bevan could be expected to resign from the Cabinet in 1954 assuming, as seems likely, that Morrison supported American rearmament of West Germany. And if, in summer 1956, Morrison had initiated unilateral action against Nasser's nationalisation of the Suez Canal – a response that he implied support for in reality[53] – then Bevan would no doubt have condemned his own government's 'policy of bankruptcy and despair' at a rally in Trafalgar Square.[54] The party, like the country as a whole, was deeply split on the invasion, and though Bevan might not have had sufficient support in the PLP to replace Morrison himself, he could well have inflicted enough damage to bring him down.

Assuming that Bevan could not contain his ego sufficiently to step aside for protégés such as Harold Wilson, Barbara Castle or Richard Crossman, a revisionist such as Gaitskell or Durbin would have been best placed to succeed. The civil war that engulfed Labour in opposition in reality might in this scenario have done so in government. The steadying hand of Attlee, stilled in Mesopotamia some four decades earlier, would be missed, the red flag it held fought over while the Tory enemy advanced.

Notes

1   With thanks to Duncan Brack, Alex Mavrou-Stone and my two other anonymous reviewers for their useful comments.
2   John Bew, *Citizen Clem: A Biography of Attlee* (London: Riverrun, 2017), pp. 8–9.
3   Michael Jago, *Clement Attlee: The Inevitable Prime Minister* (London: Biteback, 2017), p. 45.
4   Ibid., p. 60.
5   In 1919, 35 million days were lost to industrial disputes across the country, eclipsing the levels of the pre-war 'labour unrest'. See Peter Clarke, *Hope and Glory: Britain 1900–2000* (London: Penguin, 2004), p. 107.
6   Simon Hannah, *A Party with Socialists in It: A History of the Labour Left* (London: Pluto, 2018), p. 20.
7   Ibid., p. 31.
8   Grigory Zinoviev was a leader of the Russian Communist Party and the supposed author of a message attributed to the Communist Third International for its tiny British section, which the *Daily Mail* printed four days before the election. Its veracity remains hotly contested but its instructions, exhorting insurrection, were used effectively to smear the Labour Party, in which some communists remained members. See David Thomson, *England in the Twentieth Century, 1914–63* (Suffolk: Penguin, 1977), pp. 96–7.
9   Francis Beckett, *Clem Attlee: Labour's Great Reformer* (London: Haus, 2015), pp. 117–18.
10 Jago, *Clement Attlee*, pp. 81–2.
11 Beckett, *Clem Attlee*, p. 150.
12 Hannah, *A Party with Socialists in It*, p. 59.
13 Thomson, *England in the Twentieth Century*, pp. 129–34.
14 David Cohen, *Churchill & Attlee: The Unlikely Allies Who Won the War* (London: Biteback, 2018), pp. 141–2.
15 Beckett, *Clem Attlee*, p. 165.
16 Hannah, *A Party with Socialists in It*, pp. 72–3.
17 Bew, *Citizen Clem*, p. 198.
18 Ben Pimlott, *Labour and the Left in the 1930s* (Cambridge: Cambridge University Press, 1977), p. 26.
19 Lord Morrison, *Herbert Morrison: An Autobiography* (London: Odhams, 1960), p. 115.
20 Tony Cliff and Donny Gluckstein, *The Labour Party: A Marxist History* (London: Bookmarks, 1996), pp. 183–4.
21 Ibid., pp. 185–8.
22 In reality, it was Morrison (seconded by Attlee) who put a resolution, narrowly defeated, to the Labour NEC to delay a decision on Cripps's expulsion until party conference. See Pimlott, *Labour and the Left in the 1930s*, p. 178.
23 Morrison, *Herbert Morrison*, pp. 172–5.
24 Cohen, *Churchill & Attlee*, pp. 190–91.
25 Pimlott, *Labour and the Left in the 1930s*, p. 186.
26 Bew, *Citizen Clem*, pp. 256–7.

27 Quoted in John Simkin, 'Herbert Morrison', Spartacus Educational, January 2020, https://spartacus-educational.com/TUmorrison.htm – though Dalton reported that this *bon mot* was actually at the expense of Emanuel Shinwell, the Minister for Fuel and Power – see Hugh Dalton, *High Tide and After: Memoirs 1945–60* (London: Frederick Muller, 1962), p. 212.

28 Cliff and Gluckstein, *The Labour Party*, pp. 207–8.

29 Morrison, *Herbert Morrison*, p. 263.

30 Hannah, *A Party with Socialists in It*, pp. 113–14.

31 Bew, *Citizen Clem*, p. 312.

32 Dalton, *High Tide and After*, pp. 8–10.

33 Morrison, *Herbert Morrison*, p. 246.

34 Paula Bartley, *Ellen Wilkinson: From Red Suffragette to Government Minister* (London: Pluto, 2014), p. 122.

35 These two suggestions are also made in Eric Midwinter, 'Prime Minister Morrison and municipal socialism', in Francis Beckett (ed.), *The Prime Ministers Who Never Were* (London: Biteback, 2012). My post-war speculations share several similarities with this engaging piece but were sketched out before I read it.

36 Bartley, *Ellen Wilkinson*, p. 131.

37 Morrison, *Herbert Morrison*, pp. 261–3.

38 John Simkin, 'What kind of society would we have if Evan Durbin had not died in 1948?', Spartacus Educational, 28 June 2018, https://spartacus-educational.com/spartacus-blogURLiii.htm

39 Dalton, *High Tide and After*, p. 136.

40 Ibid., p. 193.

41 Paul Foot, *Immigration and Race in British Politics* (London: Penguin, 1965), p. 116.

42 Bartley, *Ellen Wilkinson*, p. 126.

43 Ibid., p. 88.

44 David Kynaston, *Austerity Britain: Smoke in the Valley* (London: Bloomsbury, 2007), p. 60.

45 Morrison, *Herbert Morrison*, p. 329.

46 Dalton, *High Tide and After*, p. 299.

47 Morrison, *Herbert Morrison*, pp. 268–9.

48 Beckett, *Clem Attlee*, p. 427.

49 John Newsinger, *The Blood Never Dried: A People's History of the British Empire* (London: Bookmarks, 2006), p. 135.

50 Ibid., pp. 145–52.

51 Ibid., p. 159.

52 Morrison, *Herbert Morrison*, p. 281.

53 James Eayrs, *The Commonwealth and Suez: A Documentary Survey* (Oxford: Oxford University Press, 1964).

54 Aneurin Bevan, quoted in *New Statesman*, 4 February 2010, https://www.newstatesman.com/uk-politics/2010/02/aneurin-bevan-1956-speech

Chapter 3

What if General Maxwell had not executed the leaders of the 1916 Easter Rising?

Graham Kirby

'*Nuair a bhíonn deacracht ag Sasana, bíonn deis ag Éirinn.*' (Usually translated as 'England's difficulty is Ireland's opportunity.')
Daniel O'Connell (1775–1847), Irish political leader and campaigner

There were ten in the room, all dressed in the military uniform of the British Empire. None of them spoke. They looked towards the man at the head of the table and waited.

Out of the window, Dublin still smouldered. Its air smelled of cinders and sulphur. There was, though, quiet: the sound of machine-gun fire no longer broke out every other minute.

It had started when Irish rebels posted a proclamation on the door of the General Post Office on Sackville Street. Its message was uncompromising:

We declare the right of the people of Ireland to the ownership of Ireland and to the unfettered control of Irish destinies, to be sovereign and indefeasible. The long usurpation of that right by a foreign people and government has not extinguished the right, nor can it ever be extinguished except by the destruction of the Irish people. In every generation, the Irish people have asserted their right to national freedom and sovereignty; six times during the past three hundred years they have asserted it in arms. Standing on that fundamental right and again asserting it in arms in the face of the world, we hereby proclaim the Irish Republic as a Sovereign Independent State, and we pledge our lives and the lives of our comrades in arms to the cause of its freedom, of its welfare, and of its exaltation among the nations.

Its seven signatories declared themselves the provisional government of a new Irish Republic.

For six days, the rebels controlled a few square miles in central Dublin. It was impressive, even the men at the table had to admit; 1,000 or so volunteers held out against the might of the British Empire.

The volunteers had trained for street fighting. The British, unprepared and conditioned for the Western Front, had not. At one point, the Royal Navy's HMY *Helga* steamed up the Liffey and shelled the city streets remorselessly until Sackville Street was a burning wreckage. The rebels had secured and defended their posts, but tactics were no substitute for strategy. The GPO, the rebellion's headquarters, held little critical value. They failed to capture Trinity College or Dublin Castle, the symbolic seat of imperial power. When the British forces adjusted to the extraordinary situation and employed new tactics, they broke the Irish defences.

It may not have been a damn close-run thing, as Wellington had said of Waterloo; without a general uprising, the rebellion was doomed – and the rebels knew it. However, it had been bloody and had only ended when Pádraig Pearse, the republic's self-declared President, ordered his army to surrender to avoid more unnecessary deaths. In total, 485 people were killed. Of those, 143 were British military and police personnel, but 260 were civilians. The man at the head of the table knew that his own men were responsible for numerous civilian deaths and injuries.

The whole thing sickened him.

Home Rule was, at last, on the statute books. Even the Tories admitted it was unavoidable. That it had not been implemented was not the fault of the British but of the Great War – a war that had brought Ireland the biggest deployment of troops in its history. Nearly 90,000 Irishmen had enlisted over two years. The 10th Irish Division had served honourably in the Gallipoli campaign and suffered huge losses. Catholic leaders such as John Redmond had defied their Pope to support the war effort. Indeed, Redmond had even served himself, as did his brother William.

Yet the rebels had taken an explicit side against their fellow countrymen fighting in the trenches. Their proclamation referred to 'our gallant allies in Europe'. Who else could they mean but Germany and Austria-Hungary? Now justice was being done. The British Army had arrested the rebels; court martials were being held in secret; the accused were allowed no defence. The next morning, the executions, to be staggered for maximum impact, would begin. They would become examples. The rebels would be intimidated into submission.

His instincts pulled him towards the harshest policy of retribution.

And yet. Something stopped him. He was, after all, inexperienced in Irish politics, having arrived as 'military governor' only a few days before. For 115 years, this island had been not a colony but an integral, if turbulent, part of the United Kingdom. It was the United Kingdom of Great Britain *and Ireland* – by Act of Union.

He thought. The idea of mass executions was distasteful. He had clear-cut instructions – but from a government whose drift had allowed unrest to rise and given tacit permission for the militancy of so-called loyalists. Might a cold-blooded response revolt opinion – not just here but eventually in Westminster, from where the Prime Minister, H. H. Asquith, was watching and to whom he would have to report? What if what he called justice, they called martyrdom? What if the dissidents were not cowed – or worse, what if those who had a few days previously shunned the rebellion were radicalised?

In Pretoria, a decade and a half before, as governor he had gained the trust of the population. He had even been praised for it. In Egypt, his previous post, they had noted his human kindness. The man who lost Ireland was not an epitaph he wanted on his tombstone.

Blood begets blood. It was a terrible cycle. Just then, it revolted him, and he wanted none of it. 'To hell with them! We're not doing it,' he barked. He paused and spoke more calmly, 'We'll wait to see the lie of the land.'

Before any of those at the table could respond, Lieutenant-General Sir John Grenfell Maxwell stood up and strode out of the room.

~

'We derided the moral law and said there was no law but the law of force, and the moral law answered us. Every devilish thing we did against the British went its full circle and then boomeranged and smote us tenfold.'

P. S. O'Hegarty (1879–1955), writer and former member of the Irish Republican Brotherhood Supreme Council, 1924

In his old age, Michael Collins said that Ireland, as a nation in the twentieth century, had three chapters.

The first drew to a close six years after the Easter Rising. The failed insurrection did not catalyse a Nationalist fever. General Maxwell's pause unintentionally allowed the British government to issue more lenient orders. All but the core agitators escaped jail. That their fate could have been worse robbed them of any martyrdom. Dispirited, many left Nationalist politics. Most of those who remained – but far from all – warily turned to constitutionalism. The rebellion became an unpopular memory. Normality was restored swiftly, and Asquith was able to declare that Home Rule would be a priority for his peacetime administration.

It was not to be that simple. In December 1916, Asquith was forced into resignation and the Liberal David Lloyd George 'kissed hands' at Buckingham Palace with a mandate to win the war – which he did, with the armistice on 11 November 1918.

Four years of conflict had brought terrible loss to the empire and Ireland. Some 250,000 Irishmen had served; over 50,000 had lost their lives. In war, Redmond and Edward Carson, the Unionist leader, had found a common cause: Protestant and Catholic had fought and died side by side. While many Nationalists questioned the disproportionate loss of Irish life and the harsh treatment of working-class Irish soldiers in the trenches, the effort and sacrifice helped to forge a national Irish identity.

When Redmond died in March 1918, John Dillon assumed the leadership of the Irish Parliamentary Party, the dominant pro-Home Rule party. Dillon was a courageous and passionate leader but his opposition, Sinn Féin, was a party emboldened. On the issue of governance, there was little to separate the two parties – both campaigned for Home Rule, self-government within the United Kingdom. However, as the more Nationalist of the two parties, Sinn Féin had found popular support in their opposition to the attempt to impose conscription on Ireland. After all but ceasing to exist in 1914, the party revived in the 1918 Westminster elections and scored their best result since their foundation to emerge as the second party, with thirty-four of the island's ninety seats.

Those who had a nagging fear of another betrayal – after all, had not Lloyd George's Conservative coalition partners scuppered Home Rule in 1893? – did not allow for the determination of the 'Welsh Wizard', a self-styled 'Gladstonian Home Ruler'. That an *extreme* nationalism did not command popular support meant that Lloyd George did not have to threaten war or play to Unionist demands. After the armistice, he moved swiftly on the Irish Question before Conservative hardliners could gain the ascendancy.

So, when Home Rule happened, it was not romantic. Forty years in the making, when it finally came to pass it was dull. There was no treaty, no intense wrangling, no massive disputes. No poets immortalised it. There was no need for the 'blood sacrifice' for which mystical Nationalists such as Pearse yearned.

Home Rule's jurisdiction did not apply to Antrim, Armagh, Derry, Down, Fermanagh and Tyrone. However, direct representation in Westminster – rather than an equivalent Protestant Assembly in Ulster – ensured that the Catholic minority would keep their representation and that there would be no Ulster Unionist supremacy. Taking their cue from Redmond, 'Ulster will have to follow' became the Nationalist motto.

Watched by Lloyd George and the King at the opening of the new Home Rule Parliament, Chief Minister John Dillon declared, 'This has been a long and painful labour, but it has been a victory – a victory for democracy.' And it was.

While Dillon and his new Irish National Party (INP) dominated politics for much of Home Rule's early life, its first parliament saw the election of two young members who would prove to be of greater significance to Ireland's future. Had British reprisals been more extensive, undoubtedly they would have filled the vacuum left by widespread executions – assuming they themselves had been spared. As it was, the Home Rule Parliament allowed them to climb a green if greasy pole.

The senior of the two young members was a former mathematics teacher, Éamon de Valera. During the rising, he had commanded the forces of the south-eastern approaches to Dublin and had been arrested in the aftermath. Tall and rangy, he was academic in disposition with a strong asceticism borne of his stronger Catholicism.

The other, also arrested for his role as an aide-de-camp in 1916, was Michael Collins. From County Cork, he had a large and commanding presence, but his burly appearance and good-natured peasant's face belied his shrewd, political brain.

Both were romantics, though his allies claimed that Collins's romanticism sprang from a broader spectrum. Both joined Sinn Féin, but their approaches to politics were different. De Valera, convinced that the British would renege, joined the new Irish Republican Army, who were agitating for independence and unity by 'any means necessary'. Collins, who cursed the blunders of 1916, did not. They may not have personified it, but they were examples of Sinn Féin's dual identity. Tacitly supported by some within the party, the IRA campaigned violently against the remaining British presence on the island.

The fall of Lloyd George's government in October 1922 forced the INP to forge links with the new Conservative administration in London to implement Home Rule. Meanwhile, de Valera and Collins looked abroad, with differing degrees of enthusiasm, for inspiration as to how to achieve their aim of independence.

In 1926, formalising what had existed in practice for decades, Britain granted dominion status to Australia, Canada, Newfoundland and South Africa. Younger 'Shinners', as supporters of Sinn Féin were called, became advocates of its advantages: dominion status would give Ireland greater powers than Home Rule. More importantly, although the new dominions were still part of the British Empire, their status was as equals. As a dominion, Ireland would no longer be subservient to its neighbour. In the Great War, Irishmen had fought alongside subjects from Australia, Canada and New Zealand; how could the British plausibly deny the Irish what they had given freely to others?

It took two terms for Sinn Féin to dislodge the INP from office and, when they did, it was with this as their policy. In his first speech to the Dáil, the new Chief Minister, William Cosgrave, asserted his intention to negotiate dominion status. He invited Collins to be part of the all-party delegation. Collins insisted that Dev also be part of the negotiations; if he were to make compromises, he wanted his rival to be part of the deal. Publicly invited, de Valera could hardly refuse.

The 1930 Buckingham Palace Conference lasted for four months. While Britain's new Labour ministers courted the old guard who officially led the Irish delegation, London's political salons feted the two coming men, Collins and de Valera.

The problem was not one of British resistance: the retention of an oath of allegiance to the British Crown, inherent in dominion status, was inflaming old passions. A united Ireland was not on the table. The IRA stirred. While Collins threw himself into the negotiations and often filled the vacuum left by some of the ageing rebels, de Valera suddenly absented himself from the delegation, pleading ill health. Tensions increased.

The eventual treaty was not 'independence', but it was one step closer. For many, that was not enough. 'Think – what have I got for Ireland? Something which she has wanted these past 700 years. Will anyone be satisfied with this bargain? Will anyone?' Collins remarked after the negotiations were concluded. 'I have signed my actual death warrant.'[1]

By the time Dev rose from his sick bed to put his signature – without ceremony – to the document, constitutional order was in the balance. Once again, the whiff of rebellion flavoured the air.

On their return, a fractious Dáil listened to Collins and the other delegates but deputies waited for the missing de Valera. It was not until late that he took his usual seat. Nobody knew what to expect. He rose to speak. 'Some of us learned later than others that we must take majority rule as determining policy, and be content with it, even when we think and we are convinced it is wrong,' he told the chamber. Channelling Wolfe Tone, he then declared: 'The unification of Ireland is our end. The abolition of the memory of past dissension is our means.'[2] He paused, to murmurs of approval. Conscious of the moment, he revealed his *coup de grâce*: an IRA plot to assassinate the delegation. Dramatically, he renounced the group and resigned his membership.

It was one of the finest – and most startling – parliamentary performances deputies had heard. He was no orator, but he had passion and simplicity. It was only his first move.

Over the coming months, Ireland came close to outright civil war. Both Collins and Dev played their part. To packed chambers, 'the long fellah' forensically dismantled his former allies. He pleaded with Irishmen and women to shut their doors to the IRA and not to give them shelter. He suggested ways to quell the rebels, including pardoning IRA members if they ended the violence. He proposed a Bill that would end the contentious oath. Meanwhile, 'the big fellah' joined the military campaign against the IRA until they declared, in 1933, that their war (such as it was) was over.

Although perilous and violent, the insurrection settled another Irish Question: was the country a state committed to democratic values? It also represented a moment when the next generation of leaders assumed control. Revisionists later suggested that Dev had created the situation in order to present himself as saviour. At the time, he was lauded as the man who had saved Irish constitutional democracy and assumed a position akin to Cicero's after his exposure of the Catiline conspiracy, as father of the nation. Yet in practice he elevated 'General' Collins further.

Sinn Féin lost power in 1934. When Cosgrave resigned, Collins and de Valera vied for the succession. Upon his victory, Collins offered Dev the party's deputy leadership. Perhaps unwilling to play second fiddle to an old rival, he declined. He said that it was a matter of policy differences, especially on economics.

Sinn Féin's second period in office coincided with a deteriorating European situation. In the House of Commons, the maverick former minister Winston Churchill warned of impending war with Nazi Germany and the empire's unpreparedness. Perhaps with this in mind, the new Chief Minister ensured that the memory of those who lost their lives in the Great War would not be eliminated from Irish history. He withstood pressure from de Valera to avoid the official unveiling, on 30 July 1939, of a national war memorial, sited in Parnell Square's new Garden of Remembrance, designed by Edwin Lutyens. As one minister said, 'Such a ceremony could be symbolical [sic] of the unification of all elements of the country under an agreed democratic constitution. The gesture could hardly fail to create a good impression beyond the border and upon British public opinion.'³ Here, Collins's canny judgement contrasted with de Valera's often tin ear for opinion outside his narrow Catholic constituency.

Two months later, on 1 September, the German invasion of Poland forced the British Prime Minister, Neville Chamberlain, to abandon his appeasement policy. On 3 September, Britain declared war.

Collins did not act immediately. He waited to show his independence. The Dáil debated for two days. The first to speak from the back benches was the member for Ennis. The Irish people did not want another war, Dev declared; as a young state, Ireland's survival was at stake and neutrality was the only realistic course. He begged the government to assure Chamberlain of any assistance short of war. Despite his interventions, deputies voted – on the same day as the Canadian House of Commons – narrowly to join Britain in war.

Home Rule gave Ireland jurisdiction over domestic policy. The 1931 Statute of Westminster gave the dominions autonomy over their foreign policy. Even so, some said that Ireland was bound by a declaration made in the name of a shared monarch. By declaring war separately, Ireland indisputably became an independent state in all but name.

Historians have written book after book about a small nation's contribution to a big war. Few have denied the valour of those who signed up. Other books have been written about the unlikely relationship between two leaders whose countries successfully fended off Nazi invasion. They had many obvious differences but there were similarities: both had the ability to inspire audiences, both were at heart romantics and both fancied themselves as military strategists and men of action. 'He is an Irish patriot, true and fearless,' Churchill wrote of Collins.

Equally, victory in war did not bring either the gratitude of their countries. Like Churchill, in 1945, Collins found himself in opposition.

John Redmond had prophesied that fighting in the trenches would unite Ireland's divided strands. He was nearly right. It was the Second World War that accomplished what two decades before had proved impossible. Without a Parliament of their own, the Protestants never held the kind of primacy that would have allowed them to give in to their worst instincts. Moreover, the post-war Marshall Plan allowed Ireland to recover quicker than Britain from the devastations of war. As with those of Germany and France, the post-war years were kind to the Irish economy, enabling it to weather the storms Britain threw its way.

Quietly, some Unionist politicians began to consider a united Ireland. Whereas the British war leader spoke of an Iron Curtain, Ireland's talked about bringing barriers down: in 1947, Collins declared a united Ireland within sight and said that any Irish government should be willing to make concessions in order to achieve it. The first compromise was that Ulster would not 'follow'; a united Ireland would be a new state, brought about only by the consent of the island's two communities: north and south. It became the centrepiece of Collins's campaign for a return to power.

He had one significant piece of luck: the election of Captain Terence O'Neill, in 1946, as MP for Bannside in the north. O'Neill's military background gave him status within the Unionist communities. Unlike some from previous generations, he was not an acolyte of the former Ulster

Unionist leader Edward Carson and was not virulently anti-Catholic. Within a few years of his election, O'Neill led the Unionists.

On 21 February 1949, Clement Attlee announced to the House of Commons the Independence of Ireland Bill, one piece of legislation that united the two jurisdictions of the island into one unitary state. The Anglo-Irish plan would give full sovereignty to Ireland and to representatives from both communities the ability to write their own constitution.

The negotiations started easily: the parties agreed that Ulster was not to be subsumed into the existing Irish state; the new nation would have no state religion; freedom of religious expression would be a primary article of the new constitution. Even so, the contentious issue of parades led to outbreaks of sectarian violence in Belfast and Londonderry. Unionists withdrew from the negotiations. The delegations only met again when Collins publicly suggested a commission to settle disputes. He also conceded that the British monarch would remain head of state.

The next dispute came over language. Although not part of the official negotiating team, de Valera threatened to withhold his consent. Without him, there could be no Catholic agreement. Since Unionists would not countenance an official language that few of them spoke, eventually the negotiators agreed that there would be two joint official languages. The north's reward – at no cost to Dev, who disliked proportional representation – was elections conducted under the British first-past-the-post system and a second chamber modelled after the American Senate, to best protect the Protestant minority.

On 17 March 1951, the two sides reached agreement. All that remained was to win majorities on both sides of the border.

Collins had a few tricks up his sleeve. Helpfully, someone leaked to the *Belfast Telegraph* a Dominions Office memorandum that recorded the Secretary of State's proposed offer of a united Ireland as an inducement to reconsider at some point, should the Dáil vote against a declaration of war in 1939. Collins then announced that, in order to reach beyond community divides, Sinn Féin would merge with the two Labour parties of north and south to contest the elections under a new all-Ireland, non-sectarian social democratic banner.

The referendum's result was conclusive.

Collins's new party won the following elections by a landslide. The Christian Democrats, formed loosely from the INP, became the second largest grouping. Of the few who contested the election as Independent Sinn Féin, only a handful won their seats – Dev among them. It was a new beginning.

Before the election of the Taoiseach of the first all-Ireland Dáil, Collins winked at his old rival as Dev took the Ceann Comhairle's chair – really, he could think of no better person to fill the Speaker's robes. When Collins came to speak, he declared he would only accept the position of Taoiseach for three years and with O'Neill as Tánaiste – *and his successor*. The Commonwealth of Ireland's second leader would come from the Unionist tradition.

By the opening of the third chapter, Michael Collins's great locks had grown grey. He still towered over most men, but his body was frail. The sight of him bicycling through Dublin's streets was a thing of the past. While former Speaker de Valera found a new passion in his campaign for a memorial for those who had given their lives in the cause of Irish freedom, to mark the state's tenth anniversary, 'the big fellah' enjoyed the life of an elder statesman.

During the 1950s, the country enjoyed an economic boom that allowed the long-serving Finance Minister, Seán Lemass, to crow 'We've never had it so good!' Lemass was right; the Social Democrats rewarded him with its leadership.

A veteran of 1916, the new Taoiseach was an old man in a hurry. It was for this reason that he paid a visit to Collins. Lemass's goal was to prepare for membership of the new European Economic Community (EEC). By strengthening the firm diplomatic relationships that already existed with the new bloc, Ireland could apply for membership some time after 1961. That gave him a few years to travel across Europe to make his case and to prepare the country.

Ireland was economically strong enough to apply. Its agricultural and industrial sectors were thriving; that it had avoided neutrality in the Second World War and was a member of NATO would play in its favour for those Europeans whose aspirations went beyond trade and hoped for a political union. The EEC's plans to create a Common Agricultural Policy, with price guarantees and export subsidies, would suit Ireland's agriculturally dominant economy.

But there was a problem. The sterling area, the single market and Commonwealth membership would make Irish membership difficult should Britain not be minded to apply. Already, the EEC had rebuffed Britain's ambition for a trade bloc without external tariffs that would have allowed the UK to maintain its Imperial Preference policy. 'The British need to apply. The empire is gone,' said Collins. He and Lemass then discussed the implications of a British application. What would happen if Britain successfully applied but Ireland was rejected? And if Britain did not secure membership, would Ireland have any other choice but to withdraw its application? 'We will, then, have one big obstacle,' Collins told his protégé. 'De Gaulle. Let me help.'

As Collins had predicted, Britain's direction of travel was similar to its neighbour's. When Britain received formal permission to apply, Lemass published a white paper stating his government's position. Any fears that the Irish had were soon put to rest: the West German Foreign Ministry were enthusiastic and the Six were clear that Ireland was a credible candidate.

In December 1962, with negotiation at a crucial stage, Collins travelled to Paris to meet an old wartime friend. Unlike with the Brits, there was no way that Collins could meet the French President as a superior, or even an equal; he could not offend that way. Instead, he played the supplicant. The next month, de Gaulle, at a theatrical press conference, put aside his reservations about these two islands and declared: '*Oui.*'

The pro-EEC side easily won the vote in the Dáil, by 196 votes to thirty-seven. Defeat did not stop de Valera. He could command headlines and audiences more easily than many party leaders. Now in his ninth decade, failing sight had diminished his once piercing eyes. His homburg hid a shock of white hair. His voice now cracked when he spoke. Nevertheless, he campaigned up and down the thirty-two counties during the referendum on the treaty, denouncing EEC membership.

Ireland was a great nation that could stand against the world as it had stood against British imperialism, he argued. How could a country that had just won its freedom now wish to submerge itself into the EEC?

Collins watched – and despite their differences, part of him admired the nostalgic idealism. He did not totally disagree, but it was an Ireland of an old radical's dreams. Dev could always stir the passions of the true believers but rarely had the imagination or character to speak a language that those who did not fit his notions of Irishness would hear.

This was his swansong. It was also Collins's. It was one final duel. But the result was never really in doubt. The 'Yes' campaign won 78 per cent of the vote, with thirty counties voting to join the EEC. De Valera never got to see his last defeat; after months of campaigning in all kinds of weather, he collapsed with pneumonia on the day of the referendum and was rushed to hospital. He died within the week.

Collins did not attend the funeral, but he did pay his respects at Glasnevin Cemetery. Later, an observer – one of the parish clergy – said that the old man must have stood at the graveyard for almost an hour. Not recognising him, the witness went to approach but stopped a few yards away as the solitary mourner spoke: 'We *were* Ireland for a while, weren't we? This is a new chapter.'

That evening, Michael Collins passed away peacefully in his sleep.

~

'If a nation is to learn anything at all from history, it must be willing to examine, using all it knows now, what might have happened, if different historical choices had been made. The choice to use force in 1916, and again in 1919, must be subjected to severe and honest reappraisal, in light of what we can now see might have been achieved, without the loss of life.'

John Bruton (1947–), former Taoiseach, 2016

Leo Varadkar fiddled nervously with his bow tie and looked at the portrait of John Redmond that hung on the wall behind his desk.

This would be the tenth time he had done this. It was tradition, and the longest-standing leader in the EU enjoyed it. All politicians should be allowed a certain amount of vanity. He told himself, not untruthfully, that the annual Constitution Day celebrations demonstrated a country at ease with itself, but it was also a moment for him to shine, and he was at ease with that.

It was 17 March – and, unusually, this year he liked his guest.

Exactly on time, he left Leinster House in his government Mercedes, made in his own Dublin constituency, and drove past the Éamon de Valera statue onto the streets until he arrived at the magnificent Michael Collins Festival Hall in the Docklands area. He battled through the scrum of reporters, answering only the question from CNN. On entering the building, he briefly caught the eye of Mary Lou McDonald, the opposition leader, who was talking to Mr Justice Trimble. Before he could get a drink, he felt a tug on his elbow. 'Taoiseach,' President Higgins said, 'could we borrow you for a minute?'

Varadkar followed the head of state and jostled in between Marys Robinson and McAleese, Ireland's first two Presidents. They smiled as the cameraman took their picture, then exhaled in relief.

Before he could catch his breath, an aide hurried up to him: 'His car's about to pull in.' The Taoiseach straightened his dinner jacket and walked towards the entrance. The British Prime Minister's car arrived as Varadkar breathed the night air for the first time. The grey hair of his counterpart emerged. Varadkar strode forward. 'Mr Prime Minister, thank you for coming.'

'I wouldn't miss it for the world, Taoiseach,' the new arrival replied. 'I'm just sorry I'm late.'

Varadkar smiled pityingly at Keir Starmer. His own Christian Democrats' healthy majority, cemented by their long alliance with Ulster's Conservative Union Party, meant that he did not suffer the same regular crises as Starmer, forced to rely on a rainbow coalition of parties for every vote. He did not comment directly on his guest's appearance but offered a bland 'You look tired,' and began to usher him into the theatre for the gala celebrations.

'Have you been here before, Keir?'

'No. This is my first time. What a building, though!'

'Irish architecture. Best in the world,' the Irishman said.

'But it was a British construction company that built it, I believe,' the Brit parried.

The Taoiseach flashed a stern frown at Starmer, then grinned. The pair laughed.

'I've been thinking about the next European Council,' Starmer said. 'Where is it again? Stormont?' The Taoiseach raised his eyebrows in vague assent. 'I think we essentially agree – and together we can persuade the Germans, who'll force the French on board.'

Again, Varadkar smiled – both at his colleague's business-like approach and at the relationship between the two countries that often led the way in Europe. 'I think you're right,' he replied. 'I'm sure that Gerry will be pleased if we reach a solid agreement.'

Varadkar's nomination of the former Social Democratic Taoiseach for Commission President had proved one of his early successes. Now Adams was about to stand down, an agreement on the new stimulus fund would burnish his legacy.

Their conversation moved to idle matters: the pressures of office, missed family moments and other gripes that leaders are wont to talk about when the public are not listening. 'What are you doing for Easter?' the British leader asked.

And briefly – very briefly – Varadkar thought about General Maxwell, 1916 and all that – and how it could have been very different.

'Nothing much,' he replied.

'It is my considered opinion that in the fullness of time history will record the greatness of Michael Collins; and it will be recorded at my expense.'
Éamon de Valera (1882–1975), Irish politician and statesman, 1966

Selected bibliography

Bruce Arnold and Jason O'Toole, *The End of the Party: How Fianna Fáil Finally Lost Its Grip on Power* (Dublin: Gill & Macmillan Ltd, 2011)

George Boyce, 'Ireland and the First World War', *History Ireland* (1994), vol. 2, no. 3

Tim Pat Coogan, *Michael Collins: The Man Who made Ireland* (London: St Martin's Griffiths, 1992)

Richard English, *Irish Freedom: The History of Irish Nationalism* (London: Pan Books, 1992)

Ronan Fanning, *Éamon de Valera: A Will to Power* (London: Faber & Faber, 2015)

John Horgan, 'Ireland and the EEC (II)', *The Furrow* (1971), vol. 22, no. 11

Michael Kennedy, Dermot Keogh, Eunan O'Halpin, Kate O'Malley and Bernadette Whelan, *Documents on Irish Foreign Policy Vol. XI: 1957–1961* (Dublin: Royal Irish Academy, 2018)

Donald McNamara, 'Bloody Instructions: General John Maxwell in Dublin after the Easter Rising', *Princeton University Library Chronicle* (2002), vol. 63, no. 3

Conor O'Loughlin, 'Irish Foreign Policy during World War II: A Test for Realist Theories of Foreign Policy', *Irish Studies in International Affairs* (2008), vol. 19

Brian Walker, *Irish History Matters: Politics, Identities and Commemorations* (Dublin: History Press Ireland, 2019)

Notes

1   In reality this was famously said by Collins on the signing of the Anglo-Irish Treaty in December 1921.

2   De Valera expressed these sentiments, roughly quoted, in speeches to the Dáil on 1 and 2 March 1934, when he renounced his position on the 1921 treaty. Bill Kissane, 'Éamon de Valera and the Survival of Democracy in Inter-War Ireland', *Journal of Contemporary History* (2007), vol. 42, no. 2, p. 216.

3   Said by an anonymous Nationalist of de Valera's reluctance to attend the unveiling ceremony at Islandbridge. George Boyce, 'Ireland and the First World War', *History Ireland* (1994), vol. 2, no. 3, p. 51.

Chapter 4

What if Franklin D. Roosevelt had died of polio in 1921?

Robert Waller

In 1921, FDR suffered a serious poliomyelitis attack that left him paralysed from the waist down. At times there were fears for his life. What if he had not lived to be the United States' only ever four-term President, overseeing the New Deal and the Second World War?

In the November 1932 presidential election, Franklin Delano Roosevelt, the Governor of the State of New York, inflicted a devastating defeat on the Republican incumbent, Herbert Hoover. He carried forty-two states to Hoover's six, and thus won the electoral college by 472 votes to fifty-nine and the popular vote by a margin of over 7 million. The reason for this was clear: the US was in the grip of the worst economic slump in its history, deteriorating since the Wall Street Crash of autumn 1929. Hoover's leadership had signally failed to promote relief or recovery, whereas on accepting the Democratic nomination for the 1932 race, having defeated a number of other candidates, including the 1928 nominee Al Smith, Roosevelt had promised 'a New Deal for the American people'. After he was elected, he delivered a massive surge of government activity and action, ranging from banking and financial reform through to major programmes for the recovery of agriculture (such as the Agricultural Adjustment Act, or AAA) and industry (through the National Recovery Administration, or NRA). Although no explicit civil rights measures were passed, the effective help that FDR's New Deal policies offered to the overwhelmingly poor African-American community meant those in the north who were allowed to vote dramatically switched their allegiance. Until 1932 a large majority of black voters had supported the Republicans, the party of Lincoln. By 1936 this had changed, as an estimated 76 per cent, an overwhelming majority, voted for the Democrats[1] – a phenomenon that has remained true to this day.

The scope and powers of Roosevelt's central government were ·transformed as the responsibility for the welfare of the unemployed was shifted from the states and localities, and there was a dramatic increase in Washington-financed public works. Opinions about the desirability and success of the varied New Deal programmes were wildly divergent. While providing much-needed relief for those suffering from unemployment and poverty, FDR's initiatives did not in themselves end the Depression; the unemployment rate in 1940 was still a very high 14.6 per cent, for example.[2] Despite the dramatic and extensive innovation of the New Deal since 1933, it was to be the mighty national effort required in the Second World War that finally reinvigorated the American economy. However, there can be no doubt that the New Deal was a major turning point in the history of American government, and in particular in the role of the President.

Equally important to the rise of executive control was Roosevelt's role during the war. The foreign policy of the United States had been dominated by isolationism ever since Woodrow Wilson's plans for shaping the world in the aftermath of the First World War – including the Paris peace treaties and the establishment of the League of Nations – had been rejected by Congress. In the 1930s, the same body passed a series of Neutrality Acts seeking to tie the President's hands as the second great world conflict drew ever closer. Roosevelt, despite his internationalist tendencies and strong Allied sympathies, was unable to take the US into the war before the Japanese attack on Pearl Harbor on 7 December 1941. Nevertheless, he did manage to stretch the rules to help the United Kingdom and its allies, for example by exchanging fifty American destroyer warships for rights to bases in the Caribbean in September 1940, and then by extending this assistance with the 'cash and carry' and Lend–Lease systems from December 1940 and throughout 1941. Roosevelt developed a strong, warm relationship with Winston

Churchill, which included setting out American and British goals for the post-war period in the Atlantic Charter when the two men met for four days off Newfoundland in August 1941 – over three months before the US actually entered the war. There can be little doubt that FDR's friendliness with the UK assisted greatly during its 'darkest hour'.

How might history have been altered if this remarkable and powerful man had not survived in 1921? There can be no doubt that this was far from the realms of impossibility. Even in the twenty-first century, the adult mortality rate for acute paralytic poliomyelitis is estimated at 15 per cent,[3] and 100 years ago far less was known about the prevention and diagnosis of this viral disease. There was no vaccine before Jonas Salk's work bore fruit in 1955, and in Roosevelt's case polio was not even diagnosed for two weeks after he fell severely ill. In mid-August 1921, FDR fell overboard from his yacht when cruising in the North Atlantic off the shore of Maine, the location of his holiday home, Campobello. He felt a chill the next day and retired to bed, where he developed severe pain in his back and legs and then a high fever. The next day he could not walk or move his legs. As we now know, he was never to walk unaided again – a fact which makes his manifold later achievements all the more remarkable.

Franklin D. Roosevelt had already achieved much at this stage. He had been a senator in the New York Assembly from 1910 to 1913 and an active assistant secretary of the navy from 1913 to 1919, including during the US's relatively brief participation in the First World War. Indeed, he had even been the Democratic candidate for Vice-President on the ticket of James Cox in the 1920 election to succeed Woodrow Wilson.

But let us now suppose he did pass away in that summer of 1921, at the age of thirty-nine.

~

For some time, it is unlikely that history would have been significantly different. The 1920 Democratic campaign had gone down to a decisive defeat, as the Republican team of Warren Harding and Calvin Coolidge had won the popular vote by 16 million to 9 million and the electoral college by the massive margin of 404 to 127. The American voters had decisively rejected the internationalism that Wilson – and indeed Roosevelt – had stood for.

What is more, the 1920s were to be a thoroughly Republican decade. The business of capitalism boomed throughout the 'Roaring Twenties', based both on genuine reasons for rapid growth and much more unsound speculation. Harding died in 1923, but his Vice-President Calvin Coolidge was elected in his own right in 1924, and Herbert Hoover won in 1928, all by very convincing margins. No Democratic candidate would have prospered in these circumstances.

On the other hand, slump inevitably followed boom. The Wall Street Crash of autumn 1929 was only the prelude to a depression that destroyed so many banks, businesses and farms that by the time of the presidential election of November 1932, the unemployment rate was nearly 25 per cent, with at least 15 million out of work. In these circumstances, the incumbent Hoover had no chance against any Democratic candidate.

In the absence of Roosevelt, who did the Democrats nominate? The front-runner at the convention which opened on 27 June 1932 in Chicago was their 1928 candidate: Alfred E. Smith of New York. Although he had been defeated by Hoover four years earlier, that was in very different economic circumstances. Smith was still the towering figure in the politics of the Democratic Party, having served for six years as the Governor of New York, by far the largest state in the union, commanding the greatest number of convention delegates (and electoral college votes). Although he had risen through the influence of the 'Tammany Hall' political machine that had dominated the politics of the largest city in America for decades, Al Smith (as he was universally known) had a deserved reputation for honesty rather than corruption. His plain speaking (in a very pronounced Lower East Side accent) clearly cut through to the mass of voters, particularly at a time of hardship such as 1932. He (and his highly effective lieutenants, such as the Rockland County boss, Jim Farley) overwhelmed his main opponents for the nomination – House Speaker 'Cactus Jack' Garner of Texas, Governor George White of Ohio and the leader of the Indiana delegation, Paul McNutt, regarded as fast-rising, at least in his own state. None of these three had more than local appeal, and White and McNutt split the Midwestern vote.

Smith, on the other hand, benefited in 1932 from an issue that had almost certainly prevented him from securing the nomination in 1924, and which had not helped him in 1928: Prohibition. Coming from the largest urban area in the nation, Smith had been seen as the leader of the 'wet' forces, arguing for repeal of the Eighteenth Amendment ever since his signature to approve an anti-Prohibition state measure in New York in 1923. By now, however, the circumstances of the Depression had made the wet case much more popular – not only did many people feel in need of a drink but repeal would bring badly needed legitimate jobs and also tax revenues for a hard-pressed government, which might support relief measures for the unemployed. The identification of Smith with this cause, as opposed to his three rivals, who were all from rural, agricultural, predominantly dry states, brought him the powerful support of urban bosses like Mayor Curley of Boston, who mobilised the New England Democratic machines in his favour. Smith won the 1932 nomination on the fourth ballot. Garner became the vice-presidential nominee, to balance the ticket with a rural southerner and in return for a deal to gain his delegates.

Smith duly defeated Hoover in the general election. Hoover won eleven states; it was felt that Smith's Catholicism and strong association with 'big city' New York, more than his stance on Prohibition, reduced the size of the landslide somewhat, but the 'solid south' held firm for the Democrats, and the overwhelming feeling was that Hoover had made no progress against the economic slump and had to go at all costs. The election of the first Roman Catholic President, and the first with Irish and Italian ancestry, was ensured by the economic blizzard.

Before he was inaugurated in March 1933, Smith assembled a small 'brains trust' from the advisers who had been so influential in helping him during his four terms as Governor of New York, led by the southern-born Joseph Proskauer; the visionary of parks and road systems Robert Moses; and Belle Moskowitz, in effect his chief of staff. Another influential woman, who had collaborated with Smith ever since his work on dangerous conditions in factories before the First World War, was Frances Perkins, who was to become the first-ever female Cabinet member as Secretary of Labor.

However, President Smith's approach to the Depression was to be far from radical. As Proskauer told interviewers, Smith was adamantly opposed to 'a tremendous concentration' of federal power, a force 'reaching its tentacles into every kind of social and political question on the lower level'.⁴ The fact was that Smith was a long-standing believer in states' rights, as shown most clearly by his strong and risky stance on Prohibition throughout the 1920s and by his support of the New York state-wide relaxation of enforcement provisions in repealing the Mullin-Gage Act in December 1923.

Another reason why President Smith failed to adopt anything like a 'New Deal' to treat the economic slump⁵ was his long-term commitment to governmental economy and balancing the budget. It might be remembered that the first thing he had done as the new Majority Leader and chairman of Ways and Means in the New York State Senate in 1910 was to require all 200 department heads to cut 10 per cent from their budgets in order to close the $15 million deficit.⁶ Then, in his first year as Sheriff of New York County (1915–16), Smith had cut expenditure by 3.3 per cent and increased revenues by 30 per cent.⁷ One of his major achievements as New York governor between 1922 and 1928 was to reduce dramatically the number of executive departments, so he was constitutionally disinclined to found any new agencies during his period as President, despite the problems of industry, agriculture and welfare.

Yes, the first thing that the new President Smith declared was that it was 'time for a drink', and the now thoroughly unpopular Eighteenth Amendment was fully repealed by the Twentieth within a year. Yes, his rapid declaration of a 'Bank Holiday' helped restore some of the vitally missing confidence in the financial system. Yes, two years later, in 1935, he accepted the legislation of his old New York state friend Senator Robert Wagner that improved the position of labour unions. And yes, he decided to provide encouragement for the arts through his Federal Theater Project. After all, Smith had been a very keen amateur

actor himself, gaining skills that proved extremely useful in his political career. However, as a portent of the likely economic policy of the
Smith presidency, he had long had close links with businessmen like
John J. Raskob, of General Motors and then of the company that had
constructed the Empire State Building, whom he had made chairman of
the Democratic National Committee in 1928.

Smith's policy towards industry remained decidedly *laissez-faire*
through the 1930s, and he scarcely intervened beyond the level of
Hoover's Reconstruction Finance Corporation, which was retained.
Much, including welfare and agricultural relief, was left to the rural
states, and the determined attempt to keep the federal government's
books balanced meant that the ideas of the British Liberal economist John
Maynard Keynes were stoutly dismissed. In fact, Smith flatly refused to
meet Keynes when the latter visited Washington in May 1934, saying he
'wouldn't understand his language'.[8] Overall, some thought it fortunate
for the President that the economy did slowly recover from the depths
of the Depression without a more active economic policy, as demanded
by radicals and interventionists like the Louisiana senator and former
governor Huey Long (until his assassination in September 1935 ended
his political threat to Smith), as well as the Keynesians. Others were
not surprised, as they believed that the vagaries of the capitalist system
formed inevitable cycles and could best look after themselves without
a huge injection of centralised executive intervention. In any case, the
voters must have been at least sufficiently satisfied, as they re-elected Al
Smith in 1936 to a second term (as they have most Presidents seeking to
continue; those denied re-election are usually regarded as downright
failures). Admittedly it was not a landslide victory, as the Republican
candidate Alf Landon did win fourteen states – a dozen more than the
absolute minimum of Maine and Vermont.[9]

In Smith's second term, foreign affairs played a leading role for the
first time since the Depression struck, with the rise of the power of the
European dictatorships, Italy and Germany, and of Japanese aggression
across the Pacific. Smith was singularly inexperienced in foreign policy,
and the lead was taken by Congress. In particular, the three Neutrality

Acts of 1935, 1937 and 1939 sought to keep the US out of the looming conflict, at least in Europe, along the lines promulgated by the Monroe Doctrine of 1823. Even when the Second World War actually broke out in 1939, the Smith administration remained unwilling to commit to the fight against Nazi Germany. Al Smith was strongly identified as an Irish-American, and indeed identified himself as such, although this ancestry was far more clear on his mother's side; his father was descended from Italian immigrants. He had little natural affinity with Britain, which was still strongly held responsible by the American Irish community for the great famine of the 1840s, as only part of centuries of occupation and oppression; and Italy entered the war on the Axis side in June 1940.

Perhaps if the triumvirate of Smith's long-term, Jewish advisers had still been close to him, there may have been more pressure to oppose the Nazi regime. However, Belle Moskowitz had died tragically early in January 1933, at the age of fifty-five, following a fall on the steps outside her house; Joseph Proskauer had become a judge and then Smith's second nominee to the Supreme Court in January 1938; and Robert Moses was fully occupied holding eight public offices simultaneously in New York state, including organising New York City's World Fair in 1939. Instead, the influence of others, such as Smith's former campaign manager James Aloysius Farley, another Irish-American, grew strongly.

The lack of any signs of possible assistance from Smith was undoubtedly one of the factors in the fraught British politics of the great crisis of 1940, immediately following the fall of France. If there had been more hope of help from across the Atlantic when Chamberlain resigned in May, the rather shadowy process of the selection of his successor as Prime Minister might well have led to a gamble on the black sheep of inter-war politics, Winston Churchill, who would probably have continued the fight even as the odds became apparently impossible. As it was, although the man on whom the choice did fall, Lord Halifax, did genuinely consider carrying on the fight, his decision was to accept Hitler's surprisingly generous offer of a non-aggression pact – which meant that the empire could be retained and that Britain was safe from invasion. This was strongly supported by the Cliveden set, by some very powerful press barons, and by many who had urged the appeasement of Germany in the late 1930s, including the US ambassador to Britain, Joseph P. Kennedy. In the general election of October 1940, the Conservatives under Halifax were returned with a reduced majority, as relief that peace had been secured narrowly outweighed widespread revulsion at the deal with the dictator.

It was also fortunate from the United Kingdom's point of view that the Führer's overwhelming priority was to free Germany to strike further eastwards, in the direction foreshadowed in the Lebensraum theory ever since *Mein Kampf* in the 1920s. This was dictated by the racial obsession of the Nazis, which classed Russians as inferior Slavs and the English as fellow Anglo-Saxon Aryans. Making peace with Britain allowed Hitler to accelerate his plans to break his more hypocritical agreement – the Nazi–Soviet Pact – and prepare to invade the Soviet Union in a one-front war as early as possible in 1941, without distractions across the English Channel or in North Africa. In any case, there had been strong doubts expressed about the feasibility of invading Britain – not by Goering, the head of the Luftwaffe, but certainly by the top generals in the Wehrmacht and the leading admirals in the German Navy.

Meanwhile, back in the US, Al Smith never considered the possibility of breaking the convention that Presidents should only serve two terms. There was no active fighting in Western Europe in the second half of 1940, and in any case international affairs had never been his strong suit. Among the Democrats competing for the nomination were Jim Farley (very much a continuity candidate as a Catholic and a New Yorker), the Midwesterner Paul McNutt (former Governor of Indiana), Jack Garner of Texas and Cordell Hull of Tennessee. After a hopelessly deadlocked convention in Chicago, where there was bitter opposition both to another New Yorker and to the southerners, McNutt emerged as the candidate, albeit not a strong one despite accounts of his 'astonishingly good looks'.[10]

After eight years of rather non-interventionist leadership, and with the tail end of the slump still dragging on, the election promised a good chance of a change of party. Among the Republican front-runners were the isolationist Senators Vandenberg and Taft, and Thomas Dewey, who had risen to fame as a prosecutor of gangland figures in New York. But Dewey was only thirty-eight years old – his time would come later – and the rising threat across the Pacific from an aggressive Japan on top of Hitler's triumphs was already making the isolationist case weaker. In the end, the Republican nomination at the Philadelphia convention, which started two days after France surrendered in June 1940, went to a more internationalist figure, Wendell Willkie, who cancelled out Democrat McNutt's Midwestern strength, as he was also originally from Indiana. Willkie was a businessman who had never before stood for elective office – but this does not always have to prove a bar to nomination, nor to be disastrous in practice. To many, he was an attractive figure, with a warm personality and appealing speaking style (as long as the occasion was extemporaneous and he was not reading from a prepared script). Although trained as a lawyer, Willkie had achieved high-flying success in business at an early age – often seen by many Americans as a qualification for high executive office. To balance the ticket, Willkie selected as his vice-presidential candidate a Westerner: Senator Charles McNary of Oregon.

In the general election in November 1940, Willkie proved the much more substantial candidate, sweeping the west and Midwest, including Illinois and Ohio, and winning key states in the north-east such as New York and New Jersey. The Republicans were back in the White House, but Willkie was of a very different hue to the party of the 1920s. Certainly Willkie, like President Al Smith, was not likely to favour extensive state intervention. In the 1930s he had vigorously defended his private-sector power conglomerate Commonwealth & Southern, and claimed to be a 'true liberal – who couldn't tolerate executive or legislative domination'.[11] Willkie was indeed a liberal in social as well as economic affairs, and also an Anglophile, strongly committed to an outward-looking foreign policy following that of his hero Woodrow Wilson. He was determined to stand up against aggressive powers (and for the United States' interests, of course).

Willkie was still encumbered by the Neutrality Acts and a divided

Congress, but any remaining isolationism was dispelled by the end of 1941. In July, responding to the occupation of Indochina, Willkie escalated sanctions against Japan's continuing expansion, most critically by freezing Japanese assets in the United States to prevent the purchase of the supplies needed to continue their military advances. This effectively placed an embargo on the supply of oil, a vital commodity of which Japan suffered a chronic shortage. Tensions were clearly reaching breaking point, but it was still a shock when the attack came on Pearl Harbor in Hawaii in early December.

By this time, events in the other hemisphere had been transformed. Freed from concerns on his Western Front by the agreement with Britain, Hitler had in turn been able to shock Stalin by a surprise attack on the Soviet Union as early as May 1941. True, he had needed briefly to divert into the Balkans to bail out his ally Mussolini's stuttering attempt at an invasion of Greece, but without external help the brave resistance of the Greeks had scarcely lasted longer than that of Yugoslavia, and Hitler was even able to extend his influence in the Mediterranean by seizing the island of Crete unopposed. The time he lost before the invasion on the Eastern Front nearly prevented the armies of the Reich from reaching both Leningrad and Moscow before winter completely froze their equipment and their advance – but not quite. Stalin himself retreated beyond the Urals and established a new capital in Kuibyshev, leaving his people to conduct a savage street-by-street resistance in the two chief cities as winter tightened its grip. Nevertheless, by December 1941 Hitler had suffered no apparent irrecoverable reverse in Russia. Perhaps that was one reason why he responded to the commencement of open hostilities between his Japanese ally and the United States by declaring war on the latter himself. Willkie, therefore, could face no internal obstacle to full entry into the Second World War.

If the United States was to face war on two fronts, in the Pacific and against a European foe, there was every reason for President Willkie to pull out all the stops to cement an active alliance. There can be no doubt that the US's massive potential support was one of the key factors in the remarkable events in the United Kingdom in early 1942, as Parliament (including strong factions in all major parties) ousted the government that had concluded such a humiliating truce with the Nazis. There equally could be no doubt about who the best man to lead the new government would be, despite his age of sixty-seven years. Brought out of his grumpy retirement at Chartwell in Kent (he had refused to seek sanctuary in Canada or even in the land of his mother – the US – when it looked like he might be deselected as MP for Epping or even, as a few suggested, arrested as an enemy of the pact in 1940), Winston Churchill was summoned to the highest office. He wasted no time in declaring war on Germany as well as Japan, whose rapid advance in south-east Asia had already led to the seizure of Hong Kong and an advance through Malaya towards Singapore. No imperial power could allow this to continue.

The course of the war can only be briefly summarised: the so-called Battle of Britain in the summer of 1942, when the US 'Eagle' squadrons played a supporting role in the resistance to Hitler's rather half-hearted attempt to drive Britain back out of the war by threatening – or bluff-ing – an invasion; the continued war of attrition on the Eastern Front as Stalin's forces gradually wore down the stretched Germans, eventually preventing them from advancing far beyond Stalingrad, which they had taken in such a Pyrrhic victory in the winter of 1942–43; the Soviet recapture of Moscow in the winter campaign of 1943–44. By this time the Western Allies had driven the Germans out of North Africa and commenced a long, slow and perhaps misconceived haul up the 'leg' of Italy. Despite the massive bombing campaign of the RAF and the USAF, it was not until 1945 that an invasion of France to liberate northern Europe could be considered, and by then things had changed in the US.

Wendell Willkie had proved a dynamic and popular President. A Republican, yes, but a strong supporter of the international war effort, the big, rumpled Indianan had built up positive relationships with Churchill and Stalin, and as the Pacific war gradually turned to the advantage of the US, his popularity ratings had soared. The war effort, with huge numbers in uniform and a massive production drive, had finally ended the economic depression. He was undoubtedly on track to win comfortable re-election to a second term. Whether it was the strain of the war leadership we can never know, but on 8 October 1944, at the age of fifty-two, Wendell Willkie passed away after a series of heart attacks. An additional complication was caused by the unfortunate circumstance that his Vice-President, Chares McNary, had died eight months before him, in February 1944. At that time, according to the hierarchy established in the Presidential Succession Act of 1886, the vice-presidency had to remain vacant (as it was an elected position), and so the new President was to be the Secretary of State as the senior member of Cabinet – the only time in United States history this has happened.

The 77-year-old Henry L. Stimson (the oldest ever President of the United States) had been in Cabinet as Secretary of War as early as 1911– 13, appointed by President Taft. Between 1929 and 1933, he had served as Secretary of State under Hoover, the last Republican President before Willkie. The veteran was therefore a logical choice for Willkie, whose term began in early 1941 as the dark clouds presaging war with Japan were gathering. Many suggested at the time that only in such exceptional circumstances would the United States consider a 77-year-old worthy of election to the presidency; but as the incumbent (if only for a few weeks, which may well have helped Stimson, as he had made no new enemies) and on a 'win-the-war' ticket, that was exactly what happened in November 1944.

It could be argued that the identity of the new President was crucially fortunate in one particular way: Stimson had been heavily involved in supervising the atomic bomb project, which had been proceeding with the critical help of émigré scientists from Europe. Victory in the race with the German team under Heisenberg was to prove both essential and decisive.

The nuclear-weapon project was probably delayed by about a year because of Britain's late entry into the Second World War, as their scientists too – for example, James Chadwick – were to make key contri-butions. With the Soviets gradually pushing back on the Eastern Front throughout 1944 and 1945, and the D-Day invasion postponed to May 1946, it was believed to be a close-run thing that the Allied A-bomb team managed to produce a partial deliverable weapon in the summer of 1946, before the rumoured ultimate Nazi super-weapon, produced using the Germans' undoubted lead in rocket technology, was itself aimed at the obvious target: London. The outcome is now as well-known as any in history. Just in time, in July 1946, 'Fat Man' was dropped on Hiroshima in Japan, and two days later 'Little Boy' vaporised Dresden in Germany. Both were targets designed to bring about unconditional surrender. With the threat of the next atomic weapon destroying Berlin itself, it was not entirely surprising that the remaining Wehrmacht chiefs relieved Adolf Hitler of his duties as Führer, nor that the dictator accepted the option of suicide. The role of Emperor Hirohito of Japan, while different in the nature of its execution, as he made an unprecedented intervention by radio broadcast to overrule the militaristic elements still remaining in his government and call for surrender in the light of the impact of the nuclear weapons, had a similar effect. The Second World War was over.

The dropping of the atomic bombs had another impact too. With Stalin's Soviet forces still struggling in Byelorussia around Minsk to complete the long Eastern Front haul back from behind the Urals, it was the Western Allies who were able to occupy Germany, including Berlin. One wonders whether, if the Russians had been present on German soil in 1946, they would have been able successfully to demand a share in its occupation, and whether part of Germany would have missed out on the eventual revival of a peaceful and united capitalist state in the 1950s. Perhaps the line of the 'Iron Curtain' that developed in the Cold War would have been located menacingly further west?

At least one countervailing force of international co-operation – to a degree, at least – stemmed from seeds planted during Stimson's presidency. A thoroughgoing internationalist, he had thought that the atomic bomb, 'the most terrible weapon ever known in human history', opened up 'the opportunity to bring the world into a pattern in which the peace of the world and our civilisation can be saved'.[12] Among the institutions that Stimson was influential in founding that aimed to support that pattern was the United Nations, which attained its full status in 1947, the idea having originated in Willkie's discussions with Churchill during the war.[13]

The beginnings were also laid for other key post-war institutions, such as the International Fund for Reconstruction, with a remit for development finance – lending for projects, such as ports and roads, in developing countries – and the International Reserve Bank, the guardian of the system of fixed but adjustable exchange rate parities.[14] The US's willingness to participate actively in these bodies, and indeed to host their headquarters, had much to do with the abandonment of any hint of isolationism by the internationalist Presidents Willkie and Stimson. However, the main reason why the United States wished to play such a major role throughout the post-war world was surely due to a 'realist' reading of their expanded interests as a nation state, as one of the two post-war superpowers and as the heartland of capitalism faced with the threat of the other true victor of the Second World War: the communist Soviet Union.

As the now octogenarian President Stimson declined to seek another term in 1948, things seemed bright for his Republican Party on the domestic as well as the international front. The war had transformed the US economy, especially the manufacturing industry, now returned to private-sector production and control, as there had been little tradition of governmental intervention in peacetime. True, the President could perhaps do with more administrative help, for example through the Executive Office of the President, which was eventually established in the 1960s. True, there was still a very rudimentary welfare system with no effective policy of national insurance. True, many rural areas were still in a backward state of development, even lacking electrification. But, after all, the core of the constitutional system of the US was based on limited presidential and federal power. The Republicans in particular remained electorally strong, having successfully 'won the war', and retained their electoral coalition of Protestants, the wealthy, the suburbs, the rural areas outside the south and those African-Americans who were allowed to vote.

Indeed, within two more decades, the Republicans had both supported and benefited from the civil rights movement that had developed through the 1950s and 1960s, led by inspirational figures such as Martin

Luther King Jr, who had worked with leading GOP politicians such as Nelson Rockefeller and Richard Nixon. Even in the south, African-Americans were effectively enfranchised as Nixon's Civil Rights Act and Voting Rights Act gradually took effect. However, racial and political polarisation remained a central problem in the United States, and Democrat-against-Republican partisanship continued to become more and more divisive and bitter as the twentieth century turned into the twenty-first — perhaps reaching its nadir with the disruptive career of a well-known businessman turned politician, who became a one-term Democratic Party President...

Notes

1   Harvard Sitkoff, *A New Deal for Blacks – The Emergence of Civil Rights as a National Issue: The Depression Decade* (Oxford: Oxford University Press, 2008), p. 72.

2   US Bureau of Labor Statistics, December 1940.

3   European Centre for Disease Prevention and Control, https://www.ecdc.europa.eu/en/poliomyelitis

4   Robert Slayton, *Empire Statesman: The Rise and Redemption of Al Smith* (New York: Free Press, 2001), p. 382.

5   In reality, Al Smith was a leading member of the American Liberty League, formed in 1934 to oppose FDR's New Deal, and vehemently attacked its 'communistic' policies, for example in his renowned Mayflower Hotel speech in 1936.

6   Slayton, *Empire Statesman*, p. 82.

7   Ibid., p. 114.

8   Keynes actually met Roosevelt on 28 May 1934, leading Roosevelt to declare that 'he left a whole rigmarole of figures. He must be a mathematician rather than a political economist.' Al Smith would have put it in blunter terms.

9   The two that Landon actually won against FDR in 1936. The hypothetical extra twelve are states where Landon polled over 40 per cent in that contest.

10 *Life* magazine, 7 March 1938.

11 D. L. Lewis, *The Improbable Wendell Willkie: The Businessman Who Saved the Republican Party and His Country, and Conceived a New World Order* (New York: Liveright, 2018), p. 93.

12 Stimson's actual words in 1945 in response to the nuclear attack on Japan.

13 For Willkie's strong enthusiasm for the UN idea, see Lewis, *The Improbable Wendell Willkie*, pp. 303–5.

14 These are respectively the equivalents of the World Bank and the IMF. There is a joke among economists that the Bank is actually a fund and the Fund is actually a bank.

Chapter 5

What if Ireland had joined the Allies in the Second World War?

Jason O'Mahony

The great danger with counterfactual history is the temptation to cascade. You know the theory: Archduke Ferdinand doesn't get assassinated and eventually Enver Hoxha is the ruler of all Europe, arriving at one's end destination by a series of reactions that veer further and further away from the original point of divergence.

Having said that, there are figures so key in a nation's history that their early death could not help but have a major effect on the future direction of their country. Éamon de Valera is one such figure.

De Valera died in 1975 at the age of ninety-two, having ended his second term as President of Ireland in 1973. To many he was the Irish de Gaulle, a living personification of a certain Gaelic vision of Irish independence. When he departed the office of Taoiseach (Prime Minister) in 1959, aged seventy-seven, he left behind a definite legacy in the form of the national constitution, *Bunreacht na hÉireann*. Very much the lead draughtsman, he used it to set in many ways a conservative and Catholic view of the nation.

His Fianna Fáil successor, Seán Lemass, went on to be defined in twentieth-century Irish history as the great moderniser, as Pompidou was to de Gaulle: a pragmatic white-heat-of-technology technocrat. Outward-looking, with an eye on Europe, Lemass focused on raising the living standards of the Irish people through industrialisation, in contrast to de Valera's acceptance of perennial poverty as some sort of noble Christian sacrifice for the soul.

As with Anthony Eden's late succession of Churchill, one of the great criticisms was that de Valera simply held on too long, serving thirty-two years as leader of Fianna Fáil. While it was not guaranteed that he would be succeeded by Lemass, the latter was certainly in the running. Lemass eventually came to office as Taoiseach in 1959, leaving due to poor health in 1966 but having put in place many of the modern industrial-isation strategies and first tentative moves towards European Economic Community membership that would eventually define both him and the prosperous modern Ireland of the very late twentieth century.

Irish neutrality during the Second World War – de Valera's key for-eign policy achievement – is a strategy that has not aged well outside Ireland, particularly in the context of the Holocaust. From the perspec-tive of a new state, less than nineteen years old at the outbreak of war, de Valera's primary objective was the maintenance of national sovereignty in its purest sense. One could, of course, argue that that was the aim of every country fighting the Third Reich, but in Ireland's case it came from the viewpoint of a country still bristling against its former imperial master over the partition of the island. Furthermore, Ireland had recently fought – in the mid- to late-1930s – a nasty economic war of tariffs and protectionism against the UK (and vice versa) over its outstanding debts to its former overlord.

The common understanding of the time was that if Ireland had become involved in the war, given its near non-existent military capac-ity (the country had three tanks and around a dozen Hurricane fighters, supplemented by a dozen obsolete biplanes), it would have had to do so under British military leadership – a stance that would have been polit-ically unacceptable to the great majority of people in the new state. It is true that Churchill attempted to coax de Valera into entering the war with a vague promise as to a united Ireland afterwards, but de Valera (almost certainly correctly) chose not to treat the offer as serious and ignored it.

Ireland was not the only European country to maintain neutrality during the war. Switzerland, Sweden, Spain and Portugal all did so, and all emerged without much damage to their reputations, save maybe for

Swiss bankers. Nor was Irish neutrality strictly impartial. Thousands of Irish did indeed serve in both the US and the British armed forces, and the Irish authorities tended to lean towards the Allied side rather than the Axis in matters of discretion. Weather reports from the west coast of Ireland, for example, played a significant role in Eisenhower's Overlord decision on 5 June 1944.

What remains unforgivable, nevertheless, was the decision by de Valera, against the advice of his own officials, to visit the German legation to pass on the condolences of the nation to the German people on the death of their Chancellor in 1945. The information coming out of the concentration camps had been common knowledge in Western diplomatic circles since 1943, and while the Irish government had engaged in strict censorship of the matter, de Valera and his Foreign Minister had been well aware of the crimes against humanity committed by the Nazi regime. It was a decision that went from being a questionable act of diplomatic protocol in 1945 to a source of national shame and embarrassment in Ireland today.

Would it have been different if de Valera had been removed from the picture? The odds are against it. The neutrality policy was popular, and de Valera was re-elected in two general elections during the war. But Lemass as Taoiseach was much more realistic about Ireland's position with regard to a possible war with communism, openly admitting to sharing the goals of NATO.

As for the idea that one death could cascade into a radical change in a nation's direction, it is worth noting that it is easier to radically change the direction, both politically and economically, of a small nation than a large one.

If a number of variables had changed...

~

They buried Éamon de Valera on 1 October 1942, nearly two weeks after the car crash on Rock Road, Blackrock, County Dublin, which had claimed the life of both the Taoiseach and his Garda driver. Given de Valera's iconic status in the political pantheon of state, the Minister for Supplies and de Valera's de facto successor, Seán Lemass, had delayed the traditional swift burial to allow for a ceremony more befitting 'The Chief'. Over three-quarters of a million people turned up to pay their respects as the procession made its way from the Pro-Cathedral to Glasnevin Cemetery. Two days later, the Fianna Fáil parliamentary party met and anointed the young 44-year-old minister as Taoiseach.

A week later, Lemass was visited by the US Minister to Ireland. The minister had not been a fan of de Valera, but with the new and considerably younger man now in office, he had decided to attempt to open a conversation about Ireland's stance in the war, if only to clarify for Washington where Lemass stood. The visit had been intended to be perfunctory, the diplomat visiting to pass on the respects of President Roosevelt, but as they spoke, the minister, who was well briefed as to the differences in outlook between de Valera and his young protégé, decided to take a gamble.

Lemass had a reputation for being less enamoured with Gaelic mysticism than his predecessor; he was believed to be more interested in modern solutions to the problems of the young country. By pure coincidence, the minister had on his person copies of OSS briefing documents outlining Allied intelligence on the Nazi concentration camps. Lemass read them, asked questions about their veracity, and then, to the surprise of the minister, opened a discussion with the diplomat about the post-war situation. The world, he observed, was waiting for the invasion of France, and that, in tandem with the German reversals on the Eastern Front, meant that the war was going to end, and Nazi Germany was going to be defeated.

On top of that, it was becoming very clear that the United States was going to be the dominant power – a situation with which the Irishman expressed approval. Lemass then changed the subject entirely and spoke about the challenges facing a tiny, newly independent nation like Ireland, and its place in the world. The minister, familiar with the roundabout ways of Irish-American politicians back home, took the hint. He responded with a discussion of Ireland's strategic importance as the gateway to the Atlantic; how a US presence in the country would mean significant local spending from GI pay packets; and how the US would need to help its allies rebuild, or progress economically, after the war.

Of course, Lemass stressed, there was the question of partition. The ambassador could not commit the US to any position on that question and was honest about their relationship with Britain, but he suggested that a post-war Ireland, growing in prosperity from her relationship with the United States, would be a far more attractive proposition for the Unionists in the north. Lemass surprised the ambassador by agreeing enthusiastically. He expressed the view that the reunification of Ireland would have to be achieved by consent, through enthusiasm on both sides of the border and with respect towards the different cultures on the island. He saw economic progress as the core factor to ending partition, and that in turn required a healthy affinity between the two jurisdictions on the island, as opposed to the current frosty-to-the-point-of-Arctic relationship.

However, the Taoiseach also drew the ambassador's attention to the very modest military capacity of the country. Ireland had only 40,000 barely equipped troops wearing obsolete coal-scuttle-style helmets – meaning they were regularly mistaken by ditching Allied pilots for Wehrmacht troops. Indeed, given the tiny size of the Irish forces, and their lack of equipment and training in modern warfare, they would have to serve under another Allied command. The thought of them serving under the British – perhaps under officers they had been fighting a mere twenty-two years before – was not a proposition he believed he could sell to his people.

But under US command? the minister asked, letting the idea hang.

The Taoiseach filled his pipe and puffed thoughtfully for a moment. That was a different proposition. There was, he said, a special place for America in every Irishman's heart. The great majority of Irish families probably had an American in them, whether it was those who had taken the boat to America and built a life in Boston or Chicago or New York, or cousins who spoke with American accents. He had no doubt that most Irishmen would have little difficulty serving in a US uniform.

The minister thanked the Taoiseach for his time and asked if he would be willing to study a more detailed hypothetical proposal. The Taoiseach smiled. He would always give any request from America his full consideration.

Things moved fast. In December, the minister returned, this time with a senior US Army officer in civilian clothes, who outlined the proposal. Lemass raised certain issues, which the minister felt could be addressed, and the three men shook hands, confident that an agreement could be reached.

On Christmas Eve, the minister returned, this time with a draft document. The Taoiseach reviewed it, expressed happiness with it, and pledged to put it to his government.

Lemass approached his Cabinet colleagues individually, and all agreed, with varying degrees of enthusiasm. His Foreign Minister, Frank Aiken, threatened to resign, angered by his exclusion from the negotiations, but the two men fought it out over porter in front of a fire, and the minister finally agreed to support the Taoiseach.

On 1 January 1943, US fighter aircraft from Northern Ireland began landing in Irish military airfields. A large convoy of US troops, escorted by the Irish Army, crossed the border, bringing with them large quantities of anti-aircraft and radar equipment. The same morning, Lemass called in the leaders of the four opposition parties and briefed them. W. T. Cosgrave, de Valera's predecessor as head of government and leader of the largest (and moderately more pro-British) Fine Gael, agreed with his proposals, egged on by his unashamedly pro-Allied deputy, James Dillon. The leaders of the small Labour and agrarian Clann na Talmhan parties were both won over with promises of substantial US spending – the latter with thoughts of large beef and dairy contracts with the US Army, and the former, led by William Norton, particularly pleased that the largest US base in the country was due to be located in Norton's Kildare constituency. The most vocal opposition came from a loud minority within Lemass's own parliamentary party, but even they conceded to the will of the leader, who found it helpful to call on the ethos of rigid loyalty to the leader that de Valera had imposed.

Later that day, the Taoiseach addressed the nation on radio. He told them of the evidence that had been presented to him by the United States showing that the Nazi government was engaged in the mass extermination of hundreds of thousands, possibly even millions, of civilians. He recognised the desire of the late Éamon de Valera – and indeed many in his own party – that the country stay out of the intrigues of the great powers, but he pointed out that as a nation that had experienced a similar outcome during the Great Famine, Ireland could not morally stand idly by and let so many die when they had the power to act themselves. Therefore, he said, he had instructed the Minister for Foreign Affairs to inform the German Minister to Ireland that this country was now at war with Germany and her allies.

He also informed the country that the United States had agreed a treaty with Ireland – the Treaty of Dublin – through which they entered into a mutual defence pact; US air and land forces were now entering the state to set up defences. Finally, he pointed out that the government intended to raise two divisions of volunteers, funded, equipped and trained by the United States and serving under US command. Lemass finished by stressing that he, a veteran of the GPO in 1916, had always hoped that he would have been able to steer Ireland away from war but that the defence of civilised Christian values was not a task Ireland should shirk.

The responses were mixed.

The German government announced that the declaration confirmed their belief that Fianna Fáil was a Jewish front – a concern echoed by the lone voice of Oliver J. Flanagan, a notoriously antisemitic member of Dáil Éireann. In Ireland, however, US forces moving south were stunned to be greeted by cheering crowds akin to those expected from a liberation. US Navy vessels steaming into Cork Harbour were met by boisterous crowds waving US flags. In Boston, New York and Chicago, Irish flags went up alongside US flags in Irish-American neighbourhoods, and impromptu parties broke out celebrating the old country's entry into the war.

Two nights later, US Army Air Force fighters put up a solid defence of the ports in Waterford and Cork, inflicting heavy casualties on a German bomber force operating at the edge of its range in what was almost certainly a symbolic response to the Irish declaration. The reaction of the populace was a muted acceptance of the small number of civilian casualties.

As part of the Treaty of Dublin, the US agreed to release Irishmen currently serving in the US forces to return to Ireland to serve in the Irish forces, if they so desired; it was a decision they wanted to take anyway to ensure that the new force benefited from an injection of experienced soldiers. The British, under advice from Washington, agreed to do the same.

By May 1944, over 42,000 Irishmen, including 4,000 US citizens, passed out from the Curragh camp as the first and second Irish divisions. Lemass, standing with President Hyde and the US minister, took the salute as the forces marched by, indistinguishable from US forces save for the tricolour and Óglaigh na hÉireann shoulder flashes. It was a seminal moment for the young state, watching its young men (and a small number of women) marching by in the finest equipment available, driving brand-new jeeps and trucks and tanks, part of the greatest army in the world. They were about to engage (albeit late) in the titanic struggle between good and evil that had consumed the rest of the world, yet which to Ireland had been simply 'The Emergency'.

The first Irish troops, attached to larger US formations, saw action in Italy: a bloody baptism with significant casualties. The dreaded fear of seeing a jeep pull into one's street or village with an officer, often accompanied by the local priest, to deliver the awful news to a family became the norm in many Irish communities.

Oliver J. Flanagan and the small group of fascists in Ireland, including the pro-German former Garda Commissioner Eoin O'Duffy, founder of the Blueshirts (Hail O'Duffy!), attempted to stir up dissent against Lemass and the Irish involvement in the Allied cause, but without much luck. O'Duffy, who had led a shambolic Irish contingent to fight for Franco in the Spanish Civil War, had been eventually asked to leave by the Generalissimo, although some local Dublin wags had suggested that the would-be saviours of Christian Spain had come back because they hadn't liked the foreign food. O'Duffy's pro-German speeches had little effect, with a mood of acceptance descending on the country as it recognised it was playing a role in something important.

On 6 June 1944, boys and men from Brooklyn, Belmullet, Chicago and Clonakilty died on Omaha Beach as the Allies delivered a hammer blow to Hitler's Atlantic Wall. In December 1944 and January 1945, Irish forces, increasingly placed under the command of Irish officers who had received battlefield commissions in Italy or France, fought alongside US forces in the Battle of the Bulge.

One of the more notable features of the Irish contribution was the effect that serving in US forces had on the Irishmen. Washington had integrated the two Irish divisions into US forces to such an extent that the Irish soldiers were trained and paid the same and were as well-equipped and well-fed as US forces. The Irish also found, through their Catholicism, a kinship with Italian and Polish-American troops, all sharing the same padres. Indeed, when the inevitable brawls broke out in mess halls with British troops, American troops waded in on the side of the Irish. Such was the integration that Irish troops requested, and were granted, the right to wear US flags alongside the tricolour on their uniforms.

The transformation in Ireland caused by the entry of the country into the war was on a grand scale. Kildare, home to the Curragh camp, the sprawling former British military depot, became a huge military base and US staging post. Dublin and Cork were swamped with US and Irish servicemen spending US-taxpayer-funded pay packets, and convoys from the US battling U-boats were supported by US forces based in Cork, Kerry and Foynes.

When Germany surrendered, Ireland celebrated with the rest of the Allies.

Ireland, which had been stagnating economically before the war, benefited greatly from the munificence of Marshall Aid and US military spending. Lemass was adamant about targeting the money specifically towards transforming the country into a modern industrialised nation.

Although the base in the Curragh was scaled back, President Truman was insistent that the massive US Air Force base in Shannon, County Clare, and the vast naval base in Cork were both, along with various coastal installations, vital to the Western defence of the North Atlantic. Lemass, aware both of their strategic significance and the substantial financial contribution they made to the Irish economy, agreed, and Ireland accepted the invitation of the United States to become a founder member of NATO in 1949. Those who opposed NATO membership on the grounds that it meant entering a military alliance with the United Kingdom (therefore effectively recognising partition), were drowned out by the many commercial and regional interests benefiting from US spending, and also by the trenchant anti-communism that encouraged the Catholic Church to endorse the Atlantic Alliance and the fight against the godless Soviets.

By the late 1950s, Ireland was booming. Nevertheless, the Irish-American 'special relationship' was sneered at by some in Britain, with the Tory right referring to Ireland as the US's poodle in Europe – a situation not helped by the Suez crisis of 1956. It was certainly true that the US regarded Ireland as its most openly loyal ally, and US businesses found in Ireland a competitive English-speaking base from which to access the rebuilding European market. In the government of Fianna Fáil, re-elected in 1948 on the back of massive investment in Ireland from the US, it found a party not dissimilar to the Democrats at home, pragmatic and willing to work with business to enhance prosperity. Marshall Aid spending on infrastructure was planned in tandem with American companies, allowing them to place manufacturing premises in ideal locations, including brand-new port facilities for shipping to the Continent and the UK.

But the real challenge to Ireland came in 1957, as the nations of Europe came together to negotiate an economic community. The British had decided not to participate, but Ireland, now rapidly becoming one of the most prosperous nations in Europe (helped by not having suffered any significant war damage), was encouraged by the US to join, eager to have a loyal ally at the heart of this new European project.

Lemass regarded the decision as equal in importance to his decision to enter the war. To go into Europe without the UK was a massive step, given the importance of the British market, but Lemass also believed that the British were making a mistake and would eventually have to follow Ireland in – a view backed by US President Eisenhower. The French expressed concerns, especially over the possibility that Ireland would be 'Washington's Man', but that was a proposition that appealed to the Germans and other countries eager to anchor the US in Europe. As a result, in 1957 Lemass flew to Italy to sign the Treaty of Rome, as Ireland became one of the seven founding members of the European Economic Community. He despatched the experienced Frank Aiken to Brussels as Ireland's first European commissioner.

President Kennedy visited Ireland in 1963. He was met by huge crowds and a massive military parade by US and Irish forces who had fought together, both in the Second World War and also under the United Nations flag in Korea. Also present were Irish soldiers who had fought in the Siege of Jadotville in the Congo in 1961, when a well-equipped Irish force under UN command had comprehensively defeated a much larger attacking force of Katangese secessionists. Kennedy addressed the Dáil, where he reminded the house that 'like us, you come to war reluctantly, and sometimes late, but like us, you fight twice as hard when you are there. Every American soldier can know on the battlefield that his Irish buddy always has his back. And also where to get a drink after the fighting.'

Irish cadets would later be specially requested by Jacqueline Kennedy to perform the Queen Anne Drill at her husband's funeral.

The 1960s brought continued economic progress to Ireland, with many emigrants returning from the United States and Britain. Such was the demand for labour in the south that workers from Northern Ireland began to seek employment there. Lemass, eager to build a new and mutually beneficial and respectful relationship with the northern state, responded to stories of Protestant workers being refused jobs in the south because of their faith by publicly pointing out that companies that dis-criminated against northern Protestants would find getting government contracts a challenge. He later supported legislation that harshly punished religious discrimination in the workplace, an action which did not go unnoticed among more moderate Unionist circles in the north – not that it was appreciated by the Reverend Ian Paisley, the leader of anti-Catholic extremist unionism, who condemned 'any son of Ulster who ventured south into the embrace of the Whore of Washington with her Roman breasts dripping with the Devil's buttermilk luring good Protestant boys into the fleshpots of the European Gomorrah...' His speeches tended to go on for a considerable time. Some speculated that they increased the eagerness of many a northern Protestant youth to visit their southern neighbour.

The 1961 visit of British Prime Minister Macmillan and his chief EEC negotiator, Edward Heath, was covered widely in the international press, as they sought the help of the Irish government to reverse their error of 1957 and enter the EEC. Lemass was cordial and positive, eager to bring what was still Ireland's most important export destination into the Common Market, but stressed as a quid pro quo that Britain would have to take action to ensure that Catholics were not discriminated against in the north. The British government acted on the matter through legislation before Ireland positively supported UK membership – though France's eventual veto delayed UK entry for a decade.

The fact that a loud and active Irish-American lobby in the US Congress (well briefed by the Irish Department of External Affairs) had also pushed for employment legislation reforms did not go unnoticed. The Foreign and Commonwealth Office also pointed out that there was actually an Irish Defence Forces liaison office in both the Pentagon and the State Department, and that US military uniforms were a regular sight in the Irish Department of Defence. They also noted that the US border extended as far as to have US immigration clearance in Irish airports. The British ambassador observed that there were so many US politicians flying in and out of Dublin's Éamon de Valera International Airport as guests of the Irish government, to visit their children studying on Irish-government-funded university courses, that it would 'make more logistical sense to allow Ireland to have its own senators on Capitol Hill'.

As it happened, the changes suited the young reforming Prime Minister of Northern Ireland, Captain Terence O'Neill, and he was quite happy to use pressure from Westminster to force his own Ulster Unionist Party into adopting better trading with the south and a more open approach to the north's Catholic minority. In January 1965, he visited Dublin, where he was warmly received by crowds and the Taoiseach. Journalists were stunned to hear Lemass announce a contract for Harland & Wolff to build two warships for the Irish Navy, a corvette and a diesel-powered submarine. The submarine was to be named after the master of secret warfare as the LE (Long Éireannach – Irish ship) *General Michael Collins*, and the corvette after the founding father of Ulster unionism as the LE *Edward Carson*. The naming of a ship after Carson caused a stir in republican circles, but Lemass was quick to point out not only that Carson was a native of Dublin but also that an eventual united Ireland would have to find a place for all Irishmen and women and all heritages.

O'Neill was pleased to inform Lemass that, due to the economic opportunities in the south and anti-discrimination legislation on both sides of the border, he believed that a new era in cross-border co-operation was possible. Both men issued a joint statement, which recognised differences in policy but accepted that any solution must be reached solely by peaceful means and that cross-border co-operation on the basis of mutual respect was the way forward.

The rapid economic progress in the post-war south began swiftly to change opinions in northern Unionist circles. Lemass and O'Neill agreed the Merrion Square Declaration, which recognised that while the south advocated an end to partition, both sides accepted that a change in the constitutional status of Northern Ireland would require the consent of the northern majority. The Republic agreed to insert the right to consent into its constitution in return for political and civil rights reform in the north, including the restoration of a proportional representation electoral system, a consultative Council of Ireland, seats in the Irish Senate for northern Nationalists and a power-sharing administration in the north. The Republic also agreed with the EEC to the creation of a free-port on the southern side of the border, which would permit northern products to be exported tariff-free to the Common Market. The British government was happy to rubber-stamp the arrangement, regarding Northern Ireland as a sleepy backwater of little interest to Westminster.

A very small number of ex-IRA extremists attempted to oppose Lemass's moderate approach and carried out some minor attacks on Royal Ulster Constabulary patrols, but they eventually petered out due to lack of support among the Catholic community, now beginning to benefit from O'Neill's housing and economic reforms. Similarly, loyalists who attempted to stir up trouble against the O'Neill government found little support in their community, given the number of Protestants now travelling across the border every day to work, together with the southern government's hard line on religious discrimination. O'Neill eventually retired in 1980, having led a UUP–Nationalist coalition for fifteen years, the most successful Prime Minister in Northern Irish history.

In November 1966, following the fiftieth anniversary of the 1916 Rising, and after a parade of US, Irish, French and West German troops past the GPO in Dublin provided a poignant reminder of Ireland's place among the nations, Lemass stepped down and was elected President of Ireland. He was replaced as Taoiseach by Jack Lynch, his affable, hurling-playing, middle-of-the-road Finance Minister.

Lynch found himself having to deal with the downside of such a close relationship with the United States, however, when President Johnson put serious pressure on both him and his UK counterpart, Harold Wilson, to contribute troops to the US war effort in Vietnam. As in Australia and New Zealand, Lynch, together with many in his country, felt an obligation to the United States and to the fight against the spread of communism; he also believed the US military advice that the war would soon be brought to a successful conclusion. The Johnson administration was not particularly bothered by the size of any British or Irish contribution; they wanted to claim that their fight was an effort by an international coalition, not a lone US fight with North Vietnam.

Wilson refused, but Lynch sent 800 troops, a mixture of special forces and engineers, on the advice of his own military – who, some would later claim, were a little too well integrated into US forces; most Irish officers had attended the special Irish Defence Forces annexe, Kennedy House in West Point in the US. Indeed, such was the level of integration that some noted that Irish officers had even switched from using the British pronunciation of lieutenant (leftenant) to the American (lootenent).

The refusal of Harold Wilson to send troops alongside the Irish contingent was widely mocked in Irish newspapers, with the country bragging of its special relationship with the US, and the Irish Expeditionary Force was sent off with the public blessing of the Archbishop of Dublin and cheering families.

They were not cheered on their return.

When the stories and body bags started coming back to Ireland, Irish writers conceded that the British PM might have had rather more foresight than their own. Ireland proved to be no less susceptible than the US to mass protest and civil unrest over the war, and Lynch narrowly lost the 1969 general election, mostly on the Vietnam issue. The new Taoiseach pulled Irish troops out at the insistence of his Labour coalition partners.

President Lemass died in 1971, just before Ireland, acting as a broker for the British, helped to negotiate British entry into the EEC in 1973. The policy was supported by all the Dáil parties save for Sinn Féin, which had reinvented itself as an ardently European federalist party. It opposed British membership because of partition, and also because of a fear that Britain would block the emergence of a United States of Europe. The main concession that the British had to make was support for the appointment of the first Irish President of the European Commission. The return of Fianna Fáil to power in the 1972 election, led by the urbane Charles J. Haughey, led to the country seizing its opportunity. Haughey nominated the brilliant young economist Dr Garret FitzGerald, who had already served as Irish Foreign Minister, as a candidate for President of the Commission.

It was a fitting passing of the flame to a new generation. FitzGerald was a liberal (some described him as the Irish Roy Jenkins) and very much representative of the new generation of Irish. As with other countries in Catholic Europe, the 1970s had seen the young people of Ireland demand a retraction of church power and the liberalisation of everything from women's rights, to divorce, to contraception – the irony was that the anti-birth-control policies of the Catholic Church had resulted in the country having the youngest population in Europe. Coupled with their cultural integration with the United States, a whole new generation swept out the older, more conservative leaders of the past. 'If only', one bishop mused sadly, 'there'd been some way of getting all the young people to emigrate.'

Despite his family connections (his parents had fought along-side Lemass in the GPO during the Easter Rising), FitzGerald was an Anglophile and eager to bring the UK into the heart of the European project. Very quickly, he grasped that the transformation of the EEC from a common market to a real single market was a project the British government could back with enthusiasm. When FitzGerald announced in 1978 that he would not be seeking a second term in Brussels (in order to return to Dublin to take up the leadership of Fine Gael and enter into a decade-long struggle with Haughey), there was unanimous agreement as to his successor to complete the single market project.

The following year, the first meeting between newly elected British Prime Minister Margaret Thatcher and European Commission President Edward Heath was an interesting one.

Chapter 6

Goodbye, Mr Chips: what if the *News Chronicle* had not closed in 1960?

David Boyle

Guardian obituaries, January 2021

Frank Chipping, who has died aged 100, was a lifelong journalist and editor at the *News Chronicle* well into his nineties, almost until its final demise last year. He was a key figure in the decision to carry on publishing in 1960 after the sale of the paper by the Cadbury family.

Chipping was a member of staff at the *Chronicle* for almost his whole career, except for a brief period on secondment to the BBC European Service as a copy taster during the Second World War.

He was born outside Huddersfield in 1920. His parents, Josiah and Margaret, were both agricultural labourers. Almost from the beginning, when he joined the staff of the Liberal paper as office boy and tea-maker at the age of sixteen – in the last and somewhat tipsy weeks of Aylmer Vallance's editorship – he was known as 'Chips'. In later years, any retirement, whether by himself or from the paper's staff, always provided the headline 'Goodbye, Mr Chips', after James Hilton's novella of that name, published in 1934. 'How different my life would have been', said Chipping after one of these, 'if Hilton had decided to call his book *Hello, Mr Chips…*'

He settled down to a newspaper life, starting as office boy at the *Huddersfield Examiner* at the age of fourteen before – encouraged by the editor – he arrived off Fleet Street at the Bouverie Street offices of the *News Chronicle*, shared with their stable mate, *The Star*. The *Chronicle* was then enjoying a circulation of over a million a day, following the merger in 1930 of the two papers, the *Daily News* and the *Daily Chronicle*, under George Cadbury's ownership.

Chips joined the paper in 1936, the year that Vallance was forced out, but he remained deeply influenced by his first outgoing editor, who had been causing friction with the directors because of his radicalism and alcohol consumption, and because his support for the Liberal Party was said to be 'lukewarm'.

Chipping had one of those undefined roles around the *Chronicle* office which meant he was asked to manage – and then became effective at running – small side projects, like organising the republication of the *News Chronicle Song Book*, being Big Chief I-Spy for the children's book series that the *Chronicle* owned, and running the campaign to release the *Chronicle* staffer Arthur Koestler, the future author of *Darkness at Noon*, from Franco's prison after his capture after the fall of Málaga.

He was instrumental in the decision to send Geoffrey Cox to replace Koestler as the paper's Spanish correspondent, on the grounds that the editor's choice, the long-standing correspondent Vernon Bartlett, was too vulnerable. It was also Chipping who suggested that Cox should be sent to cover the fall of Madrid, because his New Zealand passport might confuse the Falange. Chips used to take responsibility for Cox's later career running ITN.

In this way, Chips was also managing to develop some skills as a political fixer when he was asked to join Bartlett as the candidate for the anti-appeasement Popular Front at the Bridgwater by-election in November 1938. He said later that he spent most of his time engaged in the vital role of preventing a meeting between the two great rival Liberal women stars of the day: Megan Lloyd George and Violet Bonham Carter.

Later, he would claim that his first political role had in fact been helping to persuade the Liberal Ivor Davies to stand down as party candidate for the Oxford by-election some weeks before Bridgwater, to try to unite the anti-appeasement forces behind the respected master of Balliol College, A. D. Lindsay (Davies did stand down, but Lindsay failed to win). He then went from there to Bridgwater, helping to carry Bartlett around the town centre after his victory, and thence to supporting the Duchess of Atholl in Aberdeenshire, where they failed to pull off the same trick.

As a response to the Munich agreement with Hitler, the Bridgwater result may not have been that impressive, but Chips realised from Bartlett's victory that there were many liberals outside as well as inside the Liberal Party.

By the time war broke out, Chipping had been promoted to the sub-editor's desk. It was in that role that he was seconded to the BBC European Service, under the former *Telegraph* European editor, Noel Newsome. He was soon busily trying to fix the torn relationships between the governments in exile in London, and it was Chips who stood behind the future BBC stalwart Leonard Miall, who stood behind General de Gaulle as he made his historic broadcast to occupied France in 1940. It was also said to have been Chips who forgot to switch on the recording system, which meant that no original recordings now exist.

After a war spent trying to manage the fraught relationship between the two occupants of Bush House – the European Service of the BBC (the Foreign Office) and the Political Warfare Executive (the Ministry of Economic Warfare) – managing the evolving partnership between the Liberals and the SDP in the 1980s was like a tea dance, or so Chips joked in later years. Newsome was also a great Liberal who narrowly failed to be elected at Penrith & Cockermouth in 1945. Chipping helped him and his team to reorganise the Liberal Party in 1946 and then returned to the *News Chronicle* to find it struggling with paper shortages.

But it was also struggling ideologically in the new post-war world, though this had been created partly by Liberals like Keynes and Beveridge. Yet these were Liberals on the Fabian wing of the party; they were big-government thinkers, and Chips was beginning to realise that it was small-scale and local institutions that excited him, not the big, corporate ones.

Still, the late 1940s and '50s were excitingly radical days in their own way for the *News Chronicle*, with James Cameron on foreign affairs, Louise Morgan blazing a trail on health and fitness and, later, ideologues like Richard Moore (the father of future *Telegraph* editor Charles) as leader writer. These were the great pre-tabloid days of British journalism, when hacks could turn around a lead story with a couple of phone calls and some frenzied typing, and when the accepted convention was to wander into the office at ten, leave your jacket on the back of your chair – implying some vague research in the archives downstairs or some intense editorial meeting – and then push off for an early lunch at El Vino's.

Not so for Chips, who was a true believer in the main, self-confessed function of the paper: to oppose totalitarianism wherever it survived. And if that meant sometimes turning a ferocious spotlight on the behaviour of the UK government, then so it must be. So, if the editor Michael Curtis's decision to oppose the Suez invasion in 1956 exposed the paper worryingly in the market, Chips did not mind. The paper's line was normally as divided as the staff – from the usual run of conservative hacks through to the industrial correspondent Geoffrey Goodman, who was believed to be spying for Czech intelligence – but on Suez the majority of the editorial staff backed Curtis's line.

The *Chronicle* saw a disastrous dip in circulation as a result, and Curtis came up with plan after plan to save the paper. Some of these Chips approved of, like the link-up with Granada Television; some of them he deeply disapproved of, like the merger with the Labour-supporting *Daily Herald*. But it hardly mattered, because they were all rejected out of hand by the chairman and proprietor Laurence Cadbury.

Why did Cadbury fail to get the paper onto a proper basis? Nobody knew. He was a pillar of the establishment, a director of the Bank of England and an adviser to government ministers. The *Chronicle* still operated two printing plants, one in London and one in Manchester, so it might have occurred to him that this was over-capacity. Maybe he was embarrassed by the paper's radicalism. Whatever the reason, by 1960, he had decided that enough was enough. Yet even before any announcement was made, Chips had intervened to change Cadbury's mind.

At the time, Chipping was forty, and this turned out to be his moment. He had calculated that the meagre £1.5 million the paper would fetch if sold would be used up entirely on redundancy payments to the staff; one week's pay for each year of service. 'The chocolate handshake,' one of the journalists called it later.[1]

He had first heard rumours about Cadbury's intention to sell the paper from a friend at Associated Press – Chips always seemed to know everyone – some days before the announcement had been due, and while negotiations were still going on, he had gone straight over to tackle Cadbury at his flat in Curzon Street, where the latter used to eat a strange mixture of grilled bacon sprinkled with Bisto before catching the No. 9 bus for the Bank. Neither man ever revealed what was said, but Chips was clearly effective. The sale of *The Star* to the *Daily Mail* went ahead as planned, reducing the number of evening papers in London from nine (back in the days when Bernard Shaw was the *Star*'s theatre critic) to just two. But Chips persuaded Cadbury that the *News Chronicle* should be sold instead to a trust for a nominal sum.

The critical element was secrecy until the trust could be established – and, crucially, until the powerful print unions could be squared about the sale of their Manchester printing press to *The Guardian*. This meant that the announcement went ahead as previously planned. At 6 p.m. on 17 October, staff were told to stop producing the paper for the following day.

If both the *News Chronicle* and *The Star* were to be sold to the *Daily Mail*, as many as 3,500 staff would lose their jobs, the biggest mass redundancy Fleet Street had ever seen. There was an enormous public outcry, and Cadbury was pilloried on TV, excoriated in Parliament and criticised for hanging on to the franchise for Tyne Tees TV. The *New Statesman* called it murder, horrified that a newspaper with a radical tradition – from opposition to sweatshops in 1905 to opposition to Suez in 1956 – should be sold to a newspaper that had at one time supported Mussolini and Mosley.[2]

'If the *News Chronicle* could not survive, with its extraordinary advantages of tradition, and loyalty, and talent, who can, outside the great chain-stores of the trade?' complained James Cameron. 'The newspaper with the most admirable free-thinking radical tradition withered on the bough precisely at the moment when the nation was ripe to appreciate these Liberal qualities ... a potential warhorse ridden by grocers.'[3] Cadbury had to endure being called 'the butcher of Bouverie Street' by Jeremy Thorpe, the Liberal MP for North Devon, in the House of Commons.[4]

It was never clear either why Cadbury wanted to be shot of the papers, nor how Chips had persuaded him to keep quiet about the trust. But apart from repeated denials from the *Mail* that they were buying the *Croc* as well as the *Star*, the secret was kept, and Operation Phoenix was revealed to an astonished newspaper world some weeks later. The trust was established by a number of wealthy friends of Thorpe's, though it was never exactly wealthy itself. It immediately recruited a number of Liberal Party stalwarts and well-known journalists to be trustees. This meant that both the most prominent newspapers on the liberal left – the *Chronicle* and *The Guardian* – were each owned by trusts.

A sceptical press predicted failure and a further slow decline, but, in fact, the elements were in place for a revival, both of the Liberal paper and for a new version of the Liberal creed. The Torrington by-election had been back in March 1958, when Asquith's grandson Mark Bonham Carter unexpectedly topped the poll by 219 votes – the first Liberal by-election gain since 1929. The Liberals had won just 2.5 per cent of the UK vote in the general election of 1951, and their total of MPs was by then down to five. So, Torrington was a huge achievement, though there had been twitchings in Dorset North and Rochdale some months before.

It was Chipping who saw, before most of his contemporaries, that the *Chronicle*'s revival provided a political expression, in the UK at least, for the emerging anti-corporate counterculture. He understood the term in the sense that it was coined, by the American philosopher Theodore Roszak in his 1959 book *The Making of a Counter Culture*, as a gathering revolt against the prevailing technocracy. Put like that, this was a theme that could appeal to voters on the left and the right; there were other mainstream party members who would have felt homeless either in the right- or left-leaning wings of the Liberal Party. Chips imagined that the emerging counterculture was a clue about the direction liberal-minded people were going in – he was never exactly 'hip', by any means, but he could see through the haze of smoke and flower power that the roots of the counterculture were radical but individualistic, not corporate or socialist. On these foundations – and to start with almost single-handedly – he built a new Liberal idea.

That is how he managed to articulate the link between the party and the wider Liberal revival as it tuned in, turned on and dropped out – so that if any mainstream newspaper or political ideology shared the emerging values of the 1960s, it was the old *News Croc* and the Liberals. Which is why young people flocked to the party under Jo Grimond, and why its youth wing clashed so badly with the leadership in 1970.

And behind it all, there was Chips, commissioning, formulating, collecting people who could articulate the phenomenon, putting into words so many people's distaste for modernity, as promoted by a Labour and Conservative technocratic elite – from motorways and nuclear technology to tower blocks and You've-Never-Had-It-So-Good.

As the years went by, the Liberal Party never took this as far as New Age declarations. They never went off to search for ley lines – though many of their members might have done so. The party leadership was always sceptical, but the members understood that the Liberal revival was a countercultural revolt against the threat to communities from tower blocks and the over-professionalisation of services. Chips was no household name, yet his influence was widespread. So, when Newcastle's chief planner, Wilfred Burns, said in 1963 that his technocratic purpose as a planner was in 'dealing with people who have no initiative or civic pride...', Chips made sure that the *Chronicle* splashed it across the front page. Thanks to Chipping, the response to Burns's belief that 'the task surely is to break up such groupings, even though people seem to be satisfied with their miserable environment and seem to enjoy an extrovert social life in their own locality',[5] was enough to stop Newcastle's redevelopment of inner urban motorways and tower blocks in its tracks.

Chips was able to articulate how these disparate issues amounted to something more than they seemed – how individual campaigns against high-rise flats or in favour of community power were also a fundamentally Liberal approach to social policy. So was battling for complementary health, and alternative education too. Yet this approach brought in not just the committed beards-and-sandals brigade but also, because it fostered independence of mind, people who might otherwise have been attracted by Margaret Thatcher. It was this individualism that gave the ideology its populist appeal for the right, and why an old-fashioned Liberal like Chips seems to have been attracted to the idea to start with.

Why Chips? Perhaps because of his involvement with a long-standing Liberal, Elliott Dodds, the editor of the *Huddersfield Examiner*, Chips's first employer in his hometown. It was Dodds who provided Chips with his critique of the 1940s, the technocratic business of management by Whitehall experts and the white heat of technocratic revolution, streets in the sky and the revolt against them – all of which was about to fuel the phenomenon of the Liberal revival.

In fact, it was not until a couple of years after the Torrington by-election victory in 1958, and the end of control of the *News Croc* by the Cadbury family, that anyone coined the 'revival' term. That belonged in the 1960s, alongside 'Orpington man' and other phrases, but Chips was there gathering anyone who could, even remotely, whiff this new-style liberalism – commissioning them, interviewing and promoting them. He did so from his position as deputy features editor, appointed by the then editor, Norman Cursley. It continued under other editors in the 1960s, from Richard Moore to Harold Evans, under whom the paper began the series of investigations which made it famous, revealing Kim Philby as the Third Man and the devastating power of thalidomide.

To understand the position of the *Chronicle* in those days, we have to realise the legacy of the settlement that rescued it from the clutches of its rivals at the *Daily Mail*. The money provided by the trust and by contacts of Thorpe's provided enough to pay off the family and to meet the costs of redundancy and pensions for long-standing staffers; but the new trust – under the chairmanship of Richard Wainwright, later Liberal MP for Colne Valley – was otherwise desperately under-capitalised throughout. Most of the senior staff had to double up their roles. Chipping was no exception – as well as his roving features brief, he also had a news-gathering role. He was technology correspondent in the

1950s, aerospace correspondent in the '60s, energy correspondent in the '70s and business correspondent in the '80s – most of which he delegated to a number of trusted young staffers. Even well into his seventies, in the 1990s, he was the paper's green correspondent before the next hiccup to the continuity of the *Chronicle*.

These tasks gave Chips a broad overview of the trendiest areas of news, which fed into his other ideological work. It was Chipping who understood that the Liberal Party must put itself clearly into one particular camp if it was going to thrive, and if there was no obvious ideological home, then one must be shaped and articulated. That was why the 1960s marked the beginning of an attempt by the Liberals to speak for those who regarded themselves as increasingly disaffected by the direction of modernity. Chips regarded the emerging counterculture as providing a new ideological core for the party. He realised this before prominent Liberal Des Wilson became the first director of Shelter in 1966. And so it was Chipping who collected together the liberal-minded campaigners and social entrepreneurs to take over the National Council for Voluntary Organisations when it was relaunched as such in 1980. If the diverse and ebullient voluntary sector in the UK still retains its liberalism, that is down, most of all, to Frank Chipping.

There were obvious tensions between the hippies, when they emerged, and the New Age types and the other elements of the liberal counterculture, like community campaigners. But Chips managed to bring John Lennon regularly into the paper as a columnist in 1966–67, which helped hold the mixture together. That was how a paper that was struggling in 1960 had an influential voice that belied a relatively small, though growing, circulation – while the other daily papers began quickly to decline.

There were also tensions with the parliamentary Liberal Party, which did not always enjoy being linked in the public mind with complementary health therapists and anti-nuclear energy campaigners. The party leadership never warmed to Chips, which is why he never rose in the party hierarchy. Yet his activities were beginning to benefit the party's standing.

Chipping continued to go with his gut instincts for the paper, which appeared to work – a combination of self-help health, back-to-the-land weirdness and community power. (These were, coincidentally, the same issues which originally propelled the Five Star Movement to power in Italy.)

It was thanks, at least partly, to Chips that the core Liberal vote grew so steadily and that the party began to pick up seats in 1964 and 1966 and managed to hang on to them in 1970. It was how they ended up in a position to negotiate a Lab–Lib coalition in 1974 with Harold Wilson and Jim Callaghan, later abandoned by the Liberal leader David Steel after Labour's failure to keep to its commitments on electoral reform. It was how the Liberals managed to hang on to some of those gains again after the reaction against the coalition in 1979 (though arguably Margaret Thatcher did better because she borrowed some of Chips's language to win people over to 'independence').

By the time Thatcher gave way to John Major in 1990, the idea of independence fostered by Conservatism had palled, which meant that people like Chris Patten and Shaun Woodward were defecting from the Tories. They joined the Liberals, which set up a peculiar divide between the Liberals and their SDP allies, who had followed Shirley Williams out of Labour (Roy Jenkins, of course, joined the Liberal Party in 1980). But although Chips's party had clawed back some of the ground they had lost since the coalition with Labour, they still had no means of paying for themselves on the same scale as their rivals; like his newspaper, they had no major financial backers.

In the same way, because there was so little money to invest, the *News Croc* staff had to survive by their wits alone – attracting editors like Andreas Whittam Smith on his way to founding *The Independent* (now merged with the *Chronicle*). Or Simon Jenkins on his way to *The Times*. Or Alan Rusbridger, editor for nearly a decade from the early 2000s, and the reason why it was the *News Chronicle* that broke stories like the Trafigura scandal and the Panama Papers.

They took an early decision to go tabloid before the *Daily Mail*, though mainly for financial reasons. For the same reason, they carried on in Bouverie Street, off Fleet Street, nursing their elderly printer – still using hot metal presses well into the dotage of anyone who knew how to repair them. The printing press itself became a well-known stop for Lib Dem campaigners producing their own cut-price campaign newspapers. This was just one aspect of the two-way traffic between the party and the paper over the years – one reason why the *News Croc*'s election coverage was managed by Lord Rennard, once director of elections for the party, in recent years. It was a sad day for the party faithful when Anno Domini stepped in and the old typesetting systems, and the old printer, were sold for scrap metal and – only a generation after everyone else – the paper finally embraced computer composition. By then the *Chronicle* staff had dwindled to just one floor in Bouverie Street.

Chipping was also instrumental in the shift in marketing which meant targeting working women before the *Mail* caught on to the same idea. For decades, the *Chronicle* gave the *Mail* a run for their considerably larger moneybags – beating them to stories and innovations by the superior quality of their journalists and interns, who began to take over space from former staffers.

Now, in a future without the *Chronicle*, *The Guardian* looks set to be the main beneficiary. But Chips never trusted *The Guardian* staff, whom he regarded as social democrats and therefore not quite 'one of us'. 'They will be first with the key for the concentration camp guards if trendy opinion suggests that any of us should be put inside,' he used to say. This goes some way towards explaining the tough line he took as an old man against political correctness, which he always regarded as a way to keep the working classes out of public debate.

Just as Steel took the Liberal Party out of coalition with Labour when the Callaghan government reneged on proportional representation for Westminster elections, the Liberal Democrat leader Chris Patten took the party out of coalition with Blair for the same reason. This new coalition had been controversial in Chips's circles within the party, and so when Patten stepped down to become the EU's high representative in Bosnia, he was replaced as leader by Peter Hain. Hain's leadership of the Lib Dems was in some ways a vindication of the Chipping ideology; to have as party leader the man who had led the 'Stop the Seventy Tour' campaign against the cricket team of apartheid South Africa, in those hippy-dippy days of 1970, showed that in some ways his approach in the 1960s had paid off.

Chips was delighted to see Hain, now Leader of the Opposition after Labour's catastrophic performance in the 2010 election, performing so effectively against David Cameron in the House of Commons. The collapse in Labour votes, and the success of Hain's Lib Dems, meant that Cameron's Tories took office, and he called a Brexit vote at the next election. As we know, the opposition swung against Brexit, while the Ulster Unionists maintained Cameron's minority government in office. But now, those people who might once have made a career in Labour joined the Lib Dems. It has been a long time coming, but Chips's party may shortly take office.

It was sad, though, that Jo Grimond died in 1993, before he could see clearly what his objective of a radical, non-socialist left looked and felt like. Yet there were hints, even in his lifetime; the massive expansion of co-ops in the 1970s were thanks to Liberal legislation, as was devolution in Scotland and Wales and Northern Ireland. So were some of Chipping's other brainchildren, like the demolition of tower blocks and offices; the sovereign wealth fund paid for by North Sea oil; the mass adoption of shared-ownership housing, or rent-to-buy; and the break-up of the big banks – this one was actually enacted by Cameron under pressure from Hain.

By the 2010s, as the two parties of the left ran neck and neck, effectively cancelling each other out, the *News Croc* was also struggling. There was not the money to invest in new staff or equipment or to find a new editor to replace Alan Rusbridger, who had shifted to *The Guardian*. It was then that Lord Wallace of Saltaire, chair of the *Chronicle* trust since the retirement of Wainwright, approached the ninety-year-old Chipping and asked him if he would return and look after the paper until such a time as they could find a replacement. It was, by all accounts, a touching scene. Late in life, Chips had finally been asked to take on the top job at the institution that he loved. I believe he wept, and I am not at all surprised.

Chipping was retired, though he still haunted the corridors of the Lords. He had not been on the paper's payroll for ten years and had been drawing his state pension for a quarter of a century. But he was apparently as energetic as ever: a lifelong bachelor, he had married the supermodel Wendy Devereux in 2003 at the age of eighty-three and managed to produce three children in quick succession – so there was perhaps some reason for assuming that he might have still been up to the task.

He immediately set about easing out most of the senior staff, bringing in younger journalists and interns at the same time as launching the Reform Institute, which was designed as a link between the Lib Dems and thinkers in the broader liberal movement.

Unfortunately, during his absence from public debate, the world had changed. The voluntary sector was itself divided, and the communities sector was split between the anti-racists and the old working classes. They had little in common now with the anti-vaxxers who had turned the debate about complementary health so toxic. The inner-directed elements of what had once been a cohesive liberal counterculture appeared to have retired to the countryside.

I got to know Chips again during this period. We had first met back in the 1990s, just before one of his many retirements. It was already clear that unifying these disparate strands would probably now be impossible, partly because of the new populism of the frustrated Brexiters and Trump supporters from the US – and indirectly, too, because they had given rise to a new intolerance on the left and among the young of cynicism and 'cancel culture'. Chips's own reputation had not been helped among feminists by a controversial *Woman's Hour* interview with his wife, Wendy, in which she described her husband as 'a bit priapic'.

Chips stood down as editor at the end of the interregnum, by which time the writing was on the wall. The paper's advertising revenue had nose-dived then dried up altogether during the Covid pandemic. The *News Chronicle* finally announced that it was closing and merging online with *The Independent* in November 2020.

Frank Chipping was never recognised as the saviour of his party. In fact, he was for many stalwart Lib Dems a thorn in their side, especially after the merger with the SDP in 1988. He was always sceptical, in private and in public, about social democracy, which he regarded as 'neither social nor very democratic; at best a kind of ersatz radical liberalism'. The SDP seemed to him to be reactionaries against the countercultural values he had made his own. Party managers often tried to get him sacked from the newspaper on the grounds that he was too radical – or sometimes on the grounds that he was too conservative. He regarded the sale of council houses to tenants by the Thatcher government as the crucial step towards providing everyone with economic independence – though not the way in which they had used this as an excuse to prevent councils from building more low-cost places to live. He was, in short, hard to categorise. He never said, but I suspected him of sympathy with Brexit – probably his horror at finding himself on the same side as Boris Johnson and Michael Gove prevented any kind of public affirmation.

Though he did live to see the Lib Dems replacing Labour and on the verge, perhaps, of taking power in this year's general election, he received little credit for articulating the Liberal revival as a cultural phenomenon. Perhaps he was right that, if he had not existed, somebody else would have done so. But I'm not so sure; if Chipping had not been there, the UK could now feel very different, politically and socially. We could now be the highly centralised, rather pompous and highly technocratic nation that we seemed to be hurtling towards in the 1960s, and the Liberal revival could well and truly have run out of steam. The party could be back to a handful of MPs and could entirely have squandered the great, unexpected and undeserved gift of the counterculture.

Luckily, we don't live there.

After his retirement, Chips continued as director of the Reform Institute until his death before Christmas 2020. He is survived by Wendy and family, plus two much-loved illegitimate sons, whom he supported throughout their lives.

By a strange quirk of fate, I was there at the end, when he collapsed at home between lockdowns. We stood around him trying to make him comfortable before the ambulance arrived. 'What a pity', said one of the other guests, 'that he never went into politics himself…'

At that, Chips opened his eyes and managed to murmur something. 'What... was that... you were saying... about me... just now?' he said. 'I thought I heard you... one of you... saying it was a pity... a pity I never had... anything to do with politicians,' said Chips. 'But I have... I have...' With quavering merriment, he said, 'Yes... I have... thousands of them... tens of thousands of them... and all Liberals.'

Note by the author
Unfortunately, because Chips did not exist, the sale of the *News Chronicle* to Associated Press went ahead in 1960, despite the best efforts of Jeremy Thorpe to launch a trust and of the staff to make Operation Phoenix happen. Even so, I believe we would now be living in a different kind of UK if this liberal paper had survived.

Notes
1   'The night the blow fell', *New Statesman*, 22 October 1960.
2   'The murder of the News Chronicle', *New Statesman*, 22 October 1960.
3   James Cameron, *Point of Departure: An Experiment in Autobiography* (Oxford: Oriel Press, 1985), p. 280.
4   Hansard, 2 December 1960, vol. 631, col. 777, https://hansard.parliament.uk/commons/1960-12-02/debates/0e9f7356-5f5e-4d59-be92-0aa6b4ee7822/ClosureOfNewspapers
5   Wilfred Burns, *New Towns for Old: The Technique of Urban Renewal* (London: Leonard Hill, 1963).

Chapter 7

What if Scotland had voted 'Yes' to an assembly in 1979?

Tom Chidwick

On Wednesday 28 February 1979, readers of the resolutely conservative *Daily Telegraph* were confronted by an alarming editorial which lamented their fear of 'A Kingdom on the Brink'. While the Islamic Revolution gripped Iran – with the provisional revolutionary government having collapsed in the previous fortnight, as Ayatollah Khomeini cemented his control over the former imperial state – the editorial was, in fact, a dire warning about the durability of the United Kingdom of Great Britain and Northern Ireland.

As Scotland and Wales prepared to go to the polls the following day to determine whether to establish new legislatures in Edinburgh and Cardiff, the *Telegraph* declared that nothing short of the 'dissolution of the British state' was on the ballot paper. While London's first penny paper was less concerned by the situation west of Offa's Dyke – believing that Wales would 'quietly but decisively' reject its cumbrous devolution scheme – it was particularly concerned that the Scots would succumb to the 'simple seduction' of having greater control over their own affairs.[1]

After a decade of frenetic debate about devolving power to Scotland, James Callaghan's Labour government had finally succeeded in putting the creation of a 142-member assembly to the Scottish people. While the government believed that the assembly would build on the country's distinctive history and culture, giving it control over the bulk of Scotland's social policy, including healthcare, social welfare, education and public-sector housing, many devolutionists panned its meagre powers, as well as its inability to raise its own revenue. It would, however, provide Scotland with what Russell Fairgrieve, the Conservative MP for West Aberdeenshire, called 'an Athenian Court', where Scots could discuss, debate and decide upon purely Scottish domestic issues.[2]

Although the complexities of devolution failed to capture hearts and minds during the country's first referendum on the 'constitutional question', campaigners believed that they were engaged in a battle for the 'soul of Scotland'. Scotland in the 1970s was a nation on the move, grappling with deindustrialisation, a decade of nationwide industrial strife and the discovery of North Sea oil. This economic dislocation, allied to fears about the impact of Britain's entry to the EEC on fishing and agriculture, as well as a resurgent 'Scottishness' (encapsulated in the Scottish National Party's 'It's Scotland's Oil' campaign), presented the first major challenge to Westminster's hegemony in a generation, and had aided the election of eleven SNP MPs in October 1974. As the academic and playwright Willy Maley once remarked, the '70s was also the decade in which many primarily Scottish Labour figures (including Gordon Brown, whose *The Red Paper on Scotland* was published in January 1975) helped crystallise the idea that 'socialism could profitably be harnessed to a developing *Scottish* political identity'.[3]

While the *New York Times* thought Scotland to be the 'Jimmy Cagney of the United Kingdom' – compensating for being smaller, less populous and poorer than England by bragging about 'Scotch whiskey, Scottish football and Scottish prowess in battle' – even the SNP's charismatic and no-nonsense Margo MacDonald warned Scots that they would have to 'stop pretending to be a nation' if the country voted 'No' on 1 March 1979.[4]

Although the Scotland Act 1978 was intended to give Scots greater political control over issues which, on the whole, were already administered in Scotland by the Scottish Office, devolution's critics claimed that the government was on the verge of doing irreparable damage to the ties that tethered the component nations of the United Kingdom together. On the day before polling day, the *Daily Telegraph* warned its readers that if Scotland assented to a 'complex set of constitutional proposals which baffle the head and have no appeal to the heart', it would be launching Britain 'on a disaster course from which it is hard to see an escape'.[5] Jeremy Thorpe, the former leader of the Liberal Party, who would go on trial for conspiracy to murder in May 1979, forecast that devolution could lead to independence for both Scotland and Wales in just five to seven years.[6] Even Terence O'Neill, the antepenultimate Prime Minister of Northern Ireland, suggested that, despite the permanence of the Crown and the UK's shared economy, it was 'not impossible' that a long history of 'reluctant concessions to the "Celtic fringe"' could see the United Kingdom simply 'cease to exist'.[7]

Perhaps unsurprisingly, the proposed change in the country's governance – the most significant since the Act of Union in 1707 – had not been straightforward. In February 1977, the government's first piece of draft legislation was defeated on the floor of the House of Commons after twenty-two Labour rebels sided with Margaret Thatcher's Conservative Party, which had become increasingly hostile to devolution since she had succeeded Edward Heath as leader two years earlier. In December 1976, one of their number, Robert Hughes, the Labour MP for Aberdeen North, warned his leaders that, rather than giving Scotland a greater stake in the union, they were in danger of 'giving credence to the SNP', as well as 'destroying the solidarity of the working class' and handing greater power to 'the merchant bankers and the capitalists who have raped the resources of this country'.[8]

Nine months later, in November 1977, its replacement – the Scotland Bill, which was memorably described by a Dumfriesshire bookseller as the 'world's worst seller' – was introduced to the Commons after the advent of the Lib–Lab Pact between the incumbent ailing Labour administration and the Liberal Party. The Bill ensured that the assembly's approximately 140 members (two for each of Scotland's existing seventy-one constituencies, although the legislation did permit some particularly populated areas to have three members) would be elected by first-past-the-post rather than by a proportional system, with many devolutionists favouring the latter. It also proposed the establishment of a Scottish Executive, to be led by a First Secretary, to mirror the workings of the Cabinet in London, operating under collective responsibility and served by an extension of the home civil service. For *The Scotsman*, devolution would prevent Scotland being subject to the 'pious paternalism' of Westminster, which treated Scots as 'irresponsible children, unable to make an adult decision without the say-so of their politicians or spiritual betters'.[9]

While the government managed to get the Scotland Bill onto the statute book in July 1978, it was subject to substantial amendments in the Commons, including the concession of a referendum. The most significant amendment, however, was introduced by George Cunningham, the expatriate Scot born in Dunfermline, who represented Islington South & Finsbury. Passed on Burns Night 1978, Cunningham's amendment, which would ultimately prove too high a threshold for Scotland's voters, stated that if less than 40 per cent of those entitled to vote had voted 'Yes', then the government would be obliged to bring an order repealing the Scotland Act before Parliament to stop the assembly being established.

While Scotland voted with a small majority of just over 77,000 for 'Yes' on 1 March 1979, the assembly was torpedoed by failing to meet the conditions of Cunningham's all-important 40 per cent rule. In all, of the 2,384,439 Scots who voted (over 100,000 more than had cast their ballot at the 1975 Common Market referendum), some 1,230,937 voted 'Yes', a little over 32 per cent of the electorate. Perhaps the assembly's most prolific opponent, Tam Dalyell, put it best when he remarked that the Scotland Act was comparable to 'the Sultan of Turkey's battleship, ingenious in many ways except that it would not float'.[10]

After a decade of debate about the 'Scottish question', the assembly's demise raises an intriguing question about what would have happened had the 40 per cent rule failed to pass the House of Commons. Without Cunningham's amendment, would Scotland have secured an assembly in 1979? How would the country's first legislature in nearly 300 years have changed Scottish, and indeed British, public life? Would the assembly have tempered the country's relationship with Margaret Thatcher's Conservative governments and spared it much of the psychodrama of the 1980s? And would this in turn have lessened the chances of Scotland voting to become an independent country, which now increasingly appears to be only a matter of time?

While historians typically deal in hard facts, curating, interpreting and decoding the past, the following is an estimation of what might have been had Scotland voted for an assembly in March 1979. Everything up to and including the 77,000-vote victory for 'Yes' is historically accurate and the product of extensive original research. What follows Ronald Fraser's announcement is hypothetical, the product of educated guesses, reasonable assumptions and an informed assessment of what could have happened had the House of Commons not passed George Cunningham's 40 per cent rule. Although some may suggest that this is all purely academic – noting that Scotland obtained a Parliament in 1999, making the assembly saga little more than a sorry and better forgotten episode in the country's national story – indulge me as I suggest what might have been…

'A nation again'

As the referendum campaign drew to a close, Gordon Brown, the chairman of the Labour Party's official 'Labour Movement Yes' campaign, warned that 'to be swayed now by the scaremongering and false fears peddled by the money men of the "No" campaign would be like scoring an own goal in the last few seconds of a big match'.[11] For the former student rector of the University of Edinburgh, who would become the most famous of Raith Rovers' supporters, the referendum was a once-in-a-generation opportunity for real change north of the border. For weeks, the opinion polls had been tightening as the 'No' campaign made a remarkable comeback and began to eat into the 'Yes' campaign's sizeable lead. On the final Sunday before referendum day, System Three, the independent Scottish pollster, predicted that 'Yes', which had been leading 'No' by 64 per cent to 36 in mid-January, now had just a 52:48 advantage.

While 'Yes' campaigners frantically attempted to get the assembly over the line, there was a growing sense that the complexities of devolution and an increasingly negative campaign had failed to capture the country's imagination. As George Skinner, an Aberdonian plater, told *The Guardian* two weeks before: 'We're just concerned about our next pay packet, about prices and the cost of living.'[12] Astonishingly, even the *Daily Mirror*'s polling day coverage, which centred on two topless models who, the paper forecast, would 'get an overwhelming "Yes" vote for their assemblies', seemed to have failed to invigorate the Scottish people.[13] It was also assumed that bad weather north of the border had seriously affected the 'Yes' vote by discouraging floating voters from casting their ballots. In Aberdeen, one 'No' voter, Mrs Bella Lawrie, whose advanced years her local paper did not disclose, performed her civic duty in the rain, only to break her leg as she left the polling station at the city's Mile End Primary School.[14]

As Scotland waited to hear the assembly's fate, journalists began to gather at New St Andrew's House, the Brutalist administrative centre of the Scottish Office in Edinburgh's St James Centre, which rightly shared the 'monstrous carbuncle' epithet that the Prince of Wales once applied to an extension to the National Gallery in London. The announcement, which would be made by the chief counting officer and former Secretary of the Scottish Home and Health Department, Ronald Fraser, would be witnessed by over 200 members of the fourth estate, travelling from as far afield as South Africa, East Germany, China, Canada and Bulgaria, as well as six Parisian students who chattered excitedly in French through-out the proceedings.

After Fraser announced that Scotland had voted 'Yes' by just 77,000 votes on a turnout of 63.8 per cent, Bruce Millan, the Secretary of State for Scotland, took to his feet to congratulate Scots on making devolution a reality, although he acknowledged that his fellow countrymen had not taken the opportunity 'with the decisiveness which they ought to have done'. Nevertheless, the Dundonian, who had been the MP for Glasgow Craigton since 1959, promised to organise elections to the new assembly as quickly as possible. While some questioned whether such a small majority mandated such a major constitutional change, newspapers declared Scotland to be 'a nation again', with one admirer of Scotland's national bard celebrating 'the country o' Worth'. That evening, delirious 'Yes' campaigners lit a vast bonfire beside the incomplete National Monument atop Calton Hill and, as the flames grew, launched into an impromptu rendition of 'Flower of Scotland'. Few could have missed the extra gusto with which the SNP contingent proclaimed that 'we can still rise now, and be the nation again, that stood against him, Proud Edward's Army, and sent him homeward tae think again'.

Amidst the jubilation north of the border, few reflected on the fact that it could have been markedly different had the infamous 40 per cent rule, which had been dreamt up by 'No'-voting Labour MPs, passed the House of Commons in January 1978. The amendment, which was put to the House by Labour MP George Cunningham, was rumoured to be the brainchild of Robin Cook, the urbane and forensic MP for Edinburgh Central, and would have required at least 40 per cent of eligible voters to vote 'Yes' for it take effect. Had Cook and Tam Dalyell, the unofficial 'Leader of the Opposition' to the Bill, not had their doubts, publicly refusing to endorse it after deciding that it looked too much like 'an English trick', Scotland would now be lamenting a missed opportunity – an independent legislature which only 32 per cent of Scots had voted for.

In the days following Fraser's announcement, there was a growing sense that Callaghan's administration might not survive long enough to oversee the first round of elections to Scotland's fledgling legislature. While the current parliamentary session was not scheduled to end until October, the government – which had been without any sort of majority since the end of the Lib–Lab Pact in September 1978 – now found itself reliant on the goodwill of the Scottish National Party. As Roy Hattersley, the Prices and Consumer Protection Secretary, later recalled, the government 'lived precariously ... cobbling together majorities night by night by recruiting whatever allies were available'.[15]

Although the government's commitment to press forward with an assembly temporarily pacified the SNP (which had previously expressed its willingness to vote with the Tories to bring the government down, should devolution falter), it pushed a handful of Labour MPs from the north-east of England to consider siding with the opposition. While the Conservatives were reportedly still deliberating on when to put a no-confidence motion to the House of Commons, lobby journalists suggested that Geordie MPs – whose constituents and local councils believed that devolution would bring about an economic imbalance favourable to Scotland – *could* be persuaded to side with the Tories.

The government's problems were compounded by the fact that it was also unable to decide on when the assembly elections should be held. While the SNP favoured going to the polls in June 1979, the civil service informed the Cabinet that it would not be feasible before autumn at the very earliest. As the Prime Minister retired to Upper Clayhill Farm, his bolthole in East Sussex, for the weekend to consider his options, a small group of Cabinet ministers advanced Thursday 9 August as a possible compromise, which they believed could satisfy the SNP and allow the civil service enough time to review the country's electoral register.

While the Prime Minister sounded out his Cabinet colleagues and consulted his party's Scottish Executive, Westminster gossips suggested that he would side with the civil service, hoping to ensure that the assembly elections would coincide with an October general election. As Callaghan's critics recalled, his refusal to go to the country the previous October had arguably cost Labour its best chance of winning a majority and implied that the Prime Minister would again prefer to delay the ballots until his government had a surer footing.

When the only Royal Navy man to assume the premiership took to the despatch box on 5 March 1979 – the House of Commons' first day back after its February recess – he announced, to widespread surprise, that the first round of assembly elections would be held on Thursday 7 June. To the horror of many in Scottish Labour, the Prime Minister had complied with the Nationalists' demand for a June ballot and had, worst of all, arranged the country's inaugural devolved elections on the 650th anniversary of the death of Robert the Bruce. While Callaghan made no secret of his distaste for the Nationalists – denouncing the SNP as 'extremists' during a visit to the McLellan Galleries in Glasgow in February – his government's precarious position in Parliament made appeasing them something of a necessity.

As 'Sunny Jim' explained to an unsettled House of Commons, the assembly's use of Scotland's existing seventy-one parliamentary constituencies would allow for a prompter vote and ensure that the Scottish elections would coincide with the first ever direct elections to the European Parliament. Likewise, with one eye on the finite amount of sitting time that the government had left, Callaghan announced that it was his intention that the election of the first cohort of 'assemblymen' would be wrapped up before the election of the next UK parliament. As Callaghan concluded his statement by declaring that it was now 'Scotland's moment', Margaret Thatcher's solemn expression suggested that the Conservative front bench was now keenly aware that they had been wrongfooted by a wily and spirited Prime Minister.

While the evening news told the story of a resilient premier snatching victory from defeat, reaffirming his government's authority, many in Scottish Labour were bemused by Callaghan's eagerness to get to the polls. During the referendum campaign, the party had appeared to be drained and demoralised and, while Denis Healey later recalled being 'immensely impressed' by the quality and political nous of Labour members in Scotland, many activists had noted that the local working-class support that usually materialised in general elections was lacking in the months leading up to 1 March. Furthermore, although the 'Yes' victory had encouraged the party's devolutionists to redouble their efforts, Helen Liddell, the party's general secretary in Scotland, expressed her concern that prominent 'No' campaigners would be reluctant to campaign for candidates standing for an institution whose establishment they had actively opposed.

Although the Liberals were languishing at just under 10 per cent in the polls, the party's Scottish cohort shared the Prime Minister's eagerness to go to the country. Led by David Steel and Russell Johnston, two prominent and long-standing devolutionists, they believed the assembly would allow the Scottish Liberals to present themselves to 'Yes' voters as a viable alternative to both Labour and the SNP and offer the party – which sought to break Britain's age-old duopoly but held just thirteen seats at Westminster – a rare opportunity to secure a more stable electoral footing.

As candidates and campaigners began traipsing the streets of Scotland, distributing leaflets in their quest to win the hearts and minds of a majority of the 3.75 million Scots who were eligible to vote, contractors at Edinburgh's Old Royal High School were engaged in a race to the wire to finish the assembly's new home. After Thomas Hamilton's Athenian masterpiece was purchased by the Scottish Office in 1976 for £650,000, the Property Services Agency (PSA) of the Department for the Environment was tasked with shoring up the dilapidated Grade-A-listed former school building and creating what the *Glasgow Herald* described as 'workable and dignified accommodation' for the assembly, while 'fully respecting the character of an outstanding historic building'.[16]

Costing nearly £4 million, work had begun in September 1976 when workmen discovered that the supporting timbers of the east and west lobbies, which held the roof up, were crumbling, and the entirety of its window frames needed replacing. In the three years since, the PSA had created an extensive parliamentary campus on Calton Hill, crafting a debating chamber out of the building's Great Hall, converting outbuildings to house a press room and two radio studios and replacing the swimming pool with an emergency generator, prompting the project's director to assure the press that 'state business will continue even if the whole of Edinburgh is blacked out'.[17]

Although the assembly building was almost complete, there remained a distinct possibility that it would not be ready to welcome Scotland's new legislators, who were expected to meet for the first time shortly before the summer solstice. While the government had tried to avoid unnecessarily expensive additions, repeatedly being bombarded with questions about the effort and expense that the Old Royal High was absorbing, the assembly's state-of-the-art electronic voting recording systems were still not up and running. Its critics speculated that the building's troubles were a warning that an antique edifice would be unable to nurture a modern nation.

On Monday 2 July 1979, as television and radio crews descended on 'Auld Reekie' to capture the beginning of a new chapter in Scotland's national story, the assembly was officially opened by Her Majesty the

Queen, whose arrival on Calton Hill had been heralded by a 21-gun salute from Edinburgh Castle. After a somewhat lacklustre election campaign, the consecration of the first Scottish legislature in 272 years made for box-office viewing, as the great and the good of Scottish society and the new assemblymen began the service by parading from the home of the old Scottish Parliament behind St Giles' Cathedral to the building which had been renamed 'New Parliament House', journeying down the High Street and along North Bridge before heading along Waterloo Place and climbing the steps to the assembly's Athenian portico. While the monarch had caused some controversy during her Silver Jubilee in 1977 by declaring that she could not forget that she had been crowned 'Queen of the *United* Kingdom of Great Britain and Northern Ireland', she expressed her desire that the assembly would help the country 'to realise its full potential' by being both 'responsible and responsive to the people of Scotland'.

While the elections had resulted in only a small majority for Labour, the party took heart from the fact that, even in the dying days of what had been a tumultuous government, it could still reign supreme north of the border. In Coatbridge & Airdrie, Helen Liddell had successfully contested her home seat, with the breakaway Scottish Labour Party's Jim Sillars – who it was widely expected would lose his South Ayrshire seat at the next Westminster election – taking the other of the constituency's two assembly seats. Moreover, the election of George Foulkes – the chair of Lothian Regional Council's education committee, who had come to national attention in February 1979 when he suggested that the Scottish Education Department had 'more secrets than the Kremlin' – ensured that one of the party's most promising stars would also sit on the assembly's brown leather benches.

It was noticeable, however, that a number of the party's big-hitters had refused to stand, with many speculating that, even with a spell on the opposition benches beckoning, the likes of Donald Dewar and Gordon Brown continued to see Westminster as a bigger and brighter stage. While many activists had urged Bruce Millan to stand for the assembly, believing him to be a shoo-in for First Secretary, he had instead opted to remain at Westminster, feeling 'duty-bound', if only for a few months before a general election, to oversee the assembly's first steps. The main beneficiary of Millan's decision was Harry Ewing, his junior at the Scottish Office, whose victory in one of Stirling's two assembly seats made him a surprise favourite to head the country's first devolved executive.

While not initially the front-runner, Ewing – who narrowly beat Dr Jesse Dickson Mabon, the 'cheerful and chubby-faced' now former MP for Greenock & Port Glasgow, to his party's nomination for First Secretary – was a popular, if unforeseen, choice among his fellow assemblymen. A former foundryman and a skilled parliamentarian, Ewing had enhanced his reputation during the Scotland Act's difficult passage through Parliament and, crucially, had little time for the 'separatists' whose dogged pursuit of independence, he maintained, had cost the 'Yes' campaign innumerable votes.

Although Ewing had sound devolutionist credentials, those most opposed to his appointment as Scotland's inaugural First Secretary came from within his own party, arguing that a dour, upstanding, fervently Eurosceptic Presbyterian was not an ambitious enough choice to help forge a new and better nation. Ewing's election also took the liberalisation of abortion law (which he firmly opposed) and the long-overdue decriminalisation of homosexuality off the assembly's agenda. This disappointed Labour 'Yes' campaigners, who had hoped that a campaign by the executive – which was charged with administering abortion laws set by Westminster – to encourage Parliament to liberalise family law and improve women's rights would demonstrate the assembly's ability to move the country forward.

The elections gave the SNP a respectable showing on Calton Hill, although not the majority that some thought inevitable following the 'Yes' vote on 1 March. Despite the use of first-past-the-post to select Scotland's inaugural assemblymen, both the SNP and the Scottish Liberals were able to win a handful of seats as third parties, positioning themselves as possible power-brokers in any future hung assembly. However, as Scots went to the polls in June 1979, it was becoming increasingly evident that the SNP was plateauing, with Scottish Labour expected to receive the bulk of the credit for the assembly's establishment. In Hamilton, Margo MacDonald's decision to relinquish her candidacy for the Lanarkshire town's Westminster seat in order to stand for the assembly was vindicated with one of the biggest landslides of the election. While Winnie Ewing chose not to stand, opting to continue with her candidacy for the European Parliament, the election of Dr Robert McIntyre, the Nationalists' elder statesman and the party's first ever MP – who had been tempted out of retirement to contest the second Stirling, Falkirk & Grangemouth seat – delighted the party faithful. At nearly seventy years old, it was unlikely that McIntyre would stand for a second term, although it was expected that 'Doc Mac' would add gravitas and earthy experience to the Nationalist contingent.

Despite having campaigned for a 'No' vote, the Tories decided to contest every assembly seat on 7 June. With the party still confident of forming the next government at Westminster in October, the shadow Cabinet concluded that it could not be seen to be turning its back on Scotland before Britain went to the polls. While some speculated that the party's 'No' campaign may have hurt its chances of picking up seats in 'Yes'-voting areas, the Conservatives won a handful of seats, from rural Dumfries & Galloway across to Edinburgh's leafy suburbs and as far north as West Aberdeenshire. Tory contenders – primarily unblooded parliamentary candidates and dependable, long-serving councillors – spent the campaign hoping that Scots would heed Mrs Thatcher's warning that 'the machinery by which we are governed is of less consequence than the purpose of those who are elected to govern'.[18]

As the sun set behind Castle Rock – the 'great primitive black crag' which Muriel Spark compared to the 'statement of an unmitigated fact preceded by *nevertheless*' – fireworks from Calton Hill, Holyrood Park and The Meadows celebrated the beginning of a new era of self-government north of the border.[19] With its legislature restored, Edinburgh was no longer the 'hollow capital' which poets and historians had lamented since the Act of Union had taken effect on 1 May 1707. With the most radical Conservative government since the war on the horizon and the country's age-old industrial base winding down, Scots would now enter the 1980s 'a nation again', with a Scottish legislature deciding on the country's most pressing issues. Amidst the celebrations, though, some wondered whether the assembly would inevitably push the country one step further away from the rest of the United Kingdom.

'A conscience and a tongue'

While I have presented an approximation of what *could* have happened in the months after the referendum, 1 March 1979 surely must be regarded as a missed opportunity. As Andrew Marr reflected in 1992, Scotland had passed up the glittering prize of a nation at ease with itself – 'an argumentative, grown-up Scotland with a lively parliament' with 'a conscience and a tongue, as well as limbs and a body'.[20] Indeed, a week after Ronald Fraser announced that Scots had failed to satisfy the 40 per cent rule, archivists from the National Museum of Antiquities visiting the Scottish Office replaced a medieval wooden carving of St Andrew, cheerfully shouldering his cross, with a broken sword from the Battle of Flodden in 1513, where, as Sir Walter Scott wrote, 'shiver'd was fair Scotland's spear and broken was her shield'.

There is a sense in which Scotland is still grappling with the decision it made in 1979. While it was evidently not the nation-enhancing moment of democratic empowerment that 1999 would later become, it was without parallel in Scotland's recent history. It presented the nation with genuinely divergent paths between the status quo and a future with a national legislature deciding on issues important to Scots *in* Scotland for the first time in nearly 300 years. While the assembly's inability to raise its own revenue would have continued to be controversial, as devolved parliamentarians were forced to work within a block grant from Westminster, it would have been able to address matters which had plagued Scotland for generations.

It is highly probable that the assembly would have been obliged (much as Holyrood later was) to tackle increasing overseas interest in buying up large swathes of Scotland, with one report three weeks after polling day suggesting that over 1 million acres of land were already in foreign ownership, with more set to be sold abroad as overseas speculators exploited the country's cheap and readily available acreage. While the

SNP representatives in the assembly would most probably have been in opposition, the separatist contingent on Calton Hill would have sought significant concessions to Nationalist opinion from whichever party found themselves forming the first executive. As the SNP's strongest bastions could typically be found in predominantly rural areas, it is probable – as Hamish Watt, the SNP MP for Banffshire, had suggested during the referendum campaign – that the SNP would have encouraged the assembly to establish new protectionist institutions, such as a Scottish Fishery Protection Service, to safeguard the country's fishing industry, which accounted for over 50 per cent of the EEC's fish stock. Likewise, while the health and life expectancy of most Scots had drastically improved as urban overcrowding fell and sanitation improved, a devolved legislature would almost certainly have continued the Scottish Home and Health Department's concerted effort to tackle the root causes of Scotland's poor health. In the years after 1979, it is likely that the assembly would have told Scots, as the Scottish Office's chief medical officer, Dr John Reid, later would, that individuals must take 'greater responsibility in the maintenance of their own health and well-being'.[21]

As with all legislatures, a Scottish Assembly, no matter how inconsequential some thought its powers would have been, would have given greater opportunity to ventilate Scotland's most pressing problems. As one commentator – who questioned whether the 'auld sang' of self-government would have a 'new tune' in the 1970s – suggested, devolution offered a solution to the 'endless round of crises, recessions and failures' which had hampered British politics through the past decade and would invite 'new thinking, a willingness to break with the preoccupations of the past and take a fresh look at Scotland and its problems'.[22] Throughout the 1980s and beyond, a devolved executive of any political complexion would have provided an outlet for the country's grievances and been an effective advocate for its interests in both Westminster and Brussels.

A Scottish Assembly could also have had a far-reaching impact on Britain's party-political landscape in the 1980s. With the Conservative Party moving away from the patrician 'One Nation' politics which had dominated its thinking since 1945, and the Labour Party shifting leftwards, the makeup of both parties' caucuses in the assembly may well have determined the direction that the parties took nationally. With the creation of the Social Democratic Party by Roy Jenkins, David Owen, Bill Rodgers and Shirley Williams in March 1981, the assembly might have offered the fledgling centrist party greater purchase north of the border, persuading Labour moderates (and would-be assemblymen) such as Dickson Mabon and Vince Cable (who defected to the SDP in October 1981 and February 1982 respectively) to join its ranks. Furthermore, the rise of fiery and abrasive hardline Bennites in the Labour Party (such as Dennis Canavan, 'Red Ron' Brown and George Galloway) after 1979 undoubtedly would have improved the SDP's chances of building on Jenkins's surprise victory in the momentous Glasgow Hillhead by-election in March 1982 at the second round of assembly elections. Alternatively, it is also not inconceivable that a devolved executive – headed by moderate centre-left Scots more akin to James Callaghan's brand of Labour politics than Tony Benn's – as well as the election of Denis Healey to the party's deputy leadership in November 1980, may have prevented such an exodus and encouraged wavering Scottish Labour members to remain within the fray.

For the Conservative Party, Mrs Thatcher's growing unpopularity north of the border and the party's increasingly virulent Thatcherism may have resulted in a conspicuously anti-Thatcherite faction developing on Calton Hill. Across the decade, Scottish 'Wets' – such as Alick Buchanan-Smith and Malcolm Rifkind, who led the unofficial Conservative 'Yes' campaign after resigning from the party's front bench in 1976 to protest against their leader's opposition to devolution – may have gravitated towards the assembly in order to advance a more distinctly Scottish Conservatism.

While there is a persuasive argument to be made that an assembly would have sought more powers and greater responsibility, it could have satisfied the Scots' urge for greater political autonomy from Westminster – despite the fact that the pursuit of devolution had given Scots almost unprecedented influence during the 1970s – without necessarily weakening the essential fabric of the kingdom. Although devolution to England remained a conspicuous absence in a distinctly asymmetric scheme, devolution to Scotland and Wales in 1979 could have made more diffuse government the norm in Britain and might have lessened the tensions between Scotland and the UK government in the 1980s by disaggregating its domestic political agenda from that of Margaret Thatcher. It was arguably the failure to secure an assembly in 1979 and the election of Thatcher-led governments thrice in the 1970s and 1980s which prompted devolutionists to call for a more powerful *Parliament*, which has allowed the Scotland of 2021 to cement its political culture as divergent from that of both England and Wales.

It is not inconceivable, however, that a devolved (and subservient) assembly would still have hankered for greater powers and pushed the country towards an independence referendum in the mid-1980s. Despite widespread disapproval of Margaret Thatcher's governments north of the border, it seems unlikely that a Nationalist party with just two MPs for most of the decade would have been able to persuade a majority of Scots to break away from the United Kingdom. While Scotland would not vote on independence until September 2014, an independence poll was by no means a revolutionary idea in the 1970s and '80s; in September 1976, former Conservative Prime Ministers Edward Heath and Lord Home had called for a referendum in order to settle the issue once and for all, citing the poll in March 1973 which had asked the people of Northern Ireland whether they wished to remain in the United Kingdom as a model. Had an independence referendum been held between 1984 and 1986 – as Jeremy Thorpe predicted would happen had Scotland voted 'Yes' in 1979 – a decisive 'No' vote and an already minimal (and flagging) separatist movement might have put the issue to bed. Had that happened, Scotland in 2021 could have been a more contented component of the United Kingdom, and the country's heartfelt concerns in 2014 may well have been focused on the devastating fire at Charles Rennie Mackintosh's Glasgow School of Art and the city's hosting of the Commonwealth Games, rather than on the possible break-up of the union.

Nevertheless, it is equally possible that Scotland may have been 'Free by '93', as the SNP once claimed, and might have avoided Brexit. What if...

Notes

1 'A kingdom on the brink', *Daily Telegraph*, 28 February 1979.

2 Hansard, 13 December 1976, vol. 922, cols 1054–5.

3 Willy Maley, 'Cultural Devolution?: Representing Scotland in the 1970s' in Bart Moore-Gilbert (ed.), *The Arts in the 1970s: Cultural Closure?* (London: Routledge, 1994), pp. 81–2.

4 'The Devolution Bill last week passed another stage toward implementation', *New York Times*, 2 July 1978.

5 'A kingdom on the brink'.

6 'British government is facing key test', *New York Times*, 21 February 1977.

7 'The United Kingdom: Can it survive?', *New York Times*, 18 February 1975.

8 Hansard, 13 December 1976, vol. 922, col. 1134.

9 'Full measure', *The Scotsman*, 6 June 1976.

10 Russell Galbraith, *Inside Out – The Man They Can't Gag: A Biography of Tam Dalyell* (Edinburgh: Mainstream Publishing, 2000), p. 169.

11 'Scotland's 1979 devolution plans: forty years on from the "Yes" vote that wasn't', *Edinburgh Evening News*, 1 March 2019.

12 'Scottish oil region cools over devolution', *The Guardian*, 12 February 1979.

13 'It's D-Day: Millions vote in the big poll', *Daily Mirror*, 1 March 1979.

14 'City voting day accident', *Aberdeen Press and Journal*, 3 March 1979.

15 'The party's over', *The Observer*, 22 March 2009.

16 '£4m gamble on the Old Royal High School', *Glasgow Herald*, 14 February 1979.

17 'Flaw in plans for our new seat of power', *Aberdeen Evening Express*, 30 November 1978.

18 'Margaret Thatcher speech to Scottish Conservative conference', 15 May 1976, https://www.margaretthatcher.org/document/103028

19 Muriel Spark, 'What Images Return' in Karl Miller (ed.), *Memoirs of a Modern Scotland* (London: Faber & Faber, 1970), p. 153.

20 Andrew Marr, *The Battle for Scotland* (London: Penguin Books, 1992), p. 240.

21 'Scots must change bad health habits', *Aberdeen Evening Express*, 26 July 1979.

22 'Will the revival of the auld sang have a new tune?', *Aberdeen Press and Journal*, 1 February 1977.

Chapter 8

Imagine: what if John Lennon had not been killed in 1980?

Michael Mowlem

I

Andy returned from university to his parents' home in Warrington with a newly purchased vinyl copy of *Reborn*, the first album by the band the Blooming Dahlias. It added to his father's collection, started in the 1960s, of albums by the Beatles and its members, several of which were limited editions with some value. The Blooming Dahlias were a 'supergroup' consisting of Bono, Eric Clapton, Annie Lennox, Labi Siffre and John Lennon. The concept of supergroups was not new – George Harrison had teamed up with others, including Roy Orbison and Bob Dylan, in the late 1980s as the Traveling Wilburys, and a few years before that Band Aid had produced their famous charity single. Lennon led the *Reborn* project with legendary Beatles producer George Martin. It was released on 26 May 1992, the twenty-fifth anniversary of the Beatles' *Sgt Pepper* album. Andy lifted the needle to play brief segments of each track, including 'Nobody Told Me', the song featuring Ringo Starr, written for him more than ten years earlier by Lennon.

Andy finished his random listen in about ten minutes but flipped the record back to side one, this time to play it in full. He studied the gatefold sleeve, featuring lyrics of the eleven songs and notes. Interviews with the artists had talked of *Reborn* being about opportunities offered to the world following the fall of communism across central and eastern Europe and the release of Nelson Mandela in South Africa.

After the record had finished, he played it again. He placed the cover on the shelf between his favourite Beatles album, *Abbey Road*, and *Double Fantasy*, Lennon's solo comeback album after some years – a favourite if only for its poignancy. The dream of a Beatles reunion had long faded, and while Lennon had re-emerged in public life some years ago, this was his first album project for over a decade, since that fateful December day in New York that Andy recalled so well, even though he was aged just ten at the time. Little did Andy know, or even imagine, as he embarked on a career that he hoped would enable him to use his interest in politics, just how closely his and Lennon's lives would cross in the decades ahead.

II

In December 1980, Lennon was promoting *Double Fantasy*, his first new album for five years. He had largely kept out of the public eye in the interim, devoting himself to the raising of Sean, his second child and the only child born of his marriage with Yoko Ono. In 1978, in response to a series of articles in *Rolling Stone* urging his return to the public scene, Lennon retorted: 'I've done my part. It's everybody else's turn now.'[1] Instead, he read a wide range of books, baked bread and took Sean to weekly swimming lessons.[2] His only musical output was two songs written for Ringo Starr.

It was very different in the years between the end of the Beatles in 1970 and Sean's birth in 1975; Lennon had released six albums, all but one of which were commercially successful, albeit to mixed critical acclaim. He had lived the hedonistic life of a rock star, drinking heavily and tak-ing drugs, separating briefly from Ono. He had also developed an active and often outspoken interest in geopolitics.

Many regarded Ono, whom he had first met in London in 1966, as the major influence on his political activism. They married in early 1969 following Lennon's divorce from his first wife, Cynthia. Later that same year, he returned the MBE he had received in 1965, in protest principally at British government support for the Nigerian government in its civil war and for America in Vietnam. On their honeymoon, the couple staged two 'bed-ins for peace' at hotels in Amsterdam and Montreal, protesting against the Vietnam War. They bought full-page ads and billboards with the message 'War is over! If you want it.'[3]

In 1971, Lennon relocated to New York and was understood to have been on President Nixon's 'enemies list'.[4] A deportation order was placed on both him and Ono in 1972; in Lennon's case it was only overturned in the US Court of Appeals in 1975, just two days before Sean's birth. Lennon's protracted campaign for US citizenship involved courtroom battles and stress and prevented him from leaving the country. He finally received his green card in 1976.[5]

He followed British politics. Aware of his Irish roots through his estranged father, he spoke in support of a united Ireland (achieved through non-violent means). At a rally in 1971, he held up a sign that read: 'For the IRA Against British Imperialism', and two songs about the conflict that featured on his album *Some Time in New York City* were banned by the BBC.[6] He donated to NORAID, a charity he believed raised money for widows and orphans of republicans in Northern Ireland.[7] He supported striking shipbuilders in Glasgow, sending them roses and a cheque for £1,000.[8]

After Sean's birth, Lennon largely disengaged from politics, just as he had from music. He attended President Carter's Inauguration Ball in 1977 and publicly supported striking workers at a New York soy sauce factory in 1980,[9] but otherwise the radical activism he had demonstrated in the early 1970s was gone.

As the new decade dawned, he became inspired by the new musical trends he was hearing and began to write and compose once again. He was determined to share his new music with the world. In early 1980, following a brief solo trip to Cape Town, he chartered a yacht to sail to Bermuda. Near Hamilton, he leased a property for a six-week stay and installed a temporary studio. Among the first recordings was 'Beautiful Boy'; Sean was overjoyed when he was played the song.

Recording commenced in August in New York under much secrecy. After more than six years out of a studio, Lennon was energised by the process, and he produced enough tracks to create the platform for a follow-up album too.

Lennon described his vocals on the first single release, '(Just Like) Starting Over', as 'Elvis Orbison', dedicating the song 'for Gene and Eddie and Elvis and Buddy'.[10] On his fortieth birthday in October, a world tour was announced to much fanfare. The first single entered the top ten in the UK after three weeks. Lennon told Aunt Mimi, his mother's sister who had raised him and whom he spoke to weekly, that he would return to the UK if the single reached No. 1 and visit her in the home he had bought her in Sandbanks.[11]

Double Fantasy was released in November. Critical acclaim was muted or negative. In *New Musical Express*, Julie Burchill wrote of the first single: 'So much for McCartney writing slop and Lennon the shocking rockers!'[12] On learning that the single was 'stuck at No. 8', Lennon said: 'It's all right. We have the family.'[13]

III

Crowds would often congregate outside the Dakota Building in New York, where Lennon lived. The building itself was a landmark, and his presence was widely known to locals and visitors. Residents would find dozens of fans and curious passers-by hoping to catch a glimpse, a photograph or an autograph; Lennon generally (though not always) obliged, often with a wry joke. Some of the most persistent fans became known to their subject.

As the publicity increased ahead of the album launch, so did the crowds. One regular visitor was Paul Goresh, who had first met Lennon having posed as a TV repair man, gaining access not just to the building but to his hero's apartment. Eventually, the two would develop a rapport.[14]

On an unseasonably warm New York day, Monday 8 December, Lennon had a busy schedule, including a session with the famed photographer, and his neighbour, Annie Leibovitz for *Rolling Stone*, an interview with a radio team and a haircut.[15] As he waited with Ono in the early evening for their car to return to the studio, standing outside the Dakota Building he spotted Goresh, who showed him some recent photographs he had taken. Then another fan, bespectacled and in a crumpled overcoat, approached clutching a copy of *Double Fantasy* and a pen. Goresh clicked his camera as Lennon scribbled 'John Lennon 1980' on the cover. Without a word from the recipient, Lennon returned the album. After a few hours, the couple returned from the studio to put Sean to sleep. Lennon emerged from the limousine carrying cassettes of the recording session. Mark Chapman, the fortunate but seemingly ungrateful autograph recipient from just five hours earlier, stepped forward calmly holding his .38 revolver.

Chapman had purchased the weapon near his home in Honolulu and researched how to transport the gun and ammunition to New York. His preferred bullet choice, hollow-pointed Smith & Wesson +P cartridges, were designed for maximum stopping power and consequently maximum damage; they were banned in New York.[16] He concluded that they were too risky to carry by plane and might be detected in his luggage. Instead, he compromised his meticulous plans and used conventional ammunition. On that mild December evening, Chapman waited for Lennon to return to his apartment while reading his recently acquired paperback copy of *The Catcher in the Rye*. The crowd outside the Dakota Building was larger than normal. As the limousine approached, Chapman readied himself for his mission. Five bullets were loaded, but as the second shot fired, he concluded that he need not risk harming other fans.

Lennon slowly fell to the ground, the cassettes strewn across the lobby entrance. The doorman grabbed Chapman, forcing the gun from his hand and kicking it away. 'Do you know what you've done?' he asked the would-be assassin.

'I've just shot John Lennon,' came the reply.[17] Chapman returned to reading his book. Moments later, NYPD officers arrived at the scene, and Chapman was arrested.

Lying by the doorway still breathing, Lennon was carried to the police car and nodded when asked by an officer, 'Are you John Lennon?'[18] A mile away at the Roosevelt Hospital, Dr David Halleran awaited his patient's arrival.[19]

IV

In the days following the shooting, and with Mark Chapman in custody, Lennon lay in hospital in a coma, clinging to life. The odds were not good. He had suffered severe damage to several organs and his spine. News relayed to the public was largely suppressed, but in the immediate aftermath of the shooting, Ono summoned the courage to speak to trusted members of the media. She issued a statement urging the public to pray for her husband, quashing early rumours that he had died. The other three former Beatles flew to New York. Crowds gathered at the Dakota Building, spilling over into Central Park. Candlelit vigils were held at Strawberry Field park in Liverpool and in several other cities across the world, with people of all ages singing his songs 'Give Peace a Chance' and 'All You Need is Love'.

The medical team at the Roosevelt Hospital issued a few briefings, which relayed that Lennon was barely functioning in an induced coma and the outlook was poor. To offer hope, they referred to his relative youth and level of fitness. Nevertheless, two further operations were performed in the first week.

On New Year's Eve, Lennon emerged from his coma but was still in a critical condition. He was transferred to the Kessler Institute in New Jersey, where he started a long residence in its specialist spinal rehabilitation unit. News fell silent for several months.

Following the shooting, sales of Lennon's new album and single were transformed, with both climbing the charts. In the UK '(Just Like) Starting Over' and 'Woman' from Double Fantasy, as well as the reissued 'Imagine', each hit No. 1. Meanwhile, after attempts by his legal team to claim insanity, Chapman pleaded guilty to second-degree attempted murder. He was sentenced to between eight and twenty-five years in jail.

On the first anniversary of the shooting, Ono announced that her husband would finally be leaving hospital. She released a short audio recording to the media in which Lennon said, 'Thank you to you all and my incredible teams at both hospitals. There is only room in my heart for love. No bullets can beat that.' His voice was slow but clearly recognisable. He was not seen leaving hospital, nor in public in New

York. He returned to the Dakota Building and began a process of intense rehabilitation at home.

Lennon would later explain how he had used this long and frustrating period as a time of introspection. He considered how he might live the second half of his life, building on what he had achieved already and, more specifically, how he might be more effective in making a difference in society. He resolved to identify projects on which he could focus, and he maintained a discipline of reading voraciously.

V

Silence continued until September 1982, when a letter from Lennon appeared in the *Washington Post* following a mass shooting incident that killed eight people in a welding machine shop in Miami.[20] The letter spoke of the impact his shooting had had on his family and demanded changes to US gun laws.

Lennon's reappearance and his message surprised US law-makers and fans across the world. President Reagan, who had been shot himself in March 1981 but had always objected to further gun control legislation, acknowledged Lennon's as a legitimate contribution to the debate. He invited him to visit the White House for discussions (reminding the media that they had met in 1974, when they were interviewed in the same half-time interval during a televised American football game).[21] Shortly after, Lennon and Ono spoke to *Time* magazine about the campaign for gun control. The only photograph accompanying the article was of the glasses he had worn on the night of his shooting, blood still splattered on the lenses.[22] Ono gave a television interview on her friend Geraldo Rivera's ABC show but allowed no discussion regarding her husband's physical or mental health.

Taking on the influential gun lobby was a licence for controversy. Lennon and Ono's intervention led to comments about their past lifestyle being used against the cause in the press. Lennon retaliated, announcing the foundation and funding of a lobby group, 'Imagine No Gun Violence'. Lennon allocated a portion of the royalties from the song 'Imagine' to the group, and offices were established in Washington DC.

Senator Edward Kennedy joined the organisation as patron and sponsored a Bill to amend the 1968 Gun Control Act, which passed slowly through Congress.[23] Lennon's initiative ultimately spearheaded significant reform, not just in the US but in other countries across the world.

Before the shooting, Lennon had regarded New York as his home. He would walk the streets and in nearby Central Park with little concern for his security, and he had grown used to fans like David Goresh congregating outside his home, even befriending several of them. As he continued his rehabilitation, largely confined to his building, his perspective changed. He now longed to move his family to Britain to be with his eldest son, Julian, now aged nineteen, and to spend time with his beloved Aunt Mimi. Principally, he wanted to provide Sean, now aged seven, with what he considered would be a safer environment in which to grow up. Lennon had been growing nostalgic about Britain for some years. In Bermuda, while preparing for the recording of *Double Fantasy*, he had taken Sean to Hamilton for the Queen's official birthday parade and had felt mildly patriotic.[24] His regular conversations with his Aunt Mimi had added to his feelings of nostalgia; he had not seen her, nor visited England, since moving to New York more than ten years earlier.

In early 1983, Lennon and Ono announced that they would relocate to London. He appeared on US television for the first time since the shooting for an interview with Geraldo Rivera. His rehabilitation was proceeding well, and he walked unaided into the studio. They spoke about his health, his gun control initiative and the plans to move to London. Lennon finished by turning to the camera, exclaiming: 'I will always love New York and plan to visit many times. You certainly haven't seen the back of me!'

VI

In July 1983, Lennon, Ono and Sean arrived in London and settled into a gothic-styled home set back from East Heath Road in Hampstead. Sean was enrolled in a local private school. The normally rapacious British press gave the family the privacy they sought, and the property was quite secure.

Life in London suited Lennon. He continued his rehabilitation with long walks on Hampstead Heath and visited the Royal National Orthopaedic Hospital as an outpatient. Julian had a room at the home, and Paul McCartney, who lived nearby, would visit, as well as the other two Beatles. Lennon and Ono began to integrate with the London music and arts industry and agreed to interviews with UK print and television media. He visited Abbey Road Studios with his former producer, George Martin, and met old industry friends, as well as many of the new stars. Both came to know local celebrities, such as Melvyn Bragg and Michael Foot, former leader of the Labour Party. Lennon maintained his support for gun control; following a shooting in a McDonald's restaurant in San Diego in July 1984, in which twenty-one people were killed,[25] he visited his lobby group in Washington DC and appeared at several rallies, as well as undertaking media interviews. Ono, meanwhile, ceased her singing career to focus on her first passion: art.

Later in 1984, two incidents left a major mark. The first was the bombing of the Conservative Party annual conference in Brighton. Lennon was shocked to witness this outrage against the British government, which led to the deaths of several politicians, and it finished his waning sympathies for Irish independence. He made a public statement condemning the violence, and within months he had quietly sold Dorinish, the small island he had bought in County Mayo on Ireland's Atlantic coast years before, donating the proceeds to a local orphanage.[26]

Around the same time, Lennon and Ono witnessed a series of BBC News broadcasts on the horrors of the famine that had followed civil war in northern Ethiopia. Lennon was soon approached by Paula Yates, who had interviewed him earlier that year for *The Tube*, the music television programme she co-hosted. She visited Lennon's Hampstead home with her husband, Bob Geldof, and musician Midge Ure to discuss how the industry might respond to raise awareness and money for the victims. Yates's extraordinary suggestion was a reunion of the Beatles for the A-side of a charity single to be released in time for Christmas, with a 'supergroup' of stars assembled by the team on the other side. Lennon immediately spoke to his former Beatles colleagues. These remarkable individuals agreed to come together with Martin to record 'Happy Xmas (Hunger is Over)' – the first recording to feature all four Beatles since their split fourteen years before. Lennon insisted that the proposed B-side, 'Do They Know It's Christmas?', written by Geldof and Ure, be the A-side. On the new track, McCartney opened the singing, but it was Lennon's haunting, 'Well tonight thank God it's them instead of you,' that stuck in the mind. He also led a successful appeal to the government to waive VAT on the single. The record topped the charts across the world, including in the UK and, driven by airplay of the Beatles track, in the US.

Discussions commenced immediately about concerts to be held in London and Philadelphia in July 1985. The Beatles agreed to perform a 25-minute set halfway through the show at Wembley Stadium. It became the most watched event in global television history, with an estimated 2 billion viewers. For the first time since 1966, the Beatles performed live in front of an audience, though the foursome were clear it would be the last.

Lennon was very much back in the public eye. His life experience over the past decade had altered his perspective; he had consumed no drugs since the late 1970s, nor did he drink alcohol, and he maintained a healthy diet. His outlook had become less radical and more pragmatic. He was keen to use his fame and growing status as a 'national treasure' to maximise the difference he could make to society. Music was secondary, but he knew it gave him a platform.

His gun control campaign was reaping results in the US. In the UK, following the mass shooting of sixteen people in Hungerford in 1987, he successfully lobbied the government to change the law not just on ownership of semi-automatic rifles and shotguns, but using his own experience, also succeeded in a ban on all handguns.[27]

In 1988, Lennon led the team that organised a concert at Wembley Stadium to mark Nelson Mandela's seventieth birthday. He had been aware of Mandela's plight in jail in South Africa since 1964 and in May 1980 had visited Cape Town, meditating in the grounds of his hotel while trying to make sense of the apartheid regime. He sang at the concert with Ono, marking the last time they would perform together. In

June 1989, with South Africa's newly elected President F. W. de Klerk visiting London, Lennon met Neil Kinnock, leader of the Labour Party, and members of the Anti-Apartheid Movement. He also met de Klerk privately, at the President's request. Within a year, Mandela had been released from jail.

VII

Lennon returned to the recorded music scene briefly in early 1992, with the release of *Reborn*, an album of his compositions by the supergroup the Blooming Dahlias. He had conceived the idea following the release of Mandela; the songs were a commentary on the changes taking place internationally. He had assembled the group and led the media promotion campaign, dedicating the album to his Aunt Mimi, who had died the previous year. Accompanying the superstar line-up, Lennon's sons Julian and Sean also participated as backing vocalists on several tracks, while Ono designed the cover. The album sold well and yielded several hits across the world.

The project kept Lennon's profile high, which, in turn, helped maintain his chance of influence. Privately, he was frustrated by the result of the 1992 general election, which meant another five years of Conservative government; Labour had proved unable to win even during a recession, after thirteen years of Conservative government and the poll tax riots of 1990. The sudden death of Labour leader John Smith in 1994, however – which Lennon heard of while attending the inauguration of Mandela as South Africa's first black President – created an opportunity to get involved in helping Labour. Lennon had been impressed by Tony Blair, whom he had met through Bono. Blair had risen to become shadow Home Secretary and soon emerged as the front-runner for the leadership. Lennon met Blair again during the campaign at a restaurant in Islington, and a photograph of them appeared in the press, implying to many not only an endorsement of what proved to be the winning candidate but also the first sign of Lennon's party affiliation.

As Labour began to draw up its strategy for the coming general election, Peter Mandelson encouraged Blair to approach Lennon to stand for Parliament, with an offer of becoming Minister for Overseas Development. At first Lennon laughed and refused. However, when friend and fellow Merseysider Glenda Jackson, the sitting MP for his Hampstead & Highgate constituency, offered to stand aside for him, he realised the seriousness of the party's request.

Ono was initially opposed to the idea of her husband entering mainstream politics, mainly due to the potential risk to his personal safety. However, the couple recognised the opportunities for change that could be achieved by seizing the opportunity, and agreed. Jackson was allocated the neighbouring seat of Finchley, Margaret Thatcher's former constituency, which had been subject to a boundary change and was expected to swing to Labour as well.

Lennon was enthused by campaigning in the general election of 1997. He captivated the media and helped newspapers to swing towards Labour. His past was inevitably raised: his arrest for drug possession; the return of his MBE; his support for a united Ireland; his admission of ill-treatment of his ex-wife Cynthia; rumours of tax avoidance; and the 'bigger than Jesus' comment. He and Ono tackled his transition from rock star to would-be politician in a television interview with David Dimbleby. In a frank exchange, neither he nor his wife denied anything from their past, including their drug use, but Lennon stressed how his views and behaviour had changed over several decades, in particular since the birth of Sean and the shooting in 1980. Both pointed to the reformed family life they had shared since returning to the UK almost fifteen years earlier. To the baby-boom generation, their message resonated.

VIII

Labour's landslide election victory heralded the long Blair-led government, and Lennon was given the promised international development ministerial role under Clare Short. He was also often used to assist other projects; for example, he was in the background to the Good Friday Agreement, and his celebrity helped the process. He pursued his interest in gun control, ensuring the passage of further legislation, and made his maiden speech in the House of Commons on that subject shortly before the summer recess in 1997. He supported the campaign to abolish landmines and together with Ono became increasingly involved in the cause pursued by Princess Diana before she died. Ono would soon become a patron of the HALO Trust, which sought to eradicate landmines.

With responsibility came difficult decisions. Lennon had to consider for some time his position on the NATO bombing of Kosovo, which commenced in 1999. This was the first time he had to decide whether he would consciously support war. The left wing of the Labour Party condemned the bombing programme, but he supported his government. However, his loyalty was severely questioned when Serbia's state television station was bombed, killing sixteen people.

Lennon retained his seat at the 2001 election with an increased majority and continued his ministerial role. He paid public tribute later that year to his fellow Beatle George Harrison, who died of cancer at the age of fifty-eight – the first Beatle to pass away.

The tragic events of 9/11 led to Lennon's first official visit to New York on behalf of the government. He met the city's respected mayor, Rudy Giuliani, and New York Senator Hillary Clinton, and spoke, along with Ono, at a vigil in Central Park. As the long-term consequences of the attacks became apparent, Lennon discussed with Ono the difficult personal decisions he faced. He supported the invasion of Afghanistan, given the evidence of the terrorist training camps run by the Taliban, the appalling human rights abuses they inflicted on women and their attitude to modern culture. But as it became apparent that Blair was considering supporting President George W. Bush in the invasion of Iraq, Lennon took exception. Together with Clare Short and Robin Cook, he appealed to Blair to resist. He could not ignore the mass protests across the country, including the demonstration in London organised by the Stop the War Coalition – though he did not wish to be associated with many of those involved, particularly those Labour MPs led by Tony Benn. Less than a month later, Lennon resigned from the government. His departure captured global headlines; his behaviour was dignified, and he earned great respect.

Lennon moved to the back benches to advocate for peace. 'Give Peace a Chance' was reissued, and he became the first sitting MP to have a single in the charts.[28] He did not give up his seat in Parliament and vowed to stand again at the next election.

It was not long before he was asked by Blair, who had had no argument with the way in which Lennon had resigned, to become involved in the UK's bid for the 2012 Olympics. He would be working with Sebastian Coe and David Beckham, and the Department for Culture, Media and Sport (DCMS), where he had developed strong connections. It pitted him against New York, and his involvement aided the UK's successful bid in 2005. He joined the team overseeing the delivery project.

Meanwhile, Ono had developed a portfolio of activities while her husband was kept occupied by matters of state. She remained involved with the HALO Trust as well as the Imagine No Gun Violence lobby group in Washington DC. She also developed a role campaigning for greater understanding of the needs of women who had suffered miscarriages and stillbirths, something she knew from her own experience of multiple miscarriages. It was this role which would occupy most of her time while her husband remained in politics, and she enlisted the support of several celebrities and political leaders to this cause, including Senator Hillary Clinton.

In January 2008, due perhaps to new Prime Minister Gordon Brown's need for a bit of stardust as part of his first reshuffle as well as his role in the Olympic bid, Lennon was rewarded with a surprise return to government. He became Secretary of State at DCMS. Attending his first Cabinet meeting, Beatles fans Jacqui Smith, the first female Home Secretary, and Alan Johnson, the Health Secretary, sought to have Lennon sit next to them. He took his allocated seat instead next to Andy Burnham, the starstruck Minister for the Cabinet Office who had just been promoted from the Treasury. Burnham's mind would wander back to the hours spent listening to his Beatles vinyl album collection at his parents' home near Warrington.

Lennon, now sixty-seven, acclimatised quickly to his workload as Secretary of State for a forward-looking department. He embraced the

Olympics project. Another of his early priorities was to announce an independent inquiry into the Hillsborough tragedy, which had led to the death of ninety-six Liverpool FC fans in 1989. At a pre-match event at Anfield to mark the twentieth anniversary, he received a hero's welcome in his old city, giving a speech that was sombre and moving.

The scale of Labour's defeat in the 2010 general election brought about another startling development in Lennon's extraordinary life. Recognising the task ahead of them, many senior party figures urged him to put his name forward to replace Gordon Brown as leader, perhaps viewing him as a stopgap until someone younger could be found. Urged by Ono to accept, once he agreed, all his potential rivals fell away, recognising his enduring popularity in the country; Lennon was elected unopposed.

IX

As Leader of the Opposition, Lennon had a strong mandate in his party and proved popular in the country; he quickly topped the opinion polls. The coalition government's leaders, David Cameron and Nick Clegg, were both fans of the former Beatle and struggled to work out how to deal with this unconventional seventy-year-old politician.

He had first to develop a comprehensive policy platform. Other than a few specific issues such as gun control and opposition to war, his time in Parliament had been largely opportunistic and reactive. Lennon developed a clear position of opposition to austerity against a government focused on cutting public spending. He formed a strong and loyal team around him, with Peter Hain becoming a close confidant (they had worked together on the Mandela campaigns years before), together with Alan Johnson, Andy Burnham, Harriet Harman and Alastair Campbell. Other senior figures in the shadow Cabinet included David Miliband, Ed Balls and Sadiq Khan.

It proved an eventful and testing period. Lennon was forced once again to compromise his anti-war stance on two occasions in quick succession: he supported military action in Libya to depose Colonel Gaddafi in 2012; and following an alleged chemical attack by President Assad against his own people, he supported decisive action as part of an international coalition in Syria, which brought about a swift end to a looming civil war. His relationship with Hillary Clinton, then US Secretary of State, had informed his understanding of the situation in both Libya and Syria. He learned how leaders must make tough decisions, although he remained committed to the position that had led to his resignation in 2003 ahead of the invasion of Iraq.

Domestically, Lennon had to respond to riots across England in summer 2011 and calls for Scottish independence, on which Cameron announced a referendum to take place in 2014. Labour had been losing popularity in Scotland for many years, to the benefit of the SNP, and Lennon knew that the party had to recover its position there in order to be able to form a Westminster government. He actively campaigned to reject independence and Labour appeared to recover some of its former support. Meanwhile, the Conservatives were dominated by the issue of Europe. Cameron pledged to hold a referendum on EU membership should his party win the 2015 election. Lennon held the view that continued membership was necessary and support was politically expedient, even if he was not an especially enthusiastic supporter of the EU.

The 2012 Olympics in London solidified Lennon's standing in the polls, and while Cameron and London Mayor Boris Johnson were popular, it became apparent that with continued support in Scotland, Labour could win the 2015 election, especially if the Conservative vote split over Europe. Lennon's manifesto majored on opposition to austerity, and he proved an admirable campaigner, winning a working majority of twenty. He drew support equally from working-class voters, who recognised him to be on their side, due in part to his upbringing, and from middle-class supporters, where his long-term fame was key. He went to meet the Queen and at the age of seventy-four became the oldest incoming Prime Minister since Churchill in his second term – after whom Lennon had inherited his middle name.[29] As they entered Downing Street, Lennon and Ono represented the first mixed-race couple to occupy No. 10.

He set about building a government, working with a small inner circle of advisers to shape his Cabinet. Alan Johnson was appointed Deputy Prime Minister and given authority beyond that normally invested in the usually titular role. In the first Budget, Lennon and Chancellor Burnham introduced modest tax rises, scrapped university tuition fees and reversed several austerity cuts made by the coalition. Sweeping environmental initiatives to reduce carbon emissions were implemented.

Several foreign leaders came to London to meet Lennon, including President Obama, in what would be his last visit to the UK before the end of his second term. Many EU leaders visited, especially before the European summit due to be held in Brussels in December 2015. Involvement in the internal machinery of the EU was a part of the Prime Minister's role that Lennon found especially tedious, but he was energised by the discussions at the summit on the migrant crisis facing Europe as a consequence of growing poverty and environmental degradation in North Africa and the Middle East.

Shortly after his return from the EU summit, Lennon suffered a minor heart attack, and subsequent tests revealed he was suffering from a chronic condition in need of constant observation. Neither his heart attack nor his condition was revealed to the public, but he recognised that he would have to reduce his commitments. The following summer, he and Ono took the decision that he would step down at the end of the year. Before departing, he broke with protocol during a trip to the US, to meet and imply support for Hillary Clinton. Ono went further and openly endorsed their friend and candidate, and perhaps it was the backing of this celebrity couple that contributed to her winning the 2016 election to become the first female US President after a particularly heated campaign against Donald Trump.

At the start of 2017, Lennon, now seventy-six, announced his retirement. The leadership election was fiercely contested; in the end Lennon's chosen successor, Burnham, beat David Miliband. Prime Minister Burnham prepared to move into Downing Street with his family and his collection of Beatles and John Lennon albums.

X

As he left Downing Street with his wife – still a very unconventional political couple – Lennon reflected on the second half of his life and the chances afforded him by the medical teams in New York almost forty years earlier.

He had softened his radical political tendencies and found that he could use his fame to make a real difference that he could look back on with pride. His gun control campaign had changed laws at home and across the world – especially in the US, where he had co-operated with President Obama to finish the work he had started with Ted Kennedy years earlier. This initiative had saved lives; mass shootings in the US were now rare, and in the UK they had been limited only to terrorist incidents after the Hungerford shooting thirty years earlier. While he'd had to compromise over his opposition to war on several occasions over the years, he considered that the decisions he had made, often after long discussion with his wife, had been balanced ones. British society was more cohesive, the union was more settled and the country found itself in a more comfortable place as a key member of the EU.

He had delivered the wishes of millions of fans for one last Beatles concert, and he had helped to tackle a famine in the process.

On a personal level, he was a grandfather through both Sean and Julian. He lived a contented life in London with Ono and their extended family. He looked forward to turning eighty – though perhaps not, as he had predicted as he neared his fortieth birthday, 'in rocking-chairs'[30] – and he would see what would come next. There were still songs to write.

Notes

1 Kenneth Womack, *John Lennon 1980: The Last Days in the Life* (London: Omnibus Press, 2020), p. 3.

2 Ibid., pp. 10, 28, 68.

3 James Patterson with Casey Sherman and Dave Wedge, *The Last Days of John Lennon: The Assassination That Changed a Generation* (London: Century, 2020), p. 192.

4 Womack, *John Lennon 1980*, p. 200.

5 Hunter Davies, *The John Lennon Letters* (London: Weidenfeld & Nicolson, 2012), p. 242.

6 Frances Mulraney, 'Celebrating John Lennon's Irish roots and fierce support of Irish independence on his birthday', 10 December 2016, www.irishcentral.com/roots/history/john-lennon-ira. Two tracks on the album *Some Time in New York City* were 'The Luck of the Irish' and 'Sunday Bloody Sunday'.

7 Ray Connolly, *Being John Lennon: A Restless Life* (London: Weidenfeld & Nicolson, 2018), p. 352.

8 Keith Bradman, *The Beatles Diary, Volume 2: After the Break-Up, 1970–2001* (London: Omnibus Press, 2001), p. 45.

9 Ibid., p. 201.

10 Womack, *John Lennon 1980*, p. 161.

11 Mark Lewisohn, *Tune In: The Beatles – All These Years* (New York: Crown, 2013), p. 825.

12 Womack, *John Lennon 1980*, p. 200.

13 Yoko Ono, 'John Lennon's Last Days: A Remembrance by Yoko Ono', *Rolling Stone*, 23 December 2010.

14 Womack, *John Lennon 1980*, pp. 29–31.

15 Bradman, *The Beatles Diary*, pp. 271, 272.

16 Patterson, *The Last Days of John Lennon*, p. viii.

17 Ibid., pp. 310, 311.

18 Ibid., p. 317.

19 Ibid.

20 'A man of frightening contrast', *Miami Herald*, 21 August 1982.

21 Bradman, *The Beatles Diary*, p. 144.

22 The image appeared on the cover of a Yoko Ono album and she has since tweeted it several times; see www.johnlennon.com/music/with-yoko-ono/season-of-glass/ and www.twitter.com/yokoono/status/1336308015465689088?s=24

23 'Kennedy Set to Compromise to Obtain Gun Control Bill', *New York Times*, 2 April 1981.

24 Womack, *John Lennon 1980*, p. 121.

25 Dana Littlefield, 'New documentary explores 1984 McDonald's massacre in San Ysidro', *San Diego Union-Tribune*, 21 September 2016.

26 Ono sold the island shortly after Lennon's death, see 'Islands of Ireland: Mayo, John Lennon and Sid's commune', *Irish Examiner*, 14 September 2020.

27 The Firearms (Amendment) Act 1988 was passed following a report on the shooting at Hungerford in 1987. The Act broadened the range of prohibited weapons to include semi-automatic rifles and shotguns but did not ban handguns. The latter were banned by two further amendments introduced in 1997.

28 The only MP to have had chart success in the UK is Pete Wishart, an SNP MP since 2001; he was a member of the folk-rock band Runrig and had several UK chart hits with them in the 1980s and 1990s.

29 Davies, *The John Lennon Letters*, p. 7.

30 Womack, *John Lennon 1980*, p. 160.

Chapter 9

What if Margaret Thatcher had won the 1990 Conservative leadership election?

Ben Monro-Davies

'Y ou've got to do something. You're going to lose.' Peter Lilley and Michael Howard had decided to be frank. Her private office, all too aware the leadership campaign was hopeless, were delighted to give two Cabinet allies a snatched quarter of an hour in the House of Commons with the Prime Minister.

Lilley told her: 'Heseltine's been in touch with me about a job. With me! I haven't heard a word from your side. Morrison is completely useless. He stays; you go.'

Howard chipped in: 'Alan Clark just told me he found Morrison asleep at his desk. He goes round tapping his waistcoat pocket saying we have the numbers, but he's a drunk.'

Peter Morrison was Thatcher's parliamentary private secretary. His alcohol habit was well known at Westminster. The rumours about his private life were also rife – the MP then in charge of Thatcher's efforts to stay in No. 10 is now believed to have been a sex offender.

The Iron Lady was not happy. 'I've won three elections. Why should I have to go begging to these MPs for my job? They owe theirs to me. I'm off to Paris any moment to mark the end of the Cold War, and they're just playing games.'

Eventually, Lilley's remonstrations that MPs are 'pliable clay' – and that's life – won through. She agreed to tell Morrison to hand over control to the Whip *par excellence* Tristan Garel-Jones. Providing yet more evidence of a loss of touch, she assumed that he would be delighted to accept.

Instead, Garel-Jones was deeply conflicted. His wing of the party had been aghast when a few days earlier in the Commons, Thatcher had deviated from a carefully written script in a debate on Europe:

> The President of the commission, Mr Delors, said at a press conference the other day that he wanted the European Parliament to be the democratic body of the community; he wanted the commission to be the executive and he wanted the Council of Ministers to be the Senate. No. No. No.

Geoffrey Howe, her one-time Chancellor and Foreign Secretary, who had been demoted in 1989, was always opaque about the point at which he decided to resign. Thatcher's official biographer, Charles Moore, thinks it was already decided. Others think that the triple 'No' – followed by what all agreed was an unjustified public humiliation at the next Cabinet meeting – were the catalyst. As Howe, now Leader of the House, outlined the pending parliamentary timetable, Thatcher launched into him in front of all her colleagues. 'He was the Deputy Prime Minister, and she tore him into him as if he were an errant schoolboy. That was a disgrace,' the Secretary of State for Scotland, Malcolm Rifkind, later recalled.

Howe may have been the only one then to quit, but the pro-European wing of her party – then a sizeable number and including Garel-Jones among them – were exasperated. By making his resignation speech about Europe, Howe's farewell became a rallying call.

The speech caught Thatcher completely by surprise. She was sitting next to her party chairman, Kenneth Baker, as it was delivered. As Howe sat down, she whispered: 'I never thought he'd do that.' She'd also misunderstood the impact of a parliamentary innovation she'd always been wary of: the televising of the Commons. Howe's speech went straight to the living rooms of Middle England. The medium as much as the message meant that this could not be dismissed as the shenanigans of what is now termed the Westminster bubble.

Thatcher was facing an insurrection, the foundation of which was the most unpopular tax in living memory – to which she had managed to add the nitroglycerine of Europe. She'd responded by appointing an alcoholic to marshal her defence. Andrew Morrison, her then private secretary, recalled: 'She had a weakness for tall, posh men.' It nearly did for her. Had Thatcher gone in 1990, she would have been the assassin as much as Heseltine.

After Lilley and Howard told Garel-Jones that Thatcher wanted him to run her campaign, a meeting was held at the Whips' Queen Anne House in Victoria. It later became known as the 'Catherine Place Conspiracy' among the Tory right – something that amused Garel-Jones as its eventual resolution was to do everything to save their heroine.

He was motivated above all by fears for the party:

If she had gone then the Conservative Party would have broken. The electorate were tired of her, the members even more devoted. And although the real problem was the poll tax, she would have gone down as a martyr to sovereignty in the battle over Europe. I'd seen how even Heath's exit had unleashed bitterness over Europe – and no one liked him. To turf out a three-time election winner, on an issue of such sensitivity, led me in a way to put party before country. I'm still not sure I did the right thing.

An almost unspoken understanding was reached that only took flesh post-ballot. All would be done to save her. But if successful, the Cabinet would be the masters now. Alan Clark had somehow managed to invite himself to the meeting, despite being an acolyte of the leader he dubbed 'The Lady'. In his *Diaries*, he recalled being unclear if he'd helped save her or condemn her. 'She was their hostage now,' he wrote.

Michael Mates, Heseltine's campaign manager, reflected that the rebels were on course to force a secret ballot until 'Tristan' was let loose. Garel-Jones had run Thatcher's campaign the year before against the stalking-horse challenger Sir Anthony Meyer, so was in no way beginning from a standing start. The neglected foot soldiers' phones began to ring. Dwindling hopes of advancement began to revive. Another Heseltine lieutenant, Richard Ottaway, remembers the tea rooms suddenly being flooded with grandees preaching the value of continuity and yet promising a new direction. 'We'd had the place to ourselves when Morrison was in charge,' he regretfully mused.

As a consolation, Morrison was still allowed to phone through the result to Paris. Seeing her face in the mirror as she took the call, Charles Powell, her foreign affairs adviser, could tell she didn't know quite how to react. The result was 216 votes to Heseltine's 140. With abstentions, 156 out of 372 MPs had voted against her – a fact thrown at her by journalist John Sergeant as she descended the steps of the British Embassy in Paris.

She had dodged a second ballot; she was still Prime Minister and Heseltine conceded gracefully. But from that moment, as her Chief Secretary to the Treasury, Norman Lamont, recalled, 'She was in office but not in power.'

On her return, her close friend and Energy Secretary John Wakeham suggested she hold a series of one-to-one meetings with her Cabinet. He says it was so she knew how perilous her position had been. 'Had she seen them all together, they would never have given her an honest picture of her position,' he said thirty years on. She later saw it as the beginning of what Charles Powell called 'a squalid coup'.

Defence Secretary Tom King – flying back and forth to the Gulf ahead of the invasion of Kuwait – suggested she pre-announce her departure. 'Say you'll go sometime after the election.' Several others followed suit, using a similar form of words, which made her suspicious. But her ability to fight was hampered by the resignation of Rifkind, who said that the scale of opposition was too great for her to continue. The personal began to mingle with the political.

At an event to celebrate Winston Churchill's arrival at Harrow, her husband, Denis, had told Cabinet Secretary Robin Butler that he'd wanted his wife to go in 1989, on her tenth anniversary in power. Now he was adamant. All those close to her, both professionally and personally, wanted an intimation of closure. Powell had written a letter to her in the wake of her 1987 triumph saying she should not fight another election. She'd never responded, and he'd let it drop. Now, like Denis, he was more direct. 'You can't keep fighting them,' he told her. 'You've won enough battles.'

A Thatcher relaunch strategy emerged – with the abandonment of her previous 'on and on' pledge at its heart. She announced that she would leave sometime in the middle of her next term. The Community Charge was euthanised, prompting endless headlines along the lines of 'The Lady Is for Turning'. A new emollience on Europe was agreed. Her pantomime truculence could no longer became the regular party act at European summits. In terms of personnel, Ken Clarke replaced David Waddington at the Home Office. The three main offices of state were held by men – Clarke, Major and Hurd – who could not be described as Thatcherites. The circle had turned; at the beginning of her premiership, she'd had a Cabinet she didn't want. The only victory she scored was blocking a return for Heseltine. The prospect was raised once – but never again.

The ploy worked – largely thanks to Saddam Hussein. War made Westminster intrigue seem petty. And it provided a tableau which suited her primary colours. Falkland-esque pictures of her in tanks in the desert were gobbled up by the tabloids and fanned concerns about Labour leader Neil Kinnock's attitude to international security. 'Desert Maggie or Deserter Kinnock?' was one headline in *The Sun*.

In private, she'd been ready to support a move on Baghdad after the Iraqis were ejected from Kuwait, but she was too weak to take on Hurd and the Foreign Office. His carefully crafted coalition would have splintered the minute troops set foot in Iraq; her failure to argue the case haunted her when Saddam Hussein began to massacre the Marsh Arabs. 'I promised then never again to turn a blind eye to tyranny,' she wrote in her memoirs. Her regrets over Iraq were the catalyst for her final fatal battle with colleagues over the Balkans.

But, in 1991, the public had never heard of Yugoslavia's emerging strongman, Slobodan Milošević. The Iron Lady began the year shorn of the controversies that had dogged her third term: the poll tax and Europe. Against that, the economy continued to tank. Chancellor of the Exchequer John Major urged waiting until 1992 for an election; her party chairman, Kenneth Baker, said spring 1991. The four-year electoral cycle had served her well, the latter argued – and this poll would be about the suitability of Neil Kinnock for the job, not the actual record or prospectus of the Conservatives.

Baker's reasoning won out as much because Major and others were keen to bring forward Thatcher's departure. The expected defeat would allow a new leadership, which could then make hay against a Labour government inheriting a recession.

The central issue of the April 1991 election appeared to be tax. The image of the campaign saw the Prime Minister, who had slashed income tax, standing in front of a poster warning of Labour's tax bombshell. In a way the poster wasn't needed; John Smith's slickly produced shadow Budget unashamedly announced tax hikes to pay for improved public services and pensions. Labour was never defensive about their plans.

By contrast, the Conservatives' fiscal offer was far more attractive – though, on reflection, far less credible. Major toured the studios saying he had no plans whatsoever to raise taxes. In his autobiography, he was to argue this was not a lie – rather, he was just proved wrong. In the long term, voters were not to appreciate the distinction. He attributed his failure to win the leadership to these perceived broken promises rather than the coming ERM debacle.

But beneath the rows on economic credibility, Baker was absolutely correct in divining that the electorate saw the contest as a choice between Thatcher and Kinnock. One was a three-time Prime Minister whose only obvious U-turn was on the poll tax – a volte-face widely welcomed. The other was a man who'd changed his mind on virtually everything, from nuclear weapons to the market economy. His flirtation with proportional representation at the business end of the campaign highlighted Thatcher's quality of consistency against his own meandering ideological journey.

The rallies of the final week crystallised the strengths and flaws of the two prospective Prime Ministers. Margaret Thatcher was poised in front of a crowd, in many ways diminished but still sure-footed; Neil

Kinnock, by contrast, was overexcited in front of the masses in Sheffield. When Basildon stayed true blue, a fourth term had been won.

It was a victory that quickly became hard to decipher. To her disciples this was the latest example of her greatness, defying critics to win once more. But Thatcher herself was again unsure what to make of the outcome. She had won four elections in a row; but a politician used to electoral triumphs, she did not win a landslide. Indeed, her majority of ten was distinctly 1970s. She'd hated the fudge and compromise of that decade, which she now realised were as much the product of parliamentary arithmetic as Ted Heath's character. Her Health Secretary, William Waldegrave – who'd been part of Heath's inner circle – warned her the next day to be ready for guerrilla rather than conventional warfare, especially with the Maastricht Treaty negotiations gathering pace.

She could hardly take revenge on the 'Catherine Place Conspirators' by sacking them and giving Heseltine the allies he needed on the back benches. 'Why do I feel like I've lost?' she lamented to her private office. Indeed, there was pressure for her to bring forward her vaguely agreed departure date, eventually forcing a commitment from her to be gone by 1994.

Approaching Maastricht, the Cabinet appeared united on a policy of so-called opt-outs. Britain would support the treaty, but only as long as the country was essentially exempt from the drive towards monetary union and the social chapter, a series of provisions strengthening workers' rights across the community. Thatcher wanted to go further and rhetorically certainly did. It was crystal clear that her position on the single currency was 'not now, not ever'. Her press secretary, Bernard Ingham, was delighted with the picture he staged of her reading *The Sun* as it launched a 'Save the Pound' campaign. John Major insisted the position was more nuanced – no to economic and monetary union for now, but not for ever. Daily political discourse became an exercise in what the Conservatives' position on sterling actually was. Various agreed lines failed to last the week – and although Thatcher was able to emerge from the Dutch city with the opt-outs, her Cabinet's big guns blocked an open-ended commitment to the pound.

Kinnock's replacement, the newly elected John Smith, found a way for his party to oppose Maastricht even though, off the record, nearly all Labour MPs agreed that they supported it. And Mrs Thatcher had to campaign for a treaty most believed she and many of her MPs opposed. Sketch writer Simon Hoggart called it the most fertile material he'd ever been blessed to work with.

Even with the opt-outs there was plenty to outrage a growing band of backbenchers who believed the treaty read as 'Superstate, Chapter 1'. Among them was the new member for Chingford, Iain Duncan Smith. He later said that he and many colleagues only allowed the treaty through the Commons because Thatcher asked them to. The man he'd replaced, Norman (now Lord) Tebbit, was less forgiving, defying her on the party conference stage. There were rebellions and late-night votes – but nothing too agonising arithmetically.

Psychologically, though, it was tortuous, Thatcher herself seemed a little bewildered. Her only hope of seeing it out to her agreed mid-term departure date was keeping her Cabinet on board – which entailed a Wilsonian approach that she despised.

Into that vortex tumbled the ERM debacle, as the government withdrew sterling from the European Exchange Rate Mechanism under huge speculative pressure. Again, Thatcher found herself defending a policy she'd always privately derided, even after it had collapsed. Her reputation as the Iron Lady and the ultimate conviction politician was crumbling by the day.

But she remained totally unready for life outside Downing Street. Kenneth Clarke remembered how she still had no hinterland. The new house in Dulwich was largely empty; she continued to detest holidays, always cutting them short; Thatcher was trapped between her political weakness and the flaw in her personality that left her unsuited to life as anything but Prime Minister.

Major was the man who, on the Treasury steps late at night, had to announce the departure from the ERM at a cost of billions to the tax-payer. In the background, you can see his then special adviser, David Cameron, walk past the cameras. And Thatcher may have opposed the ERM all along, as she was constantly to remind those close to her. 'Lawson and Howe forced me in,' she accurately recalled. Perhaps out of gallantry, the *Sun* editor Kelvin MacKenzie said they were 'pouring a bucket of s**t on the Chancellor's head, not on the coiffured thatch of the Prime Minister'. But her poll ratings were plummeting even faster than her government's.

That in part stemmed from the need to raise taxes. As economic recovery remained a mirage, her Cabinet refused to sanction cuts to public spending that would inevitably impact the poor. Plans to privatise both the railways and the post office were shelved for a lack of support on the green benches. 'Thatcher lives, Thatcherism dies', was the headline for a comment piece by a young Conservative commentator called Boris Johnson.

Some have argued that her Cabinet splitting over the Balkans was a form of displacement. She wanted to have a conflict over Europe; instead, she chose a conflict in Europe. Thatcher felt the war in Yugoslavia personally. Hurd said that her ego saw victory in the Cold War as hers, so the less felicitous consequences of its resolution were her responsibility too. As the bloodletting flowed, her pronouncements of outrage, laced with threat, left an ever-widening gap with the Foreign Office line that this was an internal affair. It is one of the many ironies of her fourth term that on the Balkans she felt European; on Brussels, British.

As the Serbs grabbed ever more territory, she found herself increasingly uncomfortable with her government's foreign policy, as well as its economic direction of travel. Her discipline just about held on Europe and the tax rises; it utterly snapped on Bosnia. In an interview with the BBC, the Prime Minister savaged her own government's position. She said to David Dimbleby that Bosnia's Muslims should be armed to defend themselves against Serb attacks and backed with 'full air cover and, if need be, with ground attack'. The *New York Times* noted that she appeared near tears. Dimbleby later put it down more to her sense of showmanship.

She declared that the Serbs should be given an ultimatum to accept the peace plan put forward by negotiators David Owen and Cyrus Vance, or 'we would have to move in'. And then an equivalent to the 'No, no, no' speech in the House of Commons that had nearly forced her out in 1990: 'I am ashamed of the European Community, that this is happening in the heart of Europe and that they have not done more to stop it. The West, by not doing more, has been a little like an accomplice to massacre.'

Mrs Thatcher added: 'I never thought to see another Holocaust in my life, but the West say it's enough to feed them and to try to get a ceasefire.' Douglas Hurd's endlessly articulated argument that arming the Muslims would prolong and worsen the conflict and increase pressure on Russia to arm the Serbs was trashed on television.

Her break with Cabinet responsibility set the example for others. Sir Malcolm Rifkind called the remarks 'emotional nonsense'. The next day Hurd resigned. His speech explaining his departure avoided the venom of Geoffrey Howe's – another former Foreign Secretary who was sitting next to him as he delivered his speech. Hurd had always had a good relationship with Thatcher. Other than his wry observation that the 'Balkans are a little more complicated than the Falklands', he concentrated on what was an irreconcilable difference of opinion.

She had, he said, fallen victim to the 'something must be done' school of foreign policy. Intervention might seem brave, but it would only serve to ease the conscience of those intervening rather than genuinely improving the plight of the Bosnian Muslims. He then attacked what he saw as a growing argument from across the Atlantic – articulated eloquently by Labour's rising star, Tony Blair – that Western military power should be used to bring down tyrants and spread democracy.

Victory in the Cold War has granted the West military hegemony. But just because we can now comfortably win wars, it does not mean we should wage them. The military battle would likely be straightforward, at least in a conventional sense, but what then? We would own the former Yugoslavia and surely quicky become resented as an occupying force. It is perfectly possible that the former Yugoslavia without Milošević would be worse than it is now.

It was an elegant articulation of one tradition of Conservative foreign policy – one which had the majority of the party behind it.

Thatcher's bellicosity had also begun to alienate her colleagues on the issue of Northern Ireland. The UK was in the midst of the latest mainland IRA bombing campaign. But while the revulsion grew deeper, especially in the wake of the Warrington attacks in February 1993, there was a growing argument for talks with the paramilitaries. The view of securocrats such as John Chilcot in the Northern Ireland Office was that the IRA was losing the war. Infiltration by intelligence agents – above all, one codenamed 'Stakeknife' – had led to a series of military successes for British forces. It had also prompted internal recrimination within the IRA.

Thatcher's Northern Ireland Secretary, Peter Brooke, believed that Gerry Adams and Martin McGuinness no longer thought a united Ireland could be achieved by the bullet. To entice them towards the negotiating table, in November 1990 he had declared that the UK had no selfish or strategic economic interest in the province. The two sides were inching towards each other – but not with Thatcher in the lead. Understandably perhaps, Thatcher found it impossible to consider talking to the organisation that had so nearly killed her in the 1984 Brighton bombing – and killed some of her friends. Publicly, she maintained her strident tone of the 1980s, to the despair of officials. Blair claims that the Good Friday Agreement of 2002 would have come much earlier but for her refusal to engage.

Her tone also began to grate more widely. In a decade when people were rejoicing in post-Cold-War peace, her register on Bosnia was wrong. Thatcherism's supporters might argue that ideologically it was timeless, but culturally it wasn't. Gay rights, the rise of hip hop, the overnight internationalism of the Premier League: all helped to leave a radical looking reactionary.

Events then moved very quickly. She had already pledged to go by 'mid-term', which in calendar terms was 1994. In April 1993, that seemed an unfeasibly long time away to those who wanted to succeed her, as well as to the backbench malcontents led by grandees such as Hurd and Heseltine. After adding to that a husband who wanted to play more golf, Thatcher made the choice to be herself at the cost of leaving office.

In PR terms, it was presented as part of the plan. The niceties were observed. With her Cabinet hailing the greatest Prime Minister since Churchill, she informed the 1922 Committee of her decision to stand down, menacingly promising to continue the fight for what she believed in.

The battle the Conservatives had postponed in 1990 began. The 'pro'-Europeans had options. From the older generation, Heseltine was still too divisive, with an enthusiasm for monetary union that was poison to the backbench selectorate; Hurd had no enemies – but could an Old Etonian ever be Prime Minister again? Most felt Douglas-Home was surely the last – including Hurd.

By contrast, John Major's humble backstory fitted perfectly the times of a new generation of Thatcher's children. He quickly became their choice, though he was encumbered by being the face of the government's disastrous economic policy. The green shoots of recovery that he and Norman Lamont had promised from the Treasury were conspicuously absent. And the Labour leader, John Smith, never failed to remind voters who had been more honest – his word – about tax. His comparison of the Conservative promise of growth to the April 1993 'Grand National that never was' (the race was declared void after a false start) cut through.

The Thatcherites were less blessed in star quality. Ideological bedfellows during her premiership, such as John Moore and Nicholas Ridley, had tended to come unstuck. But there was a new man on offer, elevated to the Cabinet after the 1990 leadership tussle, who promised much. Michael Portillo, now Defence Secretary, was certainly Eurosceptic – so much so that his hostility to Maastricht prompted John Major to be overheard calling him a bastard. But he was also the son of a Spanish émigré who had fled Franco in the civil war. It was hard to label him a Europhobe.

He also used the next generation argument that has often proved powerful in Tory leadership battles. It resonated in particular as his opponent at the next election, John Smith, would be a Labour leader who had served as far back as Jim Callaghan's Cabinet. Added to that, he was ready to campaign to save the pound in a fashion Thatcher could not; sterling would be safe for ever with him as Prime Minister, and 'Keep the Pound' was a far simpler sell than Major's carefully constructed position.

While the number of Europhile MPs now far exceeded their non-existent numbers later in the twenty-first century, the Eurosceptic right was on the rise. The 1991 intake included Bernard Jenkin, Iain Duncan Smith, Nigel Evans and John Whittingdale. Through candidate selection, the membership was slowly pushing the parliamentary party away from the grandees.

Portillo's victory was a source of delight to his predecessor – though she marred the handover with a clumsy joke about being a back-seat driver. And her glee infuriated Major, who felt she owed him her support. The final battle with the Heathites – a caricature, but one which reflected her world view – had been won.

But in embracing Portillo's credentials, MPs forgot that they were taking a gamble. He was the most inexperienced Prime Minister since Ramsay MacDonald, and lapses in judgement followed. In his first speech to conference, he chose to embrace Britain's special forces, saying, 'The SAS have a motto: "Who Dares Wins". We dare. We will win.' The audience were ecstatic – everyone else cringed.

He had to apologise after telling some students at Southampton University that 'if any of you've got an A-level, it's because you've worked for it. Go to any other country; if you've got an A-level, it's because you've bought it or because you're a friend of the minister.' His decision to celebrate his tenth anniversary as an MP with a party at Alexandra Palace prompted more guffaws.

On top of that, the divisions would not heal. John Major accepted a move away from the Treasury – but the new Home Secretary still questioned the parentage of his boss, providing *Private Eye* with an almost biweekly front page. Ken Clarke, William Waldegrave, John Gummer were also all now out of office; it was judged to be the most experienced government back bench ever.

More distastefully, rumours began to circulate about Portillo's sexuality. They had always been there but dismissed as nonsense, not least when, live on a TV Q&A show, a Cabinet minister was asked if he and Portillo were lovers. Significant damages were paid.

Lord Tebbit told the BBC that the rumours were a matter of concern, as they questioned the Prime Minister's honesty. When asked for his views on homosexuality, Tebbit replied: 'Quite clearly it is deviancy. If you look at the definition of "deviancy", it is departure from the norm.' In the twentieth century, such innuendo mattered to many Conservatives. It also infuriated those now dubbed modernisers, who felt that the infamous Clause 28 of the Local Government Act 1988, prohibiting the 'promotion of homosexuality', was both morally wrong and electorally toxic. Another faultline in an already divided party was emerging.

After leaving Downing Street, Portillo admitted to homosexual experiences in his past but never spoke of the matter again. It is much debated whether he should be counted as the UK's first gay Prime Minister. His Chancellor, Michael Howard, wondered whether the pressure over this issue – which was deeply unpleasant – had prompted many of his PR mis-steps.

More importantly, Portillo's trump card was taken away from him by tragedy. He was polling behind John Smith in 1994, but not irredeemably so. But the sudden death of the Labour leader and his replacement by Tony Blair left him looking like the past. There was nothing Cool Britannia about Portillo. Blair's university days as a member of a rock band were far more in tune with the times than Portillo's apprenticeship at the knee of the Peterhouse don Maurice Cowling. Blair's quip at Prime Minister's Questions that 'You were the future once' landed.

~

Following Blair's landslide victory in 1996, Conservative historians have debated what would have happened had Thatcher not held on in 1990. Her likely successor would have been John Major, and the conclusion of most is that almost anyone could have beaten Neil Kinnock, however unfair that might be on a man who rescued his party.

Major certainly thinks he would have won – and won with a bigger majority than Thatcher in 1991. But he concedes that the Maastricht negotiations would have been a nightmare. His subsequent position as an arch-Remainer confirmed that behind the ambiguity he argued for over Europe, he was more Heseltine than Portillo. IDS and co. were right to be wary of him and would never have given him the latitude they afforded The Lady.

Maybe Major could have resisted the Blair magic better. But the Conservative Party was broken on the European issue and had already stretched the elastic of democracy beyond its natural limit. The numbers might have been different, but few dispute that Tony Blair would have made it to 10 Downing Street.

As for Thatcher herself, the fourth term lowered her reputation despite her extraordinary electoral record, as did her growing Euroscepticism after office. The more she bemoaned European integration, the more she was reminded that it was her signature on the Single European Act and the Maastricht Treaty. 'Better to go in 1990; even better, 1989' was Denis Thatcher's typically pithy reflection. Few now disagree.

This piece draws on interviews with all the members of Thatcher's final Cabinet. The quotes from Thatcher on Bosnia are from an interview she gave in April 1993.

Chapter 10

What if Ross Perot had withdrawn from the 1992 US presidential election?

David Cobley

July 1992

R oss Perot appears on the CNN talk show *Larry King Live* on 16 July
to announce that he will not be seeking the presidency of the
United States. Perot, the businessman and billionaire founder of data
systems companies, has been running a campaign as an independent.
He challenged his supporters to get him on the ballots in all fifty states
and as a result was at one point leading in the opinion polls. But now
he is withdrawing, stating that he does not want the election result to
be determined in the House of Representatives if the electoral college
is split. In reality, it is his campaign team that is split; his support in
the polls is falling, and his past actions are coming back to haunt him.
Veteran host Larry King, whose show has been the venue of all Perot's
key announcements so far, is visibly disappointed that he will no longer
be at the centre of this unusual event in American politics.

~

This much actually happened – Perot did perform strongly in 1992 and
then leave the race, but this is where our paths divide. In reality, he ended
up returning to the election in the autumn (after continuing his activities
behind the scenes over the summer), taking part in all three presidential
debates. He ended up getting 19.7 million votes, with his 18.9 per cent
being the highest share of the vote by a third-party candidate since 1912.[1]

Governor of Arkansas Bill Clinton ended up winning with 43 per cent of the vote compared to President George H. W. Bush's 37.5 per cent.

Perot's impact on the race has been a subject of debate ever since. While analysis suggests he drew support evenly from both major parties, this cannot be proven, particularly given the impact he had on the overall dynamics of the campaign. Therefore, for this counterfactual, let's assume that Perot, who was a private man, decided genuinely to retreat back to his business life in July 1992, leaving the 1992 US presidential election as a straight shoot-out between George H. W. Bush and Bill Clinton.

October 1992

The first debate of this presidential campaign takes place. Both candidates come out looking bruised from the town-hall format,[2] which leaves ordinary Americans asking the questions that moderators would not. Bush is challenged on the economy and his record on taxes – he feels that he will have 'read my lips' written on his gravestone at this point. While he is able to demonstrate his undoubted strength on foreign policy, post-Cold War it feels like the electorate may not be listening.

Clinton scores with his 'It's the economy, stupid' messaging, but the nature of his trustworthiness following a string of scandals and rumours means that he cannot enjoy strong benefit from it.

A similar pattern plays through all three debates, and as polling day, 3 November, draws near, the race could still be anyone's to win. President Bush, who has been looking tired during the campaign, gets a sudden burst of energy in the final weeks, supported by the tactical plans of his son, George W. Bush, and his chief of staff, James Baker, who make 'character' the key focus of the campaign.

November 1992

274 to 264. President Bush wins a second term, taking the electoral college, and the popular vote by about 500,000, but it was close. While his campaign had never expected another result like 1988 – when even California's electoral college votes went to Bush – and, naturally,

Arkansas was going to vote for Clinton this time; this was a knife-edge result. In the end, it was the return of Wisconsin and Iowa to the Republican column, two of the few states that had voted Democrat in 1988, that swung the election away from Clinton.[3]

Even without campaigning since July, Perot, whose name remained on the ballot paper, had won over 4.5 million votes. 'A good job he pulled out,' said George W. to his father. 'I wouldn't like to be in an election closer than this one.'

'Well, it's thanks to you that we got here,' replies his father. 'Your role in this campaign has been invaluable, to the result and to me personally. That's why I've something to ask of you. When Baker came back to be chief of staff in August, he made it clear it was only to allow him to have a political role during the last months of the campaign. Now, for him, it's back to State or out to the private sector. I followed your advice when you said to get rid of Sununu,[4] and now I need someone I can trust as chief for my second term. There's no one I trust more than you. I know this means you're going to have to put your own ambitions on hold, but I guarantee you that you will have the full support of the Republican Party for any role you want after this. But now, I need you by my side.'

'As my President and my father, I will do my duty to you and to my country,' replies George.

January 1993

Hillary Clinton tells Bill she wants a divorce. 'It was always the plan – first your career, then mine. Now your career's over, and I don't need to have my future tainted by yours.'

'But Hillary, I'm the comeback kid. I'll be the presumptive nominee for '96, and after sixteen years of Republicans, this time it's sure to be a Democrat.'

'Don't you see it? There is no comeback. You couldn't even beat Bush in the height of a recession, with his tax lie out there for everyone to see. How the hell do you think you're going to run again? Who do you think you are? Nixon? Don't you see? It's over – and all because you couldn't keep it in your pants.'

'That's not fair.'

'In a result like this, what do you think it was that made the difference? And who do you think ends up looking like the lesser person because of it? Me. I meant it when I said I'm not just going to stand by my man like Tammy Wynette. Thank God you didn't get elected – you'd probably end up doing something that would get you impeached, knowing your history.'

'Can't you at least stay for the rest of my term as governor?'

'No way. My time starts here. Time to change history.'

Hillary puts out a press release the same day, pointedly under the name of Hillary Rodham, the name she was forced to stop using by the press during the election campaign less than a year before. It is clear that the Clinton marriage is no more. As the Clintons have no family home, owing to living in the governor's mansion for so long, Hillary has rapidly to find somewhere else to live for her and her daughter Chelsea. Contrary to speculation about her heading to New York, she decides to stay in Little Rock, Arkansas.

January 1994

Since her intention to divorce was announced, Hillary has been raising her profile as an independent woman. She resigns from Rose Law Firm, where there is an air of scandal relating to the Whitewater property investments of some of the partners, including Clinton. She instead sets up her own firm, with a focus on taking on pro-bono work in relation to sexual harassment and children's rights, alongside more typical corporate law cases.

The divorce is finalised in September, with Hillary gaining full custody of her daughter Chelsea – who also changes her surname to Rodham in support. As someone with a high profile both in the state and nationwide, there is much speculation as to what Hillary's next step will be.

Meanwhile, under a measure passed in the same election cycle that saw Clinton's defeat in 1992, Arkansas had introduced term limits on governors of no more than two terms. Clinton had been trying to argue that as the measure only came in during his term, only the period after its enactment should apply to him.[5] However, this is seen as just the type of slick politicking that the measure was designed to remove; while Clinton retains the personal loyalty of his close aides, there is no public clamour for him to continue as governor.

What support there is disappears when Hillary Rodham announces her candidacy for the Democratic nomination for Governor of Arkansas. Her announcement makes it clear that she will take on her former husband if necessary, and that he should not be looking to hold on to power in this way, against the spirit of the term limit measures.

Bill quickly realises that there will be no comeback and steps down. In spite of this, in a display of bitterness, he encourages his lieutenant governor, long-time Clinton adversary Jim Guy Tucker, to stand against Rodham in the primary. Tucker had stood against Clinton twice for the Democratic nomination for governor, and under Arkansas rules had acted as governor for much of 1992 while Clinton was out of the state campaigning to be President.[6] As under the rules of succession he would have become permanent governor had Clinton won the presidency, Tucker takes little persuading to stand.

May 1994

After an acrimonious campaign, Hillary Rodham easily wins the nomination to be the Democrats' candidate for Governor of Arkansas. While Tucker tries to claim that this is 'more Clinton by the back door' and 'a stitch-up like they tried to do in 1988',[7] Hillary makes it clear, through her divorce and her new work, that she is her own woman. This clarity, coupled with the personal loyalties she has built up over the years, sees her through and Tucker to his third defeat.

November 1994

President George H. W. Bush's second son, Jeb, wins election as Governor of Florida against the incumbent Democrat Lawton Chiles at his first attempt. It is felt that having his father in the White House is worth two points, which just gives him the edge.[8]

Over in Arkansas, Hillary Rodham wins election as governor, her first elected office.

July 1996

Tennessee Senator Al Gore wins the nomination for the Democrats for the 1996 presidential election. Having sat out the 1992 nomination campaign, he still has positive sentiment from his run in 1988 and from his campaign as Bill Clinton's running mate in 1992; the flaws with that latter ticket are seen to be Clinton's. Gore entered the campaign as the presumptive candidate and ran a relatively easy race to the nomination.

In contrast to usual practice, he chooses an older running mate, someone who had stood against him in 1988 but whose own presidential ambitions are thought to have passed. Learning from the errors of the Clinton campaign, he also looks to get some geographic diversity on the ticket by tapping the Senate veteran from Delaware, Joe Biden, to be his vice-presidential candidate.[9]

At the Democratic convention, Governor Rodham gives a primetime keynote address, whereas Bill Clinton is nowhere to be seen.

Gore's Republican opponents are Kansas Senator Bob Dole, with former Congressman Jack Kemp as his vice-presidential running mate. Dole had easily won the Republican primary against a crowded field, including Vice-President Dan Quayle, whose past gaffes came back to haunt him when on the campaign trail he named the wrong child as the winner of a spelling bee.

November 1996

Gore/Biden win against Dole/Kemp, beating a Republican Party that had finally run out of steam despite the booming economy. Dole's age and frailty were shown up against the more youthful Gore, twenty-five years his junior, though some Republicans wonder if a Bush defeat in 1992 might have led to more of a reset in the party that could have led to victory this time.

January 1997

On leaving the White House for the last time as President, George H. W. Bush leaves a typically generous letter to his successor, Al Gore.[10] 'You will be our President when you read this note. I wish you well. I wish your family well. Your success is now our country's success. I am rooting hard for you.'

He writes an even more generous note to his son George, who has acted as chief of staff for his full second term. 'I know I have asked you to give up more than any father should, and you have served me more greatly than any son would. My role now is to serve you, to help you achieve all you dream of for yourself, your family and your country.'

May 1997

Gore makes his first visit to the UK to meet the newly elected Prime Minister, Tony Blair. 'Glad to see that you were able to follow my lead,' says Gore.

'Gosh, yes. A real new way for government in our two countries, after all these years of the right,' Blair replies.

'But a new way – a Third Way, if you like – not just the old politics of the left.'

'Indeed. My aim is to make sure this isn't just a short-term thing, that we can do something really long term. That's why I have to be really careful over these first few years, so that I can get a second term and make changes that can really stick.'[11]

'I hear you. I'm thinking the same thing. I really want to be radical on climate, but if I do it too early then nothing will get through. That's why I'm just going to take it steady and then in my second term, in 2001, I will really do some stuff that will make the world take note.'

'Well, er, right. I was thinking of health and education, but the environment too, of course. Just as long as it doesn't impact on Formula One – got to keep the donors happy.'[12]

'Amen to that – got to keep the funds coming to keep doing good.'

November 1998

George W. Bush finally gets to start his political career by winning election as Governor of Texas. His brother Jeb is re-elected as governor in Florida, the first Republican to achieve two terms in that office.

July 2000

John McCain[13] wins the Republican nomination for the 2000 presidential election. While there was a broad field for the nomination, there was no stand-out candidate. Jeb Bush was much speculated about, having entered his second term as Governor of Florida, but he was persuaded that running just four years after his father was defeated would be too soon. Then again, he is not without ambition and is already thinking about the future. Meanwhile, George W. Bush, still early in his term as Governor of Texas, thinks about what might have been.

McCain chooses Elizabeth Dole to be his running mate, the first time the wife of a former candidate has been on the presidential ticket. Dole, though, has had a career independent of her husband, having served in the Cabinets of both Reagan and Bush and having been director of the Red Cross since 1991.

On seeing this news, Hillary Rodham tells a close aide that for her it would be the presidency or nothing, that she would not be some token Vice-President on someone else's campaign ticket.

November 2000

Gore/Biden for the Democrats are narrowly re-elected over McCain/Dole for the Republicans. The results come down to Florida, where there are only a few hundred votes in it. Controversially, Republican Governor Jeb Bush appears to be opposed to holding a recount and puts measures in place to slow it down. In the end, the Supreme Court votes to stop the recount, declaring Gore the electoral college winner by 291 to 247. It is thought that Jeb Bush is helping his own ambitions by not allowing a recount, meaning he can run against a clearer field in 2004, rather than having to campaign against an incumbent President or wait until 2008. However, he states that he is just doing what is best for the stability of the country.

September 2001

As the first plane crashes into the Twin Towers on 11 September, President

Gore is on a visit to a school in Florida. The normally confident Gore appears visibly shaken as his chief of staff informs him in the classroom.

He spends most of the day out of public sight on Air Force One, while Vice-President Biden is in the White House bunker, designed for the Second World War and without the modern communication links that would have served better.

Later that day, Gore makes a public visit to the site of Ground Zero and gives a well-received speech on the enormity of the day. In his speech to the nation and at a joint session of Congress on 20 September, he makes it clear that while he will stop at nothing to bring to justice those who carried out the attacks and those who facilitated their actions, he is not looking to use the attacks as an excuse for anything broader. Contemplating attacks on Iraq or on other states without solid justification and full UN engagement will not be countenanced.

As a result, less than one month later, US and UK forces begin a campaign of air strikes targeting the Taliban and al-Qaeda in Afghanistan, followed by a ground invasion.

January 2002

Hillary Rodham, term-limited as Governor of Arkansas, announces that she will run for the Democratic nomination for the state's Senate seat in November, against the incumbent Republican Tim Hutchinson. Her Attorney General, Mark Pryor, who had himself been considering standing for the seat that his father once held, decides to sit out the election, giving Hillary a clear path to the party's nomination.[14]

November 2002

Hillary Rodham is elected as the junior Senator for Arkansas, beating Hutchinson by 54 per cent to 46 per cent. She says: 'In this world and the world of tomorrow, we must go forward together or not at all.' Her words spark speculation that it will not be long until she is running for President herself.

Meanwhile, George W. Bush is re-elected as Governor of Texas, as his term-limited brother prepares to finish his period as Governor of Florida. Jeb Bush wastes no time in setting up a committee to explore a bid for the presidency. It is thought that this is as much to indicate his intentions to his brother as it is to the American people.

July 2004

The primary season reaches its conclusion. On the Democratic side, Joe Biden wins the nomination, but only after a long campaign. Both he and Massachusetts Senator John Kerry compete for the same voters, meaning the field is split and the activist-supported former Vermont governor, Howard Dean, is able to stay in the race. Even after Kerry pulls out after Super Tuesday, the 'Deaniacs' persuade Dean to continue in the race until the convention. Biden picks the young North Carolina Senator John Edwards (who had himself been an early candidate in the race) to be his running mate. It is rumoured that he asked Hillary Rodham to be Vice-President, but she declined, stating that she is only interested in running for the top job.

On the Republican side, Jeb Bush believes his time has come. However, he also faces a strong challenge from the left by former New York Mayor Rudy Giuliani, and from the right by his father's old foe, Pat Buchanan. The strength of Giuliani's campaign, coming off the back of his actions after 9/11, make him a formidable opponent, and Bush finds himself moving to the right to gain the supporters of Buchanan, who drops out in March. He finally makes it over the line following the Alabama primary at the start of June.

His vice-presidential nominee, Gerald Ford's Defence Secretary, Donald Rumsfeld, takes many by surprise, but Bush justifies it given the ongoing war in Afghanistan and the need to take a stronger line on terror.

Meanwhile, President Gore reflects on the ticking clock of his own presidency. After the impact of the September 11 attacks and the subsequent war in Afghanistan, he has not been able to take many of the steps he wanted to tackle climate change. He finds it an inconvenient truth that politics will always be dominated by events.

November 2004

Jeb Bush is elected President, comfortably beating Vice-President Biden, who has looked less than sure-footed on the campaign trail. This is the second time in American history that a son has followed a father as President.

January 2005

President Jeb Bush stuns the world by making the first action of his presidency an attack on Iraq. Says Bush: 'For too long we have tolerated Saddam Hussein posing a real and present threat to America. This stops now. It is vital for all Americans that we bring regime change to Iraq.' Bush declines to bring the case for invading Iraq to the United Nations, declaring that existing mandates make it clear that this is legal. This puts America's natural international partners in a quandary as to whether or not to support the move. Many do not, including France and Germany, but Prime Minister Blair, convinced that there are weapons of mass destruction in Iraq, brings the UK on side. In a vote in the Senate, the war is supported 60:40. Three Republicans vote against, but eleven Democrats support it. One of those who speaks against it most clearly is Hillary Rodham, who says: 'Any vote for war has to be a difficult vote. There is no doubt that Saddam Hussein is no friend of America. But the bar for war is a high one, and one that has not been reached. There is no immediate danger to the US, and no UN support for this action. Therefore, I vote against, and I vote with conviction.'[15]

July 2005

President Jeb Bush declares 'mission accomplished' on an aircraft carrier in the Persian Gulf, following the fall of Baghdad. The Iraqi Army was found to be ill-equipped to challenge the American and British troops. Statues of Iraqi leader Saddam Hussein have been toppled in the streets, and the apparatus of his governing Ba'ath Party has been removed. President Bush says: 'Job done; time to get our troops home.'

July 2006

President Bush announces an increase in the number of troops being sent to Iraq. Following the spring 2005 invasion and the subsequent withdrawal of US armed forces, insurgency and infighting between the different ethnic parties within Iraq had increased. The lack of planning for the aftermath, given that the decision to go to war was taken just two months after Bush's election and Gore had forbidden any work to be undertaken on Iraq, is seen to be the key driver of the problems. Bush and Rumsfeld are roundly criticised for their seeming hurry to invade. Says Senator Rodham: 'We have to salute the courage and bravery of those who are risking their lives in Iraq and wish them success in their endeavours. But we must also challenge those who sent them in the first place and their lack of planning for the consequences of their actions.'

November 2006
George W. Bush is re-elected as Governor of Texas for a second time – the first time a governor has achieved a term of more than eight years, despite the lack of term limits in Texas. However, given his brother's difficulties as President, the result is a lot closer than the previous two elections.

April 2008
President Bush announces another increase in troop numbers for Iraq, following a 'troop surge' strategy proposed by and to be led by General David Petraeus. While the strategy may be right, the communications are not, as Bush continues to be deaf to the views of much of the American people that this was a needless war at which he is throwing more American lives.

May 2008
The relatively unknown Senator Barack Obama admits defeat to Hillary Rodham in the Democratic primary for President. While his oratorical skills had caused great excitement, his experience could not compare to the record of the two-times governor and senator. He does, though, accept the vice-presidential nomination, becoming the first black candidate on a presidential ticket.

November 2008

Rodham defeats Bush in the election, making her the fourty-fourth President and the first woman to hold the role – and Jeb Bush the first one-term President since Carter in 1980, twenty-eight years before. The errors of the Bush/Rumsfeld war in Iraq, coupled with Rodham's vote against it, were seen to be the defining issues of the campaign. Says Rodham: 'To every little girl who dreams big: Yes, you can be anything you want – even President.'

In his role as anchor of ABC's *Good Morning America*,[16] Bill Clinton is asked by co-presenter Robin Roberts how it feels to see his former wife as President-elect. 'Which one?' jokes Clinton, who by now has been married a further three times. 'But seriously, I knew that she was destined for great things. She always had the better brain, the better intellect, even back in law school. In this role I have met many great people – and I know that she is one of the greatest.'

'You almost sound like you wish you were still married to her,' says Roberts.

'She was my first love, but had she stayed with me I would have only held her back. I am so pleased to see her succeed, and I know that it means so much to Chelsea too. Yes, our divorce was hard, and I reacted badly, but now I wish her nothing but success.'

Meanwhile, former President George H. W. Bush is heard to complain to his wife Barbara about Jeb's actions. 'I told him not to go for Iraq – why do you think I stopped back in '91? It only causes problems that you're just left fixing forever. It's not like there were any weapons of mass destruction that would have threatened the US there anyway. I just hope he hasn't screwed things up for George – he was always the one with the political brain; he was always the one who should have been President.'

'I just hope the American public haven't had enough Bushes,' replies Barbara.[17]

January 2010

President Rodham announces in her State of the Union address that all US troops will have left Iraq by the end of the year. Numbers had already been falling during her first year as President, ironically following the benefits seen from the troop surge approach of President Jeb Bush's final year. However, the conflict in Afghanistan still continues, and to address this President Rodham announces a troop surge of her own.

December 2010
One of Hillary Rodham's key proposals had been for healthcare reform. 'Hillarycare', as the plans are known, brings in mandates for insurance on both employers and individuals. With the country in the grip of the impact of the financial crisis, even people sympathetic to healthcare reform think it is too much too soon. Vice-President Obama is known in private to be a key voice in trying to achieve something practical, if partial, such as expanding Medicare, rather than trying to accomplish the impossible. However, Rodham feels that she would be seen as weak if she backs down and therefore carries on fighting. Despite a Democratic majority, the Bill is defeated in the Senate, and with it goes the aura of inevitability that she built up over the previous fifteen years.

November 2012
George W. Bush defeats Hillary Rodham in the presidential election. After a confrontational four years, and given the impacts of the financial crisis, it is felt that Bush's compassionate conservatism offers the country the best path back to peace and prosperity. In particular, the focus he has put on education in Texas is seen as a leading example for the country. Bush shows his separation from his brother by picking the young Hispanic Senator Marco Rubio as his vice-presidential running mate – the current superstar politician in Florida, who had built his career in the years since his brother left office. After only two years in the Senate, he is untainted by any of the issues around the vote for war in Iraq. To underline the differences, Bush also promises to bring home the remaining American troops in Afghanistan in the first two years of his presidency.

Hillary's campaign is not helped by the fact that her former husband Bill is fired from *Good Morning America* just days before the election following allegations that he had behaved inappropriately with a female member of staff at the London Olympics that summer. Clips from 1992 of her 'standing by her man' are shown on all news outlets, much to Rodham's immense frustration. 'You break the ultimate glass ceiling and still you're judged for the person you married nearly forty years ago and have been divorced from for two decades,' she cries. 'Is the media still this sexist?' Of course, she knows the answer.

Former President George H. W. Bush calls his son, President-elect George W. Bush: 'Congratulations, son. When I asked you to act as my chief of staff, I knew it meant you having to put your ambitions on hold, but I couldn't have done my second term without you, and now you get to do your first. I know it hurt that your younger brother got ahead of you, but I am so pleased that the American people have seen you for who you really are and have put their trust in you, despite having had both me and your brother in the role. I know you are the best of us and will do really great things.'

'Thank you. I will make you proud, just as you did me. Forty-one, forty-three and forty-five – that's some record for you, Poppy.'[18]

Notes

1   In 1912, former President Theodore Roosevelt came second with 27.4 per cent of the vote, running for the Progressive Party, placing him ahead of the Republican President William Taft but behind the winning Democrat Woodrow Wilson.
2   The 1992 presidential election was the first time that the town-hall debate format had been used for such an event.
3   These results have been reached by allocating the actual votes achieved by Ross Perot between Bush, Clinton and Perot, based on the assumption that Perot, who took positions that were more on the right, took more votes from Bush than from Clinton. This assumption is disputed, as noted in the introduction, but is plausible enough to make it the basis for this counterfactual.
4   John H. Sununu, President Bush's chief of staff until December 1991, when he resigned on the recommendation of George W. Bush. He remained a counsellor to the President until March 1992, when he left to host CNN's *Crossfire*.
5   By then Clinton would have been expected to have been in office for a total of fourteen years (1979–81 and 1983–95), compared to the two four-year terms that were then the limit. Until a change in the 1980s, terms for the governorship had been two years.
6   Under rules in Arkansas at that time, the governor was only governor if he or she was in the state – if not, the lieutenant-governor stood in. This is no longer the case.

7 When Clinton first thought of running for President in 1988, it was considered that Hillary should stand for Governor of Arkansas.

8 In reality, in 1994 Jeb Bush lost the Florida Governor's election by two percentage points.

9 In real life, Al Gore selected Joe Lieberman to be his vice-presidential pick, a Senator of the same age and a similar background to Joe Biden. Biden himself would have been fifty-four at this time, six years older than Gore, but maybe undeserving of this joke. He had been in the Senate for over twenty-three years, so 'veteran' is fair.

10 Actual text from Bush's note left for Bill Clinton.

11 In reality, Clinton visited Blair and the Cabinet in May 1997 and found him already thinking about re-election.

12 Labour had secretly received a donation of £1 million from Bernie Ecclestone, the owner of Formula One.

13 In reality, John McCain stood in the 2000 primary against George W. Bush, coming in second and hence strengthening his claim for another chance in 2008.

14 In reality, Mark Pryor was unopposed for the Democratic nomination.

15 Wording based on that used by Hillary Clinton to support the war on Iraq as a Senator from New York. Clinton later expressed some regret for her vote and stated that it was within the context of the threat outlined by the government of President George W. Bush. Given the more partisan nature of the case made by President Jeb Bush, and the greater experience as an elected official Senator Rodham has in this timeline, I expect that she would have voted against.

16 George Stephanopoulos, President Clinton's communications director, has since 2009 been an anchor on *Good Morning America*, and Clinton himself now has a podcast, so this isn't too far-fetched.

17 On Jeb's actual run for President in 2016, Barbara Bush was heard to say that the American public had had enough of the Bushes.

18 'Poppy' is George W. Bush's nickname for his father.

Chapter 11

What if Tony Blair had implemented the Jenkins Report and introduced AV+?

Dr Julian Huppert and Tom King

The 1999 referendum introducing an 'alternative vote plus' (AV+) system for the House of Commons was easily won by a Prime Minister at the height of his powers. When the result was announced, Tony Blair triumphantly proclaimed that at long last the people's voices would be fairly reflected:

> Labour made a commitment in our manifesto, and we have stuck to it. This is a 21st-century voting system for a 21st-century Britain. A country at ease with itself, a country where governments don't just listen to the people but represent the people. What we propose is similar to that which has served our European partners in Germany and recently been introduced in progressive New Zealand. We cannot take a lead in shaping the future if our democracy is stuck in the past.

He pointed to continuing devolution and reform, taking in Wales, Scotland, Northern Ireland and the House of Lords – why should the Commons be left unreformed?

Some expressed surprise that the leader of a party with such a large majority would want to see through such a change. Coming so soon after the historic landslide election victory of 1997, which had seen the sweeping away of a tired Conservative government – including several senior ministers and MPs in supposedly safe seats – it sat badly with the more traditional side of Blair's New Labour.

Labour's total dominance in Parliament, with 63 per cent of the seats, had been secured on the back of only 43 per cent of the vote. One trade union leader grumpily described the Prime Minister's decision as 'choosing to kick away the ladder you climbed up on'. Some more cynically pointed out that the manifesto commitment was only to hold the referendum, not try to win it. The Deputy Prime Minister, John Prescott, had many reservations about the change, but having lost the argument internally, he loyally went out to hold the government line with his usual blend of combative candour and confusion. On this occasion, he was atypically clear: this was a simple matter of pride and principle. Having won a huge majority and promised a referendum, there was no justification not to act. And once the referendum had been set in train, no PM could honestly campaign for the status quo. Losing such a vote, meanwhile, would surely be a resigning matter.

Behind the scenes, there had been detailed discussions with Labour strategists, who had engaged in a long debate about the merits of the proposals. On the one hand, Labour had undoubtedly benefited from the existing first-past-the-post system, which had consistently provided the party with a greater number of MPs than its share of votes. For some strategists, maximising seats was the obvious objective. On the other hand, others pointed out that only three leaders had ever won majorities for the Labour Party: Attlee, Wilson and now Blair. In comparison, six Conservatives had won majorities since the first of these had been in office. They argued that while the move to AV+ would cost them some seats, it would cost the Conservatives more, both in terms of seats and in opportunities to form a majority government.

Blair had created a winning political strategy based on accepting the realpolitik of the Conservative position. Campaigning from a markedly more moderate position than his predecessors as leaders, he and his Chancellor, Gordon Brown, had largely adopted the market-liberal trappings of the Thatcherite consensus. He now saw the opportunity not only to push through more radical public service reforms than the casual observer might have expected but to strike back at that still new economic settlement by pushing the Tories to the margins of political consent – a position he instinctively knew they tended to occupy in opposition.

Nonetheless, Blair and his closest advisers did not accept the unshakeable, though unprovable, belief of the long-term advocates for reform – including Paddy Ashdown, the leader of the Liberal Democrats – that proportional representation would herald a permanent 'progressive alliance', locking out the Tories for decades to come. Senior New Labour figures, especially Peter Mandelson, were pragmatic about the shape-shifting abilities of the Tories and knew that while they were currently at a low ebb, the party would find its way back to electoral relevance. It was Blair's own talent in presenting left-wing policies as simple wins for everyone across society – the 'Third Way' or 'what works' strategy – that convinced him and others that up-and-coming Conservative leadership hopefuls would learn to mirror this presentational approach. In the more pluralistic electoral system that would follow reform, centrist and moderate rhetoric would become more important; but as New Labour had already proved with its historic introduction of a national minimum wage, this did not have to mean a failure to govern radically.

Moreover, Blair and others knew that the Labour Party 'out there' did not accept his view of the world. While good relations with Ashdown's Lib Dems had been built up over the period before the 1997 election, the landslide result had seen the potential for a more formal 'realignment' or partnership quickly dissipate, as there was no longer a mathematical rationale for pursuing one. This had come as a relief to Downing Street strategists, who were painfully aware of the animus between Labour and Lib Dem activists in constituencies and local councils up and down the country.

That said, the Prime Minister remained confident that while Ashdown and leaders like him were in charge of the junior party, the Lib Dems would almost always favour an alliance, however informal, with Labour over the Conservatives. The long and slow demise of Margaret Thatcher's influence promised that the Tories would turn inwards, seeking a new way forward that would result in major internal battles, not least over the euro and the European Union itself. Blair may not have seen proportional representation (PR) as a total firewall against a future, more radically nationalistic Conservative Party, but he certainly saw it as a significant new barrier to their recovery.

The referendum itself was won comfortably, with 58 per cent in favour on a low turnout. Critics carped at the lack of requirements for a super-majority or a confirmatory referendum, but with Labour sitting on such a huge parliamentary majority – and using its political capital to secure this change so early in its term – these complaints fell on deaf ears. The Conservatives and their friends in the media were unable to generate much sympathy for a system that had so recently handed them mostly unfettered power for eighteen consecutive years.

Meanwhile, the sight of a small cross-party group of older MPs – many of whom had never had to fight seriously for their own seats – banding together to defend 'the only fair way to conduct elections' was met with derision inside a Parliament that had just passed devolution across the rest of the UK. International media poured scorn on the claim, pointing out that most of Europe, and many countries formerly part of the British Empire, were using various types of PR. Some of them even still called it 'British proportional representation'.

The transition to the new system was rapidly undertaken, following the illustrative schemes developed by the report of the Independent Commission on the Voting System – known as the 'Jenkins Commission', after its chair – that Blair had established after the 1997 election. Picking the midpoint of the range proposed by Roy Jenkins, there were to be 115 top-up seats, spread across the proposed eighty top-up areas. The remaining 544 constituency seats would be elected using the alternative vote, in which voters would rank the candidates in their order of prefer-ence; the candidate with the lowest number of votes would be eliminated and their votes redistributed to the next preference on the ballot papers, until one candidate had achieved more than 50 per cent of the total. There would be a separate vote for top-up members, which would be used to achieve a level of proportionality – albeit limited – across the House of Commons. These top-up members would serve a new role in representing the broader interests of counties and cities and help to provide representation for minority political opinion.

The reduction in constituency numbers caused considerable upset, especially to those at risk of seeing their own seats disappear, but was used by the Blairite faction to strengthen their grip on the Parliamentary Labour Party after the election. The Conservatives had an easier time of it, with an unexpectedly small number of seats after 1997 and some older hands keener to move onto the red benches. The Liberal Democrats focused heavily on the new top-up seats, as well as areas where they were optimistic that Labour votes could help them defeat Conservatives – or vice versa.

The 2001 election results showed a decent majority for the Labour Party, which ended with 365 seats, fifty-three fewer than in 1997. There were large gains for the Liberal Democrats, picking up seats in areas that had been either Labour or Conservative in the past, although the Conservatives made up their losses from the top-up seats, resulting in little net change for them. In the joy of winning a second consecutive majority for the first time in thirty-five years, even many of the dissenters accepted that the result had shown that Labour could win under the new system. Perhaps just as importantly, there did not appear to be any significant shift away from three-party politics towards more extreme viewpoints – a frequent complaint from people whose only experience of PR came from their history lessons about Germany in the 1930s.

Psephologists and election anoraks were delighted to have a trove of preference data to wade through, as they sought to understand how the public would respond to transferable voting. Many found the rankings of some voters to be utterly inexplicable. Numerous academic articles appeared, trying to analyse the rationale for those who would vote for a radically pro-migration candidate as their top preference, to be followed by an equally radical anti-migration candidate in second place. Ultimately, they concluded that some voters just enjoyed contrarianism.

Conservative leader William Hague resigned shortly after the election, after his party failed to advance. In the leadership campaign that followed, Michael Portillo and the veteran Ken Clarke argued for a more moderate, open Conservatism, arguing that it was necessary to be more inclusive to win votes back from New Labour, especially with the new transferable voting system, where they needed support from Lib Dem voters to beat Labour (and in some cases from Labour voters to hold off the Lib Dems). Both men recognised that the coldness that had come to characterise the party in the Thatcher era was not sustainable in the new political landscape, and that future negotiations over potential coalitions would not be feasible if the party's penchant for economic austerity continued.

In contrast, the Thatcherite wing put up both familiar and new voices to argue its case. Heavyweights like Michael Ancram and Michael Howard noted that the temptation in the new world would be to embark on political arms races over increased public spending and borrowing, and they warned about the likely popularity of tax increases that targeted business and what they called 'wealth creation'. Eventually, the two swung behind the youngest candidate, Iain Duncan Smith, who eagerly embraced his role as the Eurosceptic standard-bearer. He insisted that the party should stay true to its core values and not compromise those for people who were not true Conservatives. He argued that without a truly Conservative option on offer – in both economic and social terms – the party would lose its soul, and the country would lose an important counterbalance to what he called the 'craven surrender of sovereignty'.

Surveys of local Conservative associations indicated a strong preference for Duncan Smith, and it seemed inevitable that he would win a vote among the members – the true believers of the party. In response, Portillo and Clarke held secret meetings over bowls of lemon ice in the back room of Ronnie Scott's, pledging to do whatever they could to make sure they would be the two candidates to be presented to the membership, 'to ensure a fair fight'.

In the third and final ballot of the 166 Conservative MPs, the candidates were almost inseparable. However, the rules called for only the top two candidates to go through to face the membership, and so Ken Clarke on fifty-seven and Michael Portillo on fifty-five went through;

Iain Duncan Smith, with only fifty-four, did not. This shift away from traditional Thatcherism sent shockwaves through the party's Eurosceptic wing, which quickly made clear its disapproval of Portillo's more socially liberal platform by ensuring that Ken Clarke was comfortably elected.

Clarke's position was bolstered by a shock result in the Ipswich by-election. With Labour defending a healthy general election vote of 51 per cent, they slipped alarmingly, losing votes both to the Lib Dems in third place and to the Conservative candidate Paul West. West eventually won the seat by just 139 votes, having made up a deficit of 2,514 votes on the first round, mostly from Lib Dem transfers. Clarke's new brand of compassionate Conservatism seemed able to deliver results.

The Blair government continued with its progressive reform agenda, often encouraged by Clarke, who embraced a more collegiate approach to parliamentary activity. This was part of a wider attempt to position his party as 'under new management' – these were, as the media began to call them, 'the new Conservatives', not the nasty party of old.

Politics in the UK seemed very comfortable until the terror attacks of 9/11.

The Labour government's response involved radical new counter-terror powers, which were opposed by prominent backbenchers like Diane Abbott. Meanwhile, as Blair became closer to President George W. Bush, there was a growing drumbeat for war in Iraq, despite the action already taken in Afghanistan. This left many in the Labour Party feeling extremely uncomfortable, and a faction led by backbencher and outspoken anti-war campaigner George Galloway became increasingly vocal in their opposition. Tensions grew until they could not be ignored, with the Galloway-led faction growing ever more critical of their own government.

At the same time, the Liberal Democrats began a very public campaign to convince some of the more anti-war Labour MPs to defect, arguing that an unprovoked and potentially illegal war was an enormous foreign policy error that would permanently harm the UK's standing. This was not a success, with Paul Marsden the only MP to abandon Labour for the Lib Dems.

Similar pressures had also arisen on the right of the Conservatives, with a faction led by David Davis and Iain Duncan Smith rejecting the 'Labour-lite' policies of Ken Clarke, calling for a stronger focus on law and order and Britain's rightful place in the world. Duncan Smith had continued to speak stridently against his new leader, and as early as November 2001, he was one of the first Conservatives to publicly demand an invasion of Iraq, aligning himself with the 'hawks' in the American presidential administration, such as Dick Cheney.

In early 2003, these tensions finally boiled over. The vote to go to war was passed by the narrowest of margins. Clarke led his troops to vote against military intervention and was joined by the Gallowayan 'True Labour' faction and the Liberal Democrats. However, enough Conservative MPs chose to support the government against their own leader to swing the vote, which passed with a tiny majority of three.

Speaking immediately after the result, Galloway announced that no true member of the Labour Party could abide remaining in a government that relied on the votes of far-right-wing Tories and that the betrayal of the Labour tradition could go on no longer. He announced that he was reclaiming the mantle of True Labour. His new party was joined by sixty Labour MPs and most of the trade unions. Vicious fights – sometimes physical – broke out in Constituency Labour Parties across the land over which Labour Party they now belonged to. Claims and counterclaims rapidly reached the courts as to who was entitled to keep the assets and staff of the party.

In this melee, Robin Cook, who had resigned as Foreign Secretary in protest at military action, challenged Tony Blair for the party leadership but narrowly failed to defeat him. Heavily weakened, Blair struggled on leading a minority government, relying on different measures for support from either the Liberal Democrats, True Labour or the right-wing offshoot from the Conservatives, the UK First Party. Though he now led a smaller party, Ken Clarke's initial bonhomie and collaborative spirit had now largely been replaced by the growing conviction that his party now had the moral standing to lead. In a crucial test of public mood, the Brent East by-election saw True Labour win the seat, with Labour forced into a shameful fourth place. The Mayor of London, Ken Livingstone, a former MP for the constituency, had campaigned vigorously against his former party, still bitter over what he saw as a betrayal in 2000, when he had not won the Labour nomination for the mayoralty.

With an unstable government and the war not proceeding as smoothly as planned, Blair was forced to call an earlier election than he had hoped for, and he went to the polls in May 2004. Unsurprisingly, the Labour Party was punished for its pursuit of military relevance, losing a third of its seats. More unexpected were the disappointing results for True Labour, whose energetic campaign 'Respect: For the Many, Not the Few' – weaponising one of Blair's own slogans against him – appeared to have caught the imagination of many younger voters. True Labour triumphed in some parts of London and in university seats across England but lost every seat they were defending in the Midlands and the north – some back to Labour, but some to the new UK First Party, led by David Davis. Nigel Farage, a long-time political failure at Westminster level who had been elected to the European Parliament in 1999, was one of the UK First MPs returned, having convinced many of his UK Independence Party colleagues that they had an opportunity to take over this new party by force of numbers.

The final results showed a complex outcome. The largest party was the Conservatives on 228 seats, narrowly ahead of Labour on 198. The Liberal Democrats had gained slightly, winning 104 seats – the first time they had reached triple figures since the heady days of Asquith in 1923. UK First had fifty-nine seats, with True Labour on thirty-six and twenty-one others.

Charles Kennedy, the leader of the Liberal Democrats, was heavily courted by both major parties. Kennedy felt torn; his instincts had always been on the social liberal side, and he had worked well with Blair on many matters of domestic policy during the previous period of minority government, while maintaining clear dividing lines over civil liberties. On the other hand, having been outspokenly opposed to the Iraq War, it was clear that a precondition of agreement would have to be withdrawal from Iraq, which Blair was not prepared to concede. Efforts to persuade Blair to resign and hand over to Brown, who was prepared to end the military incursion, seemed to be going well until George Galloway made it clear he would not back Gordon Brown either – and a minority coalition seemed an unlikely route, especially with a party that had just suffered such a catastrophic defeat.

In contrast, Ken Clarke made a 'big, open and comprehensive' offer to Kennedy. Rushed negotiations revealed a surprising level of agreement, helped by Ken Clarke's flexibility on the Conservative manifesto – he later admitted that he had only agreed to some aspects of it to placate his members, and he was delighted to see some sections weakened.

At the joint press conference in the No. 10 Rose Garden to announce the coalition deal, Ken Clarke said:

> It is my view that we have the possibility, if we get it right, of delivering more as a coalition than a Conservative government with a small majority in Parliament could have delivered. I think the present situation, in the national interest, from the national point of view, is better than a Conservative government with a tiny majority over two opposition parties would have been.

The press immediately predicted that this coalition, born of a fractured party and a fractured electorate, would not last long, but it was more coherent than many expected, with a surprising warmth between the two leaders. The economy was booming, which meant many difficult decisions could be delayed indefinitely. Immediate steps were taken to withdraw troops from Iraq, which boosted the coalition's popularity, as well as assisting the public finances. The 2004 Higher Education Act was repealed, and with it the planned rise of student fees to £3,000 a year. As Business Secretary, the Liberal Democrat Vince Cable announced that 'Labour's plans to triple tuition fees were unacceptable for our students and our universities. I'm delighted to be part of a coalition that is on the side of students.'

The Labour Party elected a new leader in David Miliband, after a close fight with Gordon Brown, tarred as he was by the failures of the

Blair government. David appointed his younger brother, Ed, as shadow Chancellor, which was perceived as an antidote to the power struggles between Blair and Brown – for how could one brother challenge another?

After a successful period of growth and improvements to public services, the global financial crisis of 2008 suddenly tore the coalition apart. Economic policy became more crucial, and the split between Clarke and Kennedy became insurmountable, despite late night whisky-fuelled negotiations. Eventually, Kennedy led his troops out, refusing to agree to any of the cuts in vital public services that the experienced former Chancellor Clarke claimed were essential to balance the books and defend the country's credit rating.

Legislation came to an almost complete stop, with Clarke leaning on the UK First MPs for support as he staggered through a response to the crisis, resulting in a far more austere approach than he would have chosen left to his own devices. After only a few months, Clarke realised that minority government in an emergency could not continue, and he called a snap general election in the cold December of 2008.

As the country awaited the results, the parties' positions were clear.

Clarke's Conservatives were pushing for a majority in their own right, focusing on the leader's experience as former Chancellor and offering 'stability with Ken Clarke or chaos with David Miliband'.

David Miliband was pledging to rebuild 'one nation' politics, promising a much more significant fiscal stimulus directed at economic recovery, along with a renewed focus on European co-operation and a new transatlantic 'special relationship' with the new President-elect, Barack Obama.

The Liberal Democrats' official slogan had been almost universally forgotten after Charles Kennedy was overheard late one night saying his aim was 'to keep the bastards honest'. The party held great hopes of challenging Miliband's Labour and becoming the official opposition, but many also felt nervous about the potential for punishment after working so closely with Clarke's Conservatives. While the effectiveness of the third party in using its leverage to gain tangible improvements to policy was being increasingly recognised by political commentators and the media, the most frequent complaint about Kennedy personally and the party collectively was that they were very good at opposition but perhaps not ready for the ultimate responsibility: government.

David Davis's UK First Party prioritised ending international aid and massive new restrictions on immigration. Arguing that the country needed to look after its own, they heavily criticised the process of globalisation that had fuelled the recession. Their most eye-catching proposal was a referendum on continued European Union membership, as Davis and Farage banged the drum to regain sovereignty, put 'Britain First' and 'Make Britain Great Again'.

The True Labour Party, now led by Jeremy Corbyn, shared many of the same views on the EU and globalisation. But their policy prescriptions were very different. Using the many examples of poor procurement decisions and horror stories of outsourcing and waste from the ill-fated Blairite Private Finance Initiative, Corbyn and his colleagues were gaining ground by advocating a much more active state that did not shy away from direct economic intervention, including nationalisation. Early indications were that his fiery condemnations of the banks and the lack of criminal prosecutions both for the economic crisis and for the Iraq War were beginning to bear fruit.

Squeezed between the True Labour movement and the Lib Dems' credentials on foreign policy and civil liberties, the Green Party doubled down on its environmental USP. The party's outspoken leader, Caroline Lucas, used her campaign and her media performances to criticise all the major parties for failing to take action on climate change. The legislation planned by Clarke had been prevented from moving forward, and the Green Party now demanded a Climate Change Act with vast investment in new forms of renewable energy and improved transport infrastructure, all as part of the economic recovery. Lucas, too, was keen to point out the potential partnership between the UK and the incoming Democratic administration in the US.

And now we go live to Sunderland for the first result of the night...

Chapter 12

What if Eric Joyce had pulled his punches in 2012?

D. M. Bean

' This place is full of f★★★ing Tories! Ach, I've had enough o' this. I'm away home.'

A bit of an odd place is the Palace of Westminster. The Strangers' Bar, famous as the watering hole where MPs can bring their outside guests, nestles against the Commons Terrace that abuts the River Thames. To exit the building from there, the simplest route (short of jumping in the river) involves taking a right, walking a few paces to a central corridor and heading west, almost immediately coming to a set of double doors leading to the central roadway that runs through most of the building. The walkway that crosses it is covered but open to the elements from each side.

Charles Barry's unconventional design served Eric Joyce well one February night in 2012. The shock of cold air all but dissipated the red mist that had been steadily descending on him as the evening and the imbibing had worn on. He realised that he had just enjoyed a lucky escape.

His army career had ended ignominiously; he had been arrested for drink driving in his constituency two years ago. And then there was the girl. Their prototypical affair had faded away before it could become a terminal danger to his career, but in the clarity of that moment he could see the jeopardy he'd placed himself in. The thought even tickled the back of his mind that his expenses might not be entirely in order. Even before the 2009 MPs' expenses scandal, he had been scorned as Parliament's highest claimant, so to avoid further exposure that might be something else to look into.[1] Most importantly, he now knew that just moments ago he had stepped back from the brink of the unthinkable: lashing out physically at mere political opponents who, he realised, had done nothing to provoke him beside just being there.

Enough, he thought.

After all, he had a hard battle ahead of him back home. The union-affiliated Labour left, he knew, was looking for a deselection scalp in Scotland, and while he liked to believe that their leading target was Douglas Alexander in Paisley, a shadow Foreign Secretary was not likely to be cut adrift by the party machine. A backbench member for Falkirk with one notch of disgrace on his belt already was not so indispensable. He'd fought off the left in the past when his record was clean, but another sign of vulnerability now could provide the impetus they needed to vanquish him. In wait behind them lay the nationalists.

No, he had enough troubles ahead without doing his enemies' work for them. He had been a good politician once, a 'rising star'; more recently he'd enjoyed a shadow ministerial post under the current administration until his drink-driving incident had put paid to it. He could live that down in time, provided he could avoid any repetition. It was time to be his old self again. It was time to clean up. The drink had to go.

Such were his muddled thoughts as he made a still-unsteady exit from the parliamentary estate, veering left as he reached the colonnade to head up the cobbled incline for the Carriage Gates exit and Parliament Square. He might have stopped to ask at the Westminster Hall police box for a taxi to be signalled by the beacon outside but, fixated on escape, he instead hailed one by hand to take him back to his hotel.

The memory remained with him next morning as he made his way back to Parliament, foggily unsure of his whipping instructions on what seemed to him a minor item of government business about pensions uprating. Besides, there would doubtless be constituency business he could discuss with his staff, and once the House adjourned that afternoon – it being a Thursday with a non-sitting Friday to follow – he could be off back up to Falkirk. He had taken the past evening's lessons to heart. Starting this weekend, he was taking politics seriously again.

~

The 'Eric Joyce Theory' of British politics may be the archetypal real-world example of that ancient proverb, 'For want of a nail': the notion that tiny, seemingly insignificant incidents can butterfly into world-shaping events. What, after all, could be more insignificant than an unprovoked punch thrown by an angry, drunken man?[2]

It has come to be believed that the right punch thrown by the right man could indeed have had such consequences. The punches in question, delivered by Eric Joyce on 22 February 2012 against several, mainly Conservative, MPs and members of their staff, resulted in his arrest and subsequent conviction for assault, ending his political career in disgrace and requiring the selection of a new Labour candidate to contest his seat of Falkirk. The fallout from a further scandal surrounding that selection battle has been thought to bear responsibility for much that happened since.

In this chapter, we will draw out those repercussions by portraying a world where the punches were never thrown, where Eric Joyce was instead shocked into quitting the bottle and becoming a responsible politician once more. Interspersed excerpts such as this will compare the narrative with what really happened, surveying it with a critical eye.

At the time of writing, Joyce is under a suspended prison sentence following conviction for offences of possessing and repeatedly viewing child pornography.[3] It is not the purpose of this story to explore what might have driven someone to such acts, but it may not be coincidental that they began around the culmination of a downward spiral of alcohol-related behaviour. The incident in the Strangers' Bar might well have been his tipping point.

Joyce had already been required, as an alternative to expulsion, to resign his commission as a major in the army following his unauthorised authorship of a critical pamphlet published by the Fabian Society.[4] He had already been arrested and fined for failing to provide a breath test after an incident while driving in Falkirk.[5] He had already become 'very friendly' with a seventeen-year-old girl and communicated with her in ways which he subsequently accepted he got wrong.[6]

The idea that Joyce's dissolute behaviour could be reduced to a single incident, and that narrowly avoiding it might have induced a turnaround sufficient to forestall any equivalent acts leading to his enforced withdrawal as a Labour candidate, is already in some doubt. But we will soldier on, and in service of the story assume that he could have chosen to reform, and did so.

Let us continue to examine that scenario.

~

Back in Falkirk, Joyce's re-selection proceeded without serious incident, as did Douglas Alexander's over in Paisley. There had been the routine agitation prompted by salaried trade union staff in favour of what they presented as selecting more authentically Labour voices. The formerly Glasgow-based trade unionist and Tom Watson's office manager, Karie Murphy, emerged as their favourite. Local members had more immediate concerns, not least the looming 2014 referendum on Scottish independence. With no serious move emerging against him, Joyce remained as the presumptive Labour nominee for Falkirk.

He would later grow lukewarm on the union, based on what he might describe as an evolved perception of Scotland's place in it, but for the moment Joyce played his role as a good unionist party politician. The result was 55.3 per cent against separation from the United Kingdom. For his career, the real threat emerged afterwards as, in common with other parts of Scotland, the 46.5 per cent of Falkirk Council residents who had voted 'Yes' – most of whom lived in his constituency – began to coalesce around the SNP.

The result of the 2015 general election, a twelve-seat Conservative majority, stunned even the BBC, whose exit poll had shown the party falling nineteen seats short of overall control. In Scotland, where Labour, in common with the Liberal Democrats and the Conservatives, slumped to a single seat, it was enough to put paid to Joyce's hopes of retaining Falkirk, and as such his political career. Languishing in minor journalistic obscurity, he now tweets approvingly about Scottish independence from the idyllic pastoral home he shares with a *Sunday Times* columnist in Suffolk.

Those still in the Parliamentary Labour Party quickly turned their attention to the leadership contest that followed Ed Miliband's resignation, with the more optimistic among the Labour left sensing an opportunity. In their favour was a distinct leftward shift in the activist base. Miliband had been elected as a compromise left-of-centre candidate, but his failure to deliver either a radical agenda or an election win emboldened their case against moderation. Less favourable were the rules for the contest. These remained as they had been at the time of Miliband's victory, having changed little since Neil Kinnock's 1994 removal of the trade union block vote had assisted the election of Tony Blair later that decade.

Labour uses an electoral college system consisting of three sections: its elected MPs and MEPs, party members, and 'affiliated' members who belong to a formally linked trade union or socialist society. The affiliated members category is by far the largest, numbering in the hundreds of thousands; constituency members in 2015 hovered around 200,000;[7] and the number of MPs and MEPs stood at 252. Section results are weighted equally. Each candidate's votes in each section are counted, calculated as a percentage of the total number cast, divided by three and then added together with the results from the other two sections. As a result, one MP's vote is worth thousands of times that of an ordinary member. The overall lowest-scoring candidate is eliminated, with their votes redistributed according to the next-ranked preference on each ballot, until one candidate has achieved a majority.

The left had long complained that the process gives undue weight to the 'ruling class' of elected officials; they had agitated for a system based on one member, one vote. Given some impetus – if, say, the trade unions had meddled brazenly enough in a selection contest to cause a scandal – Miliband might earlier have been persuaded to back reform, but as it was the rules stood unchanged. The issue the left now faced was finding their candidate.

It was in no great spirit of optimism that the faction's most prominent members met together at the Islington home of one of their number: local MP Jeremy Corbyn. Attendees included their 2010 standard-bearer and former shadow Public Health Minister Diane Abbott; Hayes & Harlington MP John McDonnell; Kate Osamor, representing the 2015 intake; and former Environment Minister Michael Meacher, accompanied by his respected long-time researcher, Jon Lansman. As Lansman would later put it, their movement lacked momentum.

The meeting soon resembled a game of hot potato. Meacher immediately ruled himself out on grounds of his age. Lansman was strong for McDonnell, but the latter would rather avoid being the front man, instead preferring Corbyn; whereas Corbyn was adamant in declining to fight what he fully expected would be a losing battle, instead advocating an encore performance from Abbott. As the least strenuous abdicator, Abbott was adopted *nem. con.*

Assuming, of course, she could get on the ballot. In addition to support from a proportion of constituency branches (virtually assured for any left representative), candidates needed nominations from at least 15 per cent of the parliamentary party, then amounting to thirty-five. At her last attempt, despite lacking sufficient serious support from her colleagues, Abbott had succeeded in winning a slew of 'charity' nominations from supporters of other candidates, primarily of David Miliband. Some of them had held a genuine desire to broaden the scope of debate within the party; others had misunderstood the transferable nature of its electoral system and imagined that her presence could effectively split the left-wing vote to their benefit. Enough who might have inclined toward the latter notion had been so disabused of it by Ed's election that this time she very nearly didn't make it.

Nominations must be submitted in person at the office of the Parliamentary Labour Party, which, in 2015, was situated in the Palace of Westminster's West Cloister, entered from the foot of the Members' Staircase through its perpendicular neighbour. In a further quirk of parliamentary geography, the rest of the North Cloister was occupied by staff of the Conservative-affiliated Policy Research Unit, which enjoyed front-row seats as Labour MPs milled about, or rather 'caucused', as the deadline approached. One member of that staff would later describe the scene as marginally less well-organised and dignified than his worst memories of elections to a students' union. 'Well, I wanted to nominate Yvette,' he recalled one veteran Labour MP commenting to two colleagues, 'but now Diane's people are saying she might not make it on. We have to get her through so we can have a debate ... Oh, you're nominating her? I don't know if they knew that. I'll have to go and check.'[8]

They would have their wish, as Abbott made the ballot alongside Yvette Cooper, Liz Kendall and Andy Burnham. It was not a slate that fully satisfied the party. Left-wing activists were quietly dispirited at being offered a candidate who had already lost once, whereas many on its Blairite wing would have preferred the chance to back Chuka Umunna. Some had even started making exploratory noises about Sir Keir Starmer, although he was a non-starter: apart from the fact he had only just been elected as an MP, it was surely unthinkable that the Labour Party would elect its second leader named Keir before its first woman.

Campaigning as usual was swiftly derailed by the issue of the candidates' sexes, with *Guardian* and *Independent* columnists reaching paroxysms of delight that three of the four were women. Burnham, as the contest's lone man and formerly Miliband's presumptive successor, was naturally concerned. Being the first woman to aspire credibly to the leadership of a left-of-centre party was no guarantee of success – Hillary Clinton had shown that in 2008 – yet unlike Clinton's opponent, aside from hailing from the north of England, Burnham's hand lacked an identity card of its own.

His response was two-pronged. First, seeking to buttress his already strong position among trade unionists with support from the activist base, he followed the old Miliband strategy of tacking to the left; in one television interview, as advised by his team member Owen Smith, he went so far as to say that he agreed with many of Abbott's ideas, 'but we have to win an election first'. His proposals included renationalising the railways as franchises expired; creating a national infrastructure fund; and allowing councils to make compulsory purchases of rental properties once they had been available to let for at least ten years, upon the current tenancy's expiration.[9]

Second and more controversially, he pledged that his frontbench teams would always include at least 40 per cent women and 40 per cent men, and to reform the party constitution so the leader and deputy would be elected separately and must be of the opposite sex. When Harriet Harman had floated a similar idea around a decade earlier it had felt like fresh thinking, but since then intersectional concerns had so predominated among many within Labour that the result was a minor controversy over where the proposal would leave transgender MPs. Since these were currently hypothetical, the outrage was mainly confined to Twitter, but membership polling suggested that his support among the younger demographics had taken a hit of over 15 per cent.

Cooper stood aloof from the row, simply saying she was proud of the steps the party had already taken to improve prospects for women and hoped that her own candidacy might end by shattering the party's last glass ceiling. Her narrative emphasised vision over policy. Moderate and embracing, it stressed the need to grow support and throw off perceptions of hostility towards business. It was hardly a message to set activists aflame (some among the commentariat even called it boring), but her narrow focus on electability and forming the next government appealed sufficiently to wiser heads to narrow the gap with Burnham.

Liz Kendall, the relative novice, ran from the right. Although she had not entered Parliament until 2010, like the Brownite convert Burnham she had served various stints as a special adviser under Tony Blair's premiership, including under Patricia Hewitt at the Departments of Trade & Industry and Health. Vehemently though she denied it, her image was as the Blairite candidate. She was the most critical of Labour's recent performance in opposition, and while colleagues confirmed the truth of her likeable public image, the medicine she prescribed was not one the wider party showed much enthusiasm for taking.

At her opposite ideological pole stood Abbott, who ran the typical Labour left campaign of calling for nationalisations and throwing at least three expressions of half-hearted outrage into each set of remarks.

Some even made it to air. Lansman's connections helped her to establish a surprisingly effective social media operation, but her campaign was torpedoed when in the televised leaders' debate, challenged on the cost of her pledge to recruit 10,000 new police officers, she initially claimed a sum that would have left them with the princely annual salary of £30 before blundering through various other figures that might have been made up on the spot. While certainly the biggest viral moment of her campaign, this was not one well-calibrated to success.

The results saw narrow first-preference leads by Cooper and Burnham in the members' and affiliates' sections respectively, with the parliamentary section a virtual tie. Abbott trailed only slightly in the first two but scored fewer votes in the third than she had won nominees. Once second and third preferences were reallocated the result became clear. Failing their first choice, Labour members would not pass up the opportunity to elect a credible candidate as their first female leader. They had chosen Yvette Cooper.

~

Because the Eric Joyce Theory relies on no Corbyn leadership from 2015, this section lies at the heart of the matter. Our story has him deciding against standing in the first place, rather than the more traditional notion of him standing and losing. Why?

To answer this, we must examine two of the theory's key contentions: that Ed Miliband's changes to leadership election rules stemmed directly from Eric Joyce's assaults in 2012, and that they bore decisive responsibility for Corbyn's victory.

The first is the simpler case to make. What really happened was that the Falkirk selection contest necessitated by Joyce's enforced resignation became mired in controversy after an alleged attempt by the Unite trade union to rig it in favour of their candidate, Karie Murphy, who would later head Jeremy Corbyn's Labour Party leader's office. Following the election of the union's Scottish chairman as leader of the Constituency Labour Party, Unite members were recruited in bulk under circumstances of questionable legitimacy, their dues paid by the union. There was then an attempt to impose an all-woman shortlist, to Murphy's obvious benefit, and when complaints from longer-standing local members led Labour's National Executive Committee to conclude that the process had been irregular, the matter burgeoned into a scandal.[10]

In its aftermath, Ed Miliband announced a review, chaired by the trade unionist peer and former Labour general secretary Ray Collins, of the party's links with unions, and especially of its selection rules.[11] The result was a wide-ranging proposal to abolish the tripartite electoral college and move to a system of 'one member, one vote', as the left had been advocating for generations. Enacted in March 2014, it allowed members of the public to become 'registered supporters' for a low cost, initially £3, and participate in selection contests – including for the party leader – on an equal footing with other eligible voters.[12]

The Collins Review stemmed directly from the row over the Falkirk selection contest, which in turn arose from Eric Joyce's assaults. While it is conjecturally possible that other circumstances might have produced a similar outcome, there is a chain of events leading from the incident in February 2012 to the £3 supporters voting in the 2015 leadership election. Despite some late attempts to screen out applicants who belonged to other parties, this enticed hard-left activists who had previously found Labour too moderate to join in droves and vote for Corbyn.

The usual recitation of the Eric Joyce Theory has it that these voters were decisive,[13] but the results of the contest show this claim to be unsupportable. Registered supporters were indeed Corbyn's strongest constituency, handing him a first-round vote of 83.8 per cent, but he also succeeded among both party and trade union members, which he won with 49.6 per cent and 57.6 per cent respectively. His overall result of 59.5 per cent avoided any need for redistribution.

Even so, under the old rules, it is possible that Corbyn could have lost. Aside from the £3 supporters, less attention has been paid to two other features of the 2014 reforms: the abolition of the electoral college, and the restriction of the trade union franchise to members who had specifically opted in to Labour Party representation. Previously, ballots had been sent to all members of affiliated unions. As a result of the reforms, the number of ballots cast by that category in 2015 dropped significantly compared with the 2010 contest, from 211,234 to 71,546. Those union members who did not opt in likely either converted to full party membership – borne out by a jump in the number of party member votes from 126,874 to 245,520 – or were not particularly supportive of Labour and no longer had a vote, but under the previous arrangements may have backed a moderate.

We can only guess what the results in those two sections might have been in the absence of Collins's reforms, but Corbyn certainly would have lost the MPs and MEPs section decisively. With the electoral college still in place, that result would have been upweighted to be worth the same as each of the others, regardless of the vast disparity in the numbers of electors. Corbyn would have needed to carry the other two sections by large enough margins to overcome his inevitable shortfall there, relying on lower-preference votes that were less likely to favour his 'Marmite' candidacy. He would have struggled, and so we could be tempted to think that Eric Joyce's punches might have made the difference after all – just not in quite the way most people think.

Simplifying matters in this story, we have conjectured that the rule changes themselves may have been enough to make Corbyn and his supporters believe that the traditional putting-up of a left-wing candidate might have been more than a formality. In their absence, the faction settles for a candidate used to losing, who neither expects nor works for a different outcome.

~

Prime Minister David Cameron's attempts to renegotiate the UK's membership of the European Union set the stage for the promised referendum on what was coming to be termed 'Brexit'.

For soft Eurosceptics, his effort did not go well. Having embarked on a valiant quest to restore national competence over trade, migration and regulatory policy, Cameron returned with a set of watered-down concessions, including over migrants' benefits; a right to persuade fifteen other EU members to ask the European Commission to reconsider a directive; and a symbolic opt-out of the EU's commitment to 'ever-closer union'. Nevertheless, having sworn to put his resignation to the public in the form of an in–out referendum, this new deal was what he had – quickly though it was handwaved away as the campaign began.

Committed to maintaining EU membership, Cameron reached out to the leadership of the other major political parties seeking to establish a unified 'Remain' campaign, and in Yvette Cooper he found a willing associate. At her urging, along with the leaders of the Liberal Democrats and the nationalist parties, they established a steering committee to oversee its formation and strategy – a move that has been credited with helping circumvent various mis-steps that Cameron's aides have since reported were under consideration.

Cooper argued that to avoid the risk of provoking a protest vote, their parties should reject the idea of formally backing 'Remain', as should the governments of the devolved nations and the United Kingdom. Cameron was adamant that the UK government needed to establish a firm policy in favour of EU membership and marshal the resources of the state in communicating it, but Cooper's threat to withdraw co-operation from the pre-existing 'Labour In for Britain' campaign at last persuaded him to demur.

The compromise saw Cameron maintaining an official government stance of recommending a Remain vote, but without committing state resources to the campaign. Cameron would go on to participate in what he described as a personal capacity, permitting his ministers to do like-wise for either side, and agreed that the Conservative Party would join Labour in a position of corporate neutrality.

The Liberal Democrats and the nationalists did not agree to maintain neutrality for themselves, but otherwise accepted the strategy in full. The result was a unified 'Remain' campaign named 'Stronger In' (the alternative suggestion of 'Britain Stronger in Europe' being vetoed by Cooper over concerns about its acronym), which would exist primarily for the sake of administration and fundraising, and also to offer a locus for non-partisan activists. It would be buttressed by confederated, co-branded campaigns targeted and run by each party's supporters, which would take responsibility for the bulk of the ground-work. The product was in effect a refined version of the model followed by the 'Better Together' campaign that had successfully kept Scotland in the UK in 2014.

Campaigners to leave the EU had a rocky start, with the rival groups Vote Leave, Leave.EU and Grassroots Out competing for recognition as the official Leave campaign, to Vote Leave's eventual success. At the senior level, however, relations between figures such as Michael Gove, Andrea Leadsom and Boris Johnson from the Conservatives, Gisela Stuart of Labour and Nigel Farage as the leader of UKIP proved cordial.

Cooper's influence extended beyond organisational matters into the tone of the Stronger In campaign. While acknowledging earlier polling that suggested most voters would base their decision on whether or not they believed Brexit would help or harm the economy, her influence has been credited with dissuading Cameron from bearing down too strongly with prophesies of doom; voters in many communities her party represented, she argued, felt that in reality they had little to lose. Her intervention is also rumoured to have forestalled a threat from the Chancellor, George Osborne, to introduce what might have been laughed off as a 'punishment Budget' if Vote Leave prevailed. She advo-cated, instead of dark warnings about leaps into darkness, a more positive case for EU membership: that while the UK certainly could make it alone, it would be stronger, fairer and richer within the EU.

Confident that the economic case was with them, Stronger In had to acknowledge that their greatest threat was the issue of immigration, particularly after Johnson and Gove came together to propose – more in the manner of an alternative government than an opposing campaign – a radically new system based on Australian-style points. Having come to believe that her party had erred throughout the Blair years in pro-moting an open-doors policy and impugning the motives of sceptics, Cooper saw an opportunity to play Nixon in China. In general terms, she secured Cameron's assent to her giving a major policy address on the issue, ostensibly on Stronger In's behalf.

Plans were already well in train when, on 16 June, one week before referendum day, Labour MP Jo Cox was murdered by a constituent linked to the far right. Campaigning was suspended for the rest of the week. The following Monday, after leading tributes in the recalled House of Commons, Cooper gave her rescheduled, rewritten and relocated speech from Cox's constituency of Batley & Spen. She began with the anticipated excoriation of the hatred that had apparently driven the murder, but segued into a more reflective tone, conceding that her political forebears bore primary responsibility for making many feel that the sole refuge for their legitimate concerns about the impact of immigration on communities lay in extremism.

To widespread astonishment, she went on to commit a future Labour government to go beyond invoking the renegotiated concessions on migrants' benefits by seeking fundamental reform of EU migration policy. Anticipating the Vote Leave response, she argued that following EU withdrawal no acceptable deal on market access could ever be secured without the UK conceding continued free movement, so the responsible vote for achievable reform was to remain.

Cameron was infuriated with Cooper's probing at his flank, but in time for the *News at Ten* was persuaded to authorise a statement of support and a similar commitment from the government. Vote Leave rubbished the notion that British withdrawal from freedom of movement could more readily be achieved inside the EU than out, but on the whole Stronger In was relieved to have mounted what sounded like a credible challenge to Vote Leave's dominance of the issue.

By 23 June, neither side had scored a knockout in the 'air war' of the national campaign, so what proved crucial was the old-fashioned groundwork of canvassing, telling and knocking up. Stronger In's confederal model allowed vigorously recruited local activists to talk to their own voters on the doorstep and on the telephone, sharing data and intelligence to provide for a polling-day operation focused ruthlessly on driving out the vote. Vote Leave also proved highly capable but could not match its rival's scale. At 10 p.m., the BBC called a narrow win for Remain, and as the returns came in the result was confirmed, with a margin of 51.9 to 48.1 per cent.[14]

Remain supporters were predictably jubilant, while the broadsheet commentariat declared the matter settled for all eternity, with firm and frowning admonitions against even thinking about suggesting it might be revisited. Moderate supporters on both sides were indifferent; those soft Eurosceptics who had felt persuadable to back Remain if Cameron had produced a more substantial renegotiation largely accepted the result and returned to their respective folds.

The Leave faithful proved less amenable. Parliamentary parties held firm, aided on the Conservative side by prime ministerial patronage, as Cameron's long-rumoured 'reconciliation reshuffle' brought senior ex-Leavers into the Cabinet, including Johnson as Foreign Secretary and Theresa Villiers at Work & Pensions, with Gove remaining at the Ministry of Justice. Yet in the country, a stream of Conservative and Labour members, animated by his roars of betrayal and demands for a new referendum, defected to Farage's surging UKIP. The anger only grew when a brief Downing Street press note after the European Council meeting of 28 June announced that progress towards implementing the new deal would be postponed 'for further study'.

Early in 2017, rumours started to circulate that Cameron might step down as Prime Minister to continue his career in Brussels. He had concluded, went the story, that Britain's interests were best served with its biggest beasts joining the den, and his role in preserving UK membership would suffice to secure his welcome. In March, however, politics as usual was disrupted when a deadly terrorist attack on the Palace of Westminster saw an Islamist from Luton drive a car through crowds of pedestrians before crashing into its perimeter, breaching Carriage Gates and murdering an unarmed police officer. The attacker was shot and killed, but Parliament was forced into lockdown. Barely had the country time to pause for breath before a suicide bomb at the Manchester Arena a month later left twenty-two victims dead.

Terrorism had once again become the defining political issue of the day, and Cameron concluded that his response to the atrocities might secure his legacy. Always one to step up in times of crisis, his televised address promised the country 'thoughts and prayers, but also action'.

Following negotiations with Yvette Cooper to secure Labour's support, and with European partners to win quiet assurances against complications from the European Court of Human Rights, Cameron announced that he and the Home Secretary, Theresa May, would immediately bring forward a new Counter-Terrorism Bill, the provisions of which had been drawn up swiftly after the Westminster attack. They provided that, notwithstanding any relevant UK or international human rights legislation, anyone suspected of planning terrorist activity who had citizenship in another country could be stripped of any British citizenship, deported and excluded permanently. Applications to the High Court would be reviewed in closed session and require only a balance-of-probabilities burden of proof.

Despite horrified reactions from human rights campaigners and the hard left, Cooper judged that the times called for the unity shown during the referendum campaign to continue, and the Bill passed the Commons comfortably. Getting it through the Lords initially looked trickier, but when a preliminary round-up of suspects uncovered and disrupted a plot for a further attack at London Bridge and Borough Market that had been planned for early June, dissent melted away, and the Bill was promptly passed.

Cameron's concession to Labour and Europe was one it is now reckoned he had intended already: excepting the provision on migrants' benefits, the renegotiated terms of EU membership were formally abandoned. Normally this might have provoked fury, but with the national focus having shifted to combatting terrorism, the government and the official opposition united; the thwarted London Bridge assault having seemingly validated Cameron's approach, the public at large reacted with the expected doleful acceptance. Having passed the landmark Counter-Terrorism Act, rid his successor of a millstone and facilitated his subsequent rise in the Brussels elite, Cameron resigned as leader of the Conservative Party in July, paving the way for a contest set to culminate at the party conference.

Cameron's tacit support lay with his long-term ally and Chancellor, George Osborne. Long regarded as a Prime-Minister-in-waiting,

Osborne had, ironically thanks to Cooper, avoided any fatal wounds to his career over the referendum. He emerged as the continuity candidate, joined by Theresa May, who sought to capitalise on recent events by pledging to move further and harder against terrorism. She failed to gain traction owing to a prevailing view that the Counter-Terrorism Act had already pursued that issue far enough for the present.

Rounding out the contest was the hero of the Leave campaign, Boris Johnson. With no threat of arguments over a post-EU future to divide him from his old comrades, he succeeded in uniting the Eurosceptic wing. Although he made few firm commitments beyond 'keeping a watchful eye' on Brussels, pursuing migration reform and staying well away from the Euro, it was enough for them. Johnson had never been popular among the parliamentary party's old guard nor its moderates, but with eyes on UKIP's polling numbers and the fraught entreaties from their constituencies, MPs ultimately recoiled from the prospect of denying members the opportunity to vote for a Leaver as leader. Selected by MPs to face Osborne in the members' ballot, on Monday 2 October, in Manchester, Boris Johnson was announced as the new leader of the Conservative Party. That afternoon, he travelled to Buckingham Palace to be formally appointed Prime Minister.

Johnson's agenda promised to 'level up' the country, and over the next two years he and his Chancellor, Sajid Javid, slowly began turning on the spending taps. He retained the popular appeal that had won him two terms as Mayor of London, and his Vote Leave record helped consolidate support among natural Conservatives, just as backing Cameron over terrorism had for Cooper among traditional Labour voters. The 2019 European elections saw UKIP again top the polls, but its gain of only two seats from its 2014 score of twenty-four in a classically protest-orientated election felt manageable. The aftermath brought a pleasant surprise when the European Commission abandoned the vaunted Spitzenkandidat process to appoint David Cameron to succeed his old foe, Jean-Claude Juncker, as President.

On the eve of the 2020s, political observers looked forward to another close election, set for May, in which, despite UKIP's progress, the main event would see Johnson's Conservatives and Cooper's Labour once again arguing fiercely about whose programme would best take Britain forward within the confines of EU policy and law. *Plus ça change.*

~

A Remain victory in 2016 needs not follow an authentic Europhile displacing Jeremy Corbyn as Labour leader as night follows day. Labour's alternative leader must do some things differently, and here we have suggested some possibilities. Corbyn's critics argue that he showed little interest in playing a personal role or co-ordinating his party's campaign with the overall Remain effort. With accounts swiftly emerging of altered statements and unsigned letters, some even accused his office of sabotage.[15]

In this story, Yvette Cooper is active and enthusiastic. She helps arrange a structure that could better leverage the campaign's innate strengths, steers it away from some unforced errors and takes a firm stance on immigration, providing a counter-narrative that – while it was not borne out by true events – she is able to present as plausible. The story does not mention perhaps the greatest difference, which in its fictional universe would have been assumed as a given: she would have made it entirely clear that the leader of the Labour Party wished its supporters to turn out and vote Remain. That the same cannot be said of Corbyn may justly be thought of as a defining moment in his leadership.

We have chosen not to conclude matters with the Remain vote but to consider its ramifications as the decade ended. UKIP, with Nigel Farage continuing as leader, experiences a surge that mirrors the reaction among Scottish Nationalists to their referendum defeat in 2014 but is somewhat arrested by the appalling series of terrorist attacks that rocked the country in spring 2017. There is no reason to suppose these events would not have occurred as in reality, but they arrive here in the altered circumstances of stronger political leadership and a country not already consumed by an internal struggle over EU withdrawal.

Our imagined Counter-Terrorism Act is one conceivable response, which happens also to offer the outgoing Prime Minister an opportunity to jettison much of his old renegotiation and pave the way for his appointment as President of the European Commission. Some such bone thrown to the UK following a Remain vote seems likely; given that the European Commission did eventually reject the Spitzenkandidat process in 2019 in appointing Ursula von der Leyen, that high-profile role is a viable candidate.

Let us now examine what conclusions we can draw as to the overall plausibility of this story before at last we conclude the story itself.

Counterfactual history does not readily entertain absolutes. Although a superb genre for storytelling, to expect it to function as an academic discipline offering definitive answers to what-if scenarios would be too much. That is not its function; there are too many historical unknowns for even its sharpest analysis to penetrate.

What we can do is test our premises. We have seen that the Eric Joyce Theory, the notion that one punch-up in one pub on one night set the course for British politics echoing down to the Brexit vote and all that has ensued, rests on several large assumptions. Here is their summary:

That Eric Joyce would not have found some other way to screw up. Here, catching himself on the brink in February 2012 – with assistance from a parliamentary architect – was enough to startle him into reform. There are, however, innumerable possible scenarios where he avoided that night's outrage but still disqualified himself on some other occasion and triggered a selection contest that proceeded much as it did in reality.

That the forces bearing down from the unions, led by Unite, would not have found some other constituency in which to put up a questionably legitimate selection fight. This was Joyce's own explanation for doubting the theory: he expects, he said, that a similar contest would have been fought elsewhere. His bet was on Paisley,[16] but the likelihood of a sitting frontbencher falling victim to a successful challenge would seem smaller than what actually occurred. Here it simply does not happen at all.

That with the rules unchanged, neither Jeremy Corbyn nor any similar figure from the traditionally Eurosceptic Labour left would have stood for the party leadership in 2015 and won. The £3 'registered supporter' category was not essential for Corbyn to win his leadership contest, but other changes inspired by the Collins Review, particularly the abolition of the electoral college, were perhaps more significant. Their absence may have dissuaded Corbyn from standing, leaving the left with a weaker candidate.

That a full-throated Europhile, cast here as Yvette Cooper – who in reality became one of the government's greatest opponents in delivering Brexit – as leader of the Labour Party would have changed the result of the EU referendum. This may be uncertain, but it is far from implausible – provided the alternative leader could impact the campaign appropriately.

This chapter has set out neither to prove nor to debunk, but to offer a definitive account of what has been an enduringly popular theory. If readers come out feeling better equipped to assess it for themselves, it will have done its work.

~

Meanwhile, in the Chinese province of Wuhan, somebody coughed.

Notes

1   On 12 January 2015, Eric Joyce was ordered to repay £12,919.61 of incorrectly claimed expenses, following review by the Independent Parliamentary Standards Authority. The sum was subsequently reduced to £10,000 (*The Times*, 11 March 2015).

2   Joyce 'accepted he was "hammered" during the brawl' (*Daily Telegraph*, 9 March 2012).

3   BBC News, 7 August 2020.

4   *The Independent*, 14 January 1999.

5   BBC News, 19 November 2010.

6   *Daily Mirror*, 2 March 2012.

7   Estimated based on the actual number of votes cast by constituency members in that election standing at 245,675 (BBC News, 12 September 2015). In this scenario, with the leadership contest rules unchanged, Labour experienced some surge of membership following its 2015 defeat, but of a lesser extent.

8   This scene did occur in reality, except that the soul-searching concerned the candidacy of Jeremy Corbyn instead of Diane Abbott. The Policy Research Unit staff member who witnessed it was the author.

9   These are a slightly more radical variant of policies Burnham campaigned on in reality.

10 *The Guardian*, 12 May 2013, 5 July 2013.

11 Ed Miliband, speech on the union link, 9 July 2013.

12 *The Collins Review into Labour Party Reform*, Labour Party, February 2014.

13 See e.g. *Irish Times*, 13 December 2019.

14 This is, of course, the exact reverse of the actual result.

15 See e.g. BBC News, 26 June 2016.

16 *New Statesman*, 21 April 2017.

Chapter 13

What if Nick Clegg had resigned as Liberal Democrat leader in 2014?

Anonymous

Monday 26 May 2014

Nick Clegg looked in a worse state than anyone had ever seen him. The four years since his triumph in the first TV debate of the 2010 general election campaign had seen many setbacks for the Liberal Democrats. The party had plummeted in the opinion polls and had lost almost 60 per cent of its council seats. Not only were there a lot of angry ex-councillors, but it was these council seats that had provided the base for the party's earlier parliamentary breakthroughs.

The party that had once been the 'kings of by-election campaigning' had only narrowly clung on to Eastleigh after Chris Huhne's resignation the year before. For the first full parliament since 1951–55, the Lib Dems now appeared incapable of gaining any seats at parliamentary by-elections. Party membership had plummeted by a third. Financial appeals sent in the leader's name to ordinary party members asking them for funds had simply resulted in shoals of resignation letters, though major donors had remained willing to give large sums to a party of government.

But none of these setbacks had dented the Liberal Democrat leader's confidence in the way that the European election results, announced the night before, had done. The number of Lib Dem MEPs had fallen from eleven in 2009 to just one. The margin in the one remaining seat had been so close that the party had been nearly wiped out completely.

It was clear to everyone who met him in the Deputy Prime Minister's

Office at 70 Whitehall that Monday morning that Clegg had not slept a wink all night. Previous election setbacks had not concerned him too greatly. He had never had much time for those people in his party who he thought 'put too much effort into local campaigning and winning council seats'. The loss of many of them was officially described as 'an inevitable result of mid-term unpopularity in government'. The fact that the losses had begun in the first year of the coalition and that the party's coalition partners, the Conservatives, had made significant gains at the same time was never accounted for. But Clegg had held high hopes that the European elections of 2014 would restore confidence and credibility to the party and to his own leadership.

A few months earlier, he had met the party's MEPs at the European Parliament. This was where he had served as one of their number between 1999 and 2004 before turning his ambitions to Westminster. The group, then comprising twelve members (the eleven elected in 2009 plus Edward McMillan-Scott, who had defected from the Conservatives in 2010), had been delighted that Clegg would be taking on Nigel Farage of UKIP directly in head-to-head TV debates prior to the election. 'It's Nick v Nigel' had been prominent in the party's leaflets and social media presence. The message of the Lib Dem campaign was unequivocally pro-EU, with the party constantly describing itself as the party of 'In'. But the debates eventually dashed the party's hopes of reviving the spirit of 'I agree with Nick' which had followed his first TV debate encounter with Gordon Brown and David Cameron in 2010.

The post-debate polls that had propelled him in 2010 to the post of Deputy Prime Minister now showed that, in a two-cornered contest, only 27 per cent thought he had 'won' the debates. This was a far lower share than might have been expected for someone arguing in favour of continued EU membership against Brexit. He'd had some able people spinning for him, and they claimed that '27 per cent was a great result, given that the party was only polling around 8 per cent nationally at the time'. But his parliamentary colleagues knew that 27 per cent was not a great result when no representatives of the Conservatives nor Labour had been included as options. Almost 70 per cent of those polled thought Farage had won.

The Lib Dem results in the European elections were terrible. The party won just 6.6 per cent of the vote and lost ten of the eleven seats it had held previously, as well as the seat of McMillan-Scott. The longest-standing Lib Dem MEP, Graham Watson, had been defeated in south-west England, once the party's greatest stronghold.

Clegg wanted to resign. His strategy had been a failure. He had lost the trust of former Lib Dem voters. He had never expected to win back those who had switched to support Labour. But now he knew that he would not win back those who had switched to the Conservatives or to UKIP either. The Scottish Liberal Democrats were in danger of being marginalised by the SNP, even though the nationalists still held only six Westminster seats. Across the country, the Lib Dems appeared to have no prospect of retaining a significant proportion of the seats won in 2010.

Ten of the party's MPs had privately agreed that they would call for Clegg to go if the party won fewer than three MEPs; now it had just one.

Southport's MP, John Pugh, spoke to Clegg's most loyal supporter, Danny Alexander, and forcibly argued that while Clegg must go, the need to save seats meant avoiding the kind of public clash between MPs that had followed Charles Kennedy's admission of a drink problem in 2006. But Alexander, who sat in the Cabinet as Chief Secretary to the Treasury and was Clegg's closest friend in the parliamentary party, was not prepared to countenance his friend's downfall. The special advisers appointed by Clegg, and his chosen ministers, urged him to carry on. Weary and depressed, their leader decided to retire for a few hours to try to get some sleep.

Party president Tim Farron was consulted about what should happen. He in turn consulted his own campaign team, which he had set up in anticipation of the next leadership contest. Many of them were extremely hostile to Clegg, and they very much favoured an immediate leadership election. They had campaigned for Tim to be president and were campaigning for him to be leader; they expected that they would be suitably rewarded if he was successful. Entering coalition had given the Lib Dem leader powers of patronage that his predecessors had never enjoyed. These included appointing ministers, special advisers and many more peers than previously. Farron, however, counselled his team that 'now might not be the time'. He confided in them that Vince Cable would be the most likely winner of a leadership election and that, even if Farron was successful, it would be a very bad time for him to take over the leadership, 'just before impending disaster in the general election'. Most of the team, however, thought that getting Clegg out might be the first step towards averting just that disaster.

Party grandee and SDP founder Shirley Williams had earlier in the day been invited into 70 Whitehall Place to share her thoughts, and above all to try to secure her loyalty, given the great respect – almost veneration – which party members, and much of the wider public, held for her. She had told Clegg that she would, of course, give him her support if he carried on but that he must exercise his own judgement.

In scenes reminiscent of John Major's dental surgery during Mrs Thatcher's downfall, Vince Cable was conveniently away in China leading a trade mission as Secretary of State for Business. The party's first leader, Paddy Ashdown, who saw Clegg as his protégé, offered his full support. Clegg had, somewhat reluctantly, already appointed Ashdown to chair the forthcoming general election campaign after being forced to admit that he was losing the confidence of the party.

It was a bloody day, but there was a determination to avoid the debacle that had preceded Kennedy's resignation. Clegg's advisers were speaking in diplomatic terms to the key players in the party. Ministers, of course, were reminded to whom they owed their position. The group of MPs first elected in 2010 felt a greater sense of loyalty to Clegg because they had experienced the bounce in support for the Lib Dems after the first leaders' debate, and they had won their seats with Clegg as leader. Some of the more experienced backbenchers were more doubtful that Clegg should carry on, but they also believed that major donors were being directed to write large cheques to support the campaigns of those seen as Clegg loyalists, and feared that campaign funds for their own constituencies could be withheld if they were seen to be disloyal. The most 'difficult' MPs were the group led by John Pugh. They had opposed Clegg vigorously over tuition fees, support for the Health and

Social Care Act and measures like the 'bedroom tax'. But they mostly agreed that their concerns were best left out of the media. Clegg's inner circle prepared for a social media campaign which would use the #NickMustStay hashtag in case the anticipated #CleggMustGo movement gained traction.

In spite of efforts by those closest to him, the campaign to save Clegg was to collapse within hours – and people are still unsure whether this was due to cock-up or conspiracy. The immediate commentary on the Euro election results had paid less attention to the Lib Dems than the party had feared, as no one had expected them to do particularly well; but the result was worse than anticipated, and their failure to clear even such a low bar encouraged the media to focus on Clegg's broader coalition strategy.

Attention was ignited in particular by an interview with Shirley Williams on Radio 4's *World at One* that Monday. She was asked whether UKIP was now emulating the success of the SDP in the early 1980s. This led to a powerful denunciation of populist principles 'making propaganda against alleged foreign enemies who in reality are the friends that we need in an uncertain world'. But her response to the question that followed – 'But your leader, Nick Clegg, hasn't done very well at all, has he? Will he resign?' – 'Well, he wants to,' was an honest but fateful answer. 'Whether he does or not is a matter for him, but the country needs the Liberal Democrats. It needs to learn to value our membership of the EU and to counter the anti-democratic voices that seek to divide us.'

The cat was out of the bag. A skilful campaign to downplay any prospect of Clegg resigning was holed below the waterline as social media commentators now took to using the hashtags #IAgreeWithNick and #NickShouldResign. Text messages to all parliamentarians asked that no comment be made about the Williams interview. But the mainstream broadcast media led their bulletins with the news that Clegg wanted to go. Whether Williams's interview was simply 'Shirley being Shirley', an example of her saying honestly what she knew but may not have intended to say, or a more calculated move from someone who had previously shown a degree of ruthlessness was not clear. She had, for example, supported David Owen as the first leader of the SDP rather than Roy Jenkins but later opposed Owen over his 'continuing SDP'. Williams was seen by the public as the Liberal Democrat with the greatest level of integrity, and when she said that Clegg himself wanted to go, people believed her.

As a relatively new MP, in 2006 Clegg had witnessed the defenestration of Charles Kennedy. Despite being counselled to the contrary, he feared that he would be in deep trouble if he now denied that he had told Williams that he wanted to resign. 'I only wanted to think about it' would have been a poor defence. 'Being open to persuasion to stay' was not going to work well either. His dream of the Lib Dems being in coalition for twenty years had become a personal nightmare as he looked at the European election results. He had played his strongest card – his personal commitment to the EU – but the party was now back to its position twenty-five years previously, when Ashdown had admitted to doubts as to its viability as a going concern. Fighting a general election as leader when everyone believed that he had done so badly that he had wanted to quit was not an attractive option for him, his family or his future career.

At 5.55 p.m. that Monday, a text message to his MPs and leading party figures saying that he would make a statement about his future at 6 p.m. was obvious in its purpose. The BBC's *Six O'Clock News* led with Laura Kuenssberg's interview with Clegg breaking the story that he was resigning. He told her that 'the future of Liberal values, and the country's position in Europe, is too important for me to provide any barrier to protecting the country from the autocratic, mean-minded and intolerant forces that now threaten it'. He was calm and dignified but evidently exhausted by the struggle and shocked by the scale of the electoral failure.

His interview was pooled to the rest of the broadcast media and tributes and profiles were prominent that night and in the next day's papers. He won praise for having spared his party potential acrimony and providing it with some (limited) hope for a fresh start. Generous tributes were led by David Cameron: 'Nick Clegg did a great deal to save the country from bankruptcy in 2010, and his role was crucial in providing economic stability to enable recovery.' Lib Dem president Tim Farron said, 'Nick tried to champion Liberal values over Europe and immigration and deserves respect and gratitude,' but he would not confirm whether he would be a candidate for the leadership. Vince Cable issued a statement from China wishing 'Nick, Miriam and their family all the very best for the future' and saying that 'the party must now move forward together to offer the country a greater and more shared prosperity in future, and one which respects the environment more seriously'.

A parliamentary party meeting the following day featured only tributes to Clegg, who chose not to attend. Lib Dem MPs were briefed that Clegg would remain in place until a new leader had been elected, providing that this was done before the summer recess. Danny Alexander, Tim Farron and Jo Swinson all spoke in warm terms about Clegg, with some of their colleagues suggesting that they may have been making their first pitches for the vacancy. Others spoke about the immediate need to reappraise the way in which the coalition was being handled, with Andrew George (MP for St Ives) and Adrian Sanders (Torbay) saying that the party should consider ending it. Few present, however, wanted an early general election if the break-up of the coalition triggered a way round the Fixed-Term Parliaments Act.

Two days after Clegg's statement, an emergency meeting of the party's Federal Executive, chaired by Farron, approved a timetable for a new leader to be in place by August. Any candidate needed the support of six MPs (potentially including themselves) to secure nomination. It was suggested that Tim might struggle to reach the six nominations; in any case, he told his supporters that he was not keen to stand until after the general election. Alexander had hoped to succeed Clegg, but he knew that many of his fellow MPs firmly opposed him, and it was hardly possible now for Clegg to support him publicly. There was a strong feeling that at least one woman should fight the election, but none of the party's seven female MPs felt it necessary to stand.

By the Thursday of that week, it was clear that Cable would be the only candidate, even though nominations did not close for another two weeks. There was a short transition period, during which Clegg met Cable privately to ask that a number of his key advisers be retained and that Danny Alexander be looked after. Cable agreed to ask Jonny Oates to remain as chief of staff and asked for Clegg's help to ensure this.

Vince Cable officially became leader of the Liberal Democrats, and consequently Deputy Prime Minister, on 15 July 2014. He was conscious of the fact that he had just ten months to try to improve the party's position before the general election scheduled for May 2015.

In spite of Clegg's endeavours, Alexander knew that he would not continue as Chief Secretary to the Treasury and resigned from the Cabinet. While also not popular with some of the party, David Laws was restored to the position of Chief Secretary, from which he'd had to resign shortly after the formation of the coalition. Cable explained that Laws had served a period outside government and the Cabinet and that his skills were needed in what were likely to be difficult spending decisions before the general election. Laws also enjoyed great respect from Cameron and Osborne. The 'Quad' – previously Clegg, Alexander, Osborne and Cameron – which took many of the key coalition decisions was to be no more. The Coalition Committee, established in 2010 but which had almost never met, would now be convened regularly in the Quad's place.

Cable decided to remain as Secretary of State for Business, Innovation and Skills as well as becoming Deputy Prime Minister. Clegg's departure from government therefore left one vacant position in the Cabinet for a Lib Dem, according to the protocol agreed in 2010. Cable wanted to make a bold move and was determined that it would be filled by a woman. He considered appointing Lynne Featherstone, who was then a minister at the Department for International Development, but he decided to be even bolder and make Shirley Williams the first ever female Lib Dem Cabinet minister, with a key role in the Cabinet Office. It was a remarkable return for Williams, thirty-five years after she had been a member of Jim Callaghan's Labour Cabinet as Secretary of State for Education. She had lost her seat as a Labour MP in 1979, the same year Cable had tried unsuccessfully to become the Labour candidate for

Hampstead. They had gone a long way together in Labour, the SDP and the Liberal Democrats.

The move delighted most of the broadcast media, which realised that Williams was there to talk to them – though the *Daily Mail* and *The Sun* focused on her role in closing grammar schools during the 1970s. Cable told his parliamentary colleagues that a problem with the coalition so far had been that when Danny, or most other ministers apart from himself, gave interviews, 'Nobody knew if it was a Conservative or a Lib Dem speaking – but they will all know that Shirley is "one of us".'

The parliamentary party also agreed to elect joint deputy leaders (one male, one female), with Ed Davey, who continued as Secretary of State for Energy and Climate Change, and Jenny Willott, MP for Cardiff Central, being chosen. With David Laws returning as Chief Secretary, Nick Harvey, the MP for North Devon, was brought back into the government, having left two years before, as Minister of State for Schools and also with a strategic role in the Cabinet Office. It was seen as a minimalist reshuffle.

Cable had been a Cabinet minister for four years, and many people blamed him for letting the spending cuts his department had had to make fall almost entirely on higher education, including forcing the tuition fees reversal. He could not avoid the opprobrium that had previously been heaped on Clegg over this issue. But Cable tried to shift some of the blame for what Labour called 'austerity' onto the Conservatives for going too far in making Budget cuts once the economy had stabilised after 2010 and was then in need of a stimulus. He claimed to have been bounced into supporting them, revealing that neither he nor Chris Huhne had been in favour of what he called 'George Osborne's deflationary Budgets'. This supposedly private briefing of course became public – as he intended – and it sparked the first major public row between Cameron and Cable.

Cable sought to be different to his predecessor at every opportunity, while Labour claimed that he was 'much the same as Clegg'. The new leader was forced to admit how difficult it was to change much that the Conservatives wanted to do. But compared to Clegg, he saw little problem in blaming the Conservative '80 per cent of the coalition' for measures like the bedroom tax; he declared that the Lib Dems would seek in future to give more support to people finding that alternative accommodation with fewer bedrooms was not available.

Williams went further. Much as she liked Clegg, she said, 'Nick should never have allowed Andrew Lansley's supposed health reforms to see the light of day.' Speaking on her first BBC *Question Time* as a Lib Dem Cabinet minister, she argued that the House of Lords had played a crucial role in blocking the most potentially damaging aspects of the Health and Social Care Act and that Labour in government had failed to provide safeguards to make sure private-sector involvement was based on public interest. She admitted that she had nearly left the Lib Dems and gone to the cross benches over the issue but had in the end helped Clegg to stave off a major internal revolt over the health reforms at Lib Dem conference. The admissions were not universally welcomed by those who had worked on the Bill in Parliament.

Changes in personnel followed the change in leadership and were crucial to a new approach to policy and presentation as the general election approached. Polly Mackenzie had been the closest adviser to Clegg since his time as the Lib Dem Home Affairs spokesperson. She was highly intelligent, sometimes referred to as 'the brains behind Nick Clegg', and a valuable player in the Downing Street Policy Unit. But she was also blamed by some for Clegg's rapid agreement to the Lansley health reforms. She anticipated that Cable would want his own person in such a crucial role and resigned to write a book about the first four years of the coalition.

There was no shortage of people putting themselves forward for a position in Downing Street. Cable wondered if he really needed someone there at all, as opposed to trying to run a more independent DPM's operation outside it. But he was persuaded that he must have someone on the inside. He needed a person with all-round knowledge of Lib Dem Party policy and who would help to prepare a manifesto for the 2015 election as much as to fight a daily battle with Cameron's special advisers. Eventually, he settled on Duncan Brack, who had been the

Lib Dems' first director of policy and, more recently, a special adviser to Chris Huhne. Brack would bring into government more challenging green ideas than the Conservatives would accept, but this would be part of the positioning that Cable wanted as he aimed for much greater public differentiation from the Conservatives in future.

Ashdown told Cable he would stand down as chair of the Lib Dem general election campaign, but he agreed not to announce this immediately. Cable and others eventually persuaded him that continuing his role would be vital in saving the party he had helped to build. He was needed to act as a principal spokesperson for the campaign, and he received assurances that he would be given much greater freedom to criticise the Conservatives and fight an 'insurgent campaign' of the kind Clegg had not really been comfortable with. Ashdown and Cable were never close, but almost everyone recognised that only Paddy could heal some of the wounds within the party that had opened up with Clegg's resignation. The former leader did not like his protégé's demise but privately recognised that the party needed big hitters who were clearly identifiable as Lib Dems and significantly less likely to be seen as natural allies of the Conservatives than Clegg had often appeared.

Cable asked Charles Kennedy to chair the general election campaign in Scotland. Everyone knew that the task was not concerned with administrative detail but about making a distinctive impact in the Scottish media. There was no expectation of much organised activity from Kennedy, but Cable wanted to assemble a team for media comment that would be better known to the public than most of the ministers he had inherited. Most of Clegg's appointees had come from the newer intake of MPs, and the more recognisable old guard, including David Steel, Shirley Williams and Menzies Campbell, had not entered his reckoning for ministerial positions.

A consequence of Clegg's ministerial choices had been that most people could generally not identify Lib Dem ministers as Lib Dems. When interviewed, the ministers invariably found it difficult to criticise their coalition partners or to articulate what the Lib Dems wanted to do differently. Cable attempted to address this problem without changing many ministers by making some of the old guard more prominent in the media. He also set out personally to demonstrate more independence from Cameron than Clegg had appeared to show. A first step was for the new Deputy Prime Minister to sit with his Lib Dem colleagues on their front bench in the Commons, rather than next to Cameron and other Conservative Cabinet ministers. Cable would then move to the despatch box when taking questions or making statements.

Cable provoked a row with Cameron by claiming on his first campaign visit to Scotland later that year that the Conservative Prime Minister was 'attempting to renege on promises of further devolution made during the Scottish independence referendum'. His intervention provoked some opposition within the Scottish Liberal Democrats, as Cable also offered to work with the SNP in the House of Commons to guarantee that greater devolution was delivered. But Cable shrugged it off. He thought most of his colleagues would be relieved at the clear change in electoral strategy from that of his predecessor. The Euro elections had shown that the mantra produced by Clegg's strategy adviser, Ryan Coetzee – 'stronger economy, fairer society' – was not helping the party however often it was repeated. Almost all the Lib Dem MPs agreed that Coetzee had to go, and he duly departed to allow for a new approach to strategy, positioning and messaging.

The Liberal Democrat conference in Glasgow in October 2014 – delayed from its normal timing to fall after the Scottish referendum – was to be the last autumn conference before the general election. It was upbeat, with a new leader in place and in the immediate aftermath of the 'No' victory in the independence referendum. Charles Kennedy made his best speech since standing down as leader in 2006.

Cable wanted more changes behind the scenes. Too much had gone wrong in the party in recent years, and so the chief executive, Lord Rennard, was ousted. With an election approaching, an interim appointment had to be made. A successful businessman and party donor, Peter Dunphy, who chaired the party's Finance and Administration Committee, was asked to take on the role until the election.

The party received only a modest boost in the polls as a result of Cable replacing Clegg. But morale rose within the Lib Dems as awareness spread that the party would campaign clearly against the Conservatives, as well as against Labour. The Conservative papers had been hostile to the coalition since its formation, but now they took up the Conservative Party's briefing against the 'maverick Cable'. When asked about this in interviews, Cable simply explained that he had no problem with the Conservatives saying that they were different to him. He argued that coalitions had proved stable and successful in countries like Germany and the Netherlands, even though there were public rows each week about differences in policy. He said that he liked the continental model in which parties worked together in the national interest but people could still see the differences between them.

Some of Cable's early interviews had included a question about the future role of Lord Rennard. Cable observed that since a second investigation into sexual harassment allegations made the previous year was still under way, it would be inappropriate for him to comment before it was over. When it concluded, in August, that there was no basis for any form of action to be considered by the party, he said that the result must be respected. He did not, however, propose to offer him any formal role and nor, he understood, was Chris Rennard seeking one. He would, however, listen to his advice and welcome his help.

Rennard remained behind the scenes. He worked closely with a number of constituency campaigns where MPs wanted his involvement, including the leader's own constituency of Twickenham. In coalition, the Lib Dems had abandoned much of the approach to constituency campaigning that had been developed when Rennard was the party's director of campaigns and elections and had orchestrated the Lib Dem advances. An upside of coalition, however, had been more successful fundraising; some of these resources were switched to reprising the successful campaign techniques from before 2010.

Cable was horrified to learn that Clegg had proposed offering a referendum on the UK's membership of the EU in a future coalition in order to secure agreement that the Lib Dems would head a major department, such as health. Several of the leading Lib Dem peers – whom Cable was close to in a way that Clegg had never been – told him there would be resignations from their group if such a referendum was ever conceded.

In early meetings, the new leader and his team agreed to make even greater efforts to focus the future election messaging on differentiation from the other parties. Some work had already been under way on 'three things we want; three things we would stop the Conservatives doing; three things we would stop Labour doing; and one thing we would stop the SNP doing'. But Cable didn't like this shopping-list approach, feeling that it was unambitious. He said it was too like Charles Kennedy's 'ten things we propose' from the 2005 campaign – though it was pointed out to him by the group of Lib Dem peers he was using as private advisers that this had been the party's most successful campaign to date, had tested well then and should be tested again now. Market research overseen by the long-standing Lib Dem and professional market researcher Julian Ingram, who had undertaken a similar role in previous elections, showed, however, that it was too complicated.

Further research suggested instead that the party could be distinctive in 2015 by focusing its messaging framework on three principal points: first, investing in education and training to boost the economy; second, funding social care and mental health support; and third, tackling climate change. The attack messages would be simplified; they would hammer home the fact that Lib Dems wanted to stop Labour 'wrecking the economy' and the Conservatives 'making us a more unfair and less caring society'. The research suggested that the attacks earlier planned on the Conservatives had not rung true when Clegg was in place, given his close relationship with Cameron. Attacking the Conservatives with more conviction came more naturally to Cable than it had done to his predecessor.

Cable agreed to accept the election messaging, providing all the policy details would be intellectually coherent and properly costed. He had to be talked out of returning to his idea of a mansion tax (a new property tax on high-value houses) in favour of equalising the tax concession for pension contributions, currently provided at different levels for higher-rate and basic-rate taxpayers. This, it was said, would get the pension companies screaming, but the measure would raise money while avoiding the risk of reducing consumer spending when the economy was still in a fragile condition. The revenue raised would be hypothecated to funding social care, seen as an essential precondition to protect the NHS and to look after the neediest elderly people, as well as those who cared for them.

Cable's work rate was very high in the run-up to the election and during the campaign itself. He criss-crossed the country in the early months of 2015, at the same time as attending to government business and looking after his Twickenham constituency. He passed every test about whether he had the energy to lead for some years yet, and he attracted large crowds who wanted to hear him speak. Many of his appearances were made jointly with Shirley Williams or, in Scotland, with Charles Kennedy or Menzies Campbell.

As Lib Dem leader, he took part in two of the four televised leaders' debates. He performed well, though he was ambushed by the Conservatives in the first debate over a claim that he had entered coalition wanting every civil servant earning over £100,000 to have to reapply for their jobs. Some commentators were critical of this, suggesting he was 'not really fit for government', but it did him no harm in the polls. Lib Dem support rose from around 11 per cent at the start of the campaign to 14 per cent by polling day.

The final result of the general election of 7 May 2015 was Conservatives 34 per cent; Labour 29 per cent; Lib Dems 14 per cent. This left the Conservatives with 305 seats; Labour with 250; and the Lib Dems with twenty-five (down by thirty-two from 2010). The SNP won fifty seats; the Greens one; and UKIP one (Nigel Farage). On the BBC's election night programme, psephologist John Curtice observed: 'If the Lib Dems had stayed on the 8 per cent of a year ago, their number of MPs would have been down to single figures, not twenty-five.' This claim was dismissed as 'ridiculous and hypothetical' by Paddy Ashdown, speaking on the same programme. The Lib Dems had survived – but only just.

A joint meeting of the Liberal Democrat parliamentary party and the Federal Executive held on the Saturday following the election was very hostile to the prospects of another coalition – but the final decision, according to legal advice that was published, would be for the MPs alone. Cable argued that the party had to be seen to be prepared to help govern and kept his lines of communication open.

David Cameron claimed a mandate to continue as Prime Minister, even without a guaranteed majority, and remained in 10 Downing Street. Cable asked him through private channels to pause any decision about coalition and reshuffle until after the weekend, while saying publicly that 'time was needed to consider the national interest' and that 'all parties needed to work together'. But the blunt message from Cameron, delivered outside Downing Street late on the Saturday afternoon, was that 'allowing Lib Dems back into government would require agreement to an EU referendum'. Cameron was, in fact, fighting a furious battle within his own party, and he considered this step essential to his own survival as Conservative leader. He argued that 'the great divide about our place in Europe must be ended in a way that a general election could not determine'.

Cameron's own preference now was to go it alone, without a coalition. His MPs had not enjoyed the experience, and he needed to appease his Brexiter opponents within his party. He knew he could promise to introduce a Bill to enable an EU referendum, but he expected he would eventually tell his party there was no majority for it. Indeed, the Bill was later defeated, as he had privately hoped, with the help of the fifty SNP MPs and the twenty-five Liberal Democrats. The huge split in his party was widening, but his powers of patronage kept him in control.

The Labour Party was as shattered by the election results as the Lib Dems. Everyone knew that the combined total of 275 'Lib–Lab' MPs was fifty-one seats short of a majority. The SNP offered a supply and confidence arrangement for a Lib–Lab government in exchange for another independence referendum, to be held within two years, but neither Labour nor the Lib Dems could accept this.

The change of Liberal Democrat leadership in 2014 had barely rescued the party; twenty-five Westminster seats was at the bottom of the range of expectations. But it had stopped the Conservatives from winning an overall majority in the 2015 election, and it had prevented a majority in the House of Commons for an EU referendum, something which any Conservative leader now had to promise or face deselection. The Lib Dems had been battered by their experience of handling coalition, but they also felt that they had learned their lessons. With twenty-five MPs, they might be able to use the balance of power to good effect in the next parliament.

The Fixed-Term Parliaments Act remained in place, though it was more open to challenge than when two parties with a majority between them wanted to keep it there. Cameron was to spend the next five years in Downing Street complaining that the Lab–Lib–SNP coalition was blocking him from being 'a really Conservative Prime Minister'. No such formal agreement was formed, but a coalition of opposition parties to work together to bring about proportional representation was suggested by Cable at the Liberal Democrat autumn conference in 2015.

It was a sign that he had not given up the fight. He was to stay as leader until 2018, when he fulfilled his promise to his wife, Rachel, that he would stand down.

~

This chapter was written by a group of Liberal Democrats who wish to remain anonymous but who had detailed knowledge of actual events in 2014 and 2015. Their conclusion is that the Brexit referendum of 2016 could have been avoided but for the Lib Dem failure in the 2015 general election, when the party won just eight seats. Twenty-five Lib Dem MPs would not have been considered a success, but it would have left the party much better placed to rebuild and to try to use the balance of power more successfully in the parliament that followed.

Chapter 14

What if John McDonnell had fought the Labour leadership election in 2015?

Francis Beckett

It seems ridiculous now, two years into his premiership, but on 1 June 2015 it looked as though John McDonnell would not even get on the ballot paper to become Labour leader.

When nominations were about to close, he was still one short of the thirty-five Labour MPs needed to stand. But with just one minute to go, the veteran Oxford East MP Andrew Smith walked into the committee room with a nomination paper, and wonder of wonders, it had McDonnell's name on it. The race was on.

Colleagues celebrated around him, but if you looked closely at McDonnell's face, you read no triumph there. Someone had to carry the flag for the left in this election – and come bottom of the poll as usual – but John McDonnell would have preferred it to be someone else this time. He was sixty-four, and a heart attack two years earlier had left him thinking seriously about retirement. But there were only two other MPs with the experience to be credible candidates. Diane Abbott had stood last time, and she was tired of being Labour's punchbag. Jeremy Corbyn would have done it if asked, but he seemed relieved when McDonnell put his head above the parapet first.

McDonnell comforted himself with the thought that there was not the slightest chance he would win. But as the campaign wore on, the dreadful realisation slowly dawned upon him that he might do just that. Labour supporters, it became clear, badly wanted a leader who looked as little like Tony Blair as possible. And there was a new voting system.

It gave every Labour Party member a vote – and it even gave a vote to Labour supporters who were not party members for a very moderate price. As McDonnell toured the country with the other candidates, it became clear that the Labour Party might well do the unthinkable.

John McDonnell was quiet and undramatic. He would never be a great orator. But he inspired affection and confidence. He was unaffected. He smiled a lot. He seemed to like people. The chippiness colleagues had noticed before his heart attack had been replaced by a benevolent air, and if this hid a real ruthlessness at least it hid it rather well. People who met him could not make out why the newspapers hated him so much. Yes, he had opposed Tony Blair, and the Iraq War, and Gordon Brown's Private Finance Initiative. He brandished socialist credentials and was an enthusiastic advocate for public ownership. But he had a ready smile and bucketloads of emotional intelligence. It was this that distinguished him from Jeremy Corbyn, his oldest friend in politics – some said his only friend in politics – who many people thought had the emotional intelligence of a lump of coal.

By the time he listened with amazement to the first adoring chorus of 'Oh, John McDonnell' as he entered a hall, it was starting to look like a one-horse race. And by 12 September, when the results were to be announced, everyone knew that the unthinkable had happened.

Labour's top brass was horrified. 'If only it had been Corbyn,' sighed one veteran of Tony Blair's government. 'We could have coped with Corbyn. But McDonnell's got a political brain; he's dangerous.'

It would be hard to imagine anything less dangerous-looking than the small, unfashionable figure wandering about the corridors of Westminster, with his thin, cracked voice, his self-deprecating jokes, his gentle, crooked smile and a kind word for friend and foe alike. But beneath the modesty and the gentle banter, unseen by the world, the iron had entered John McDonnell's soul.

A week later, he kept a long-standing engagement to address the Fire Brigades Union's annual conference in Brighton. McDonnell had been close to the FBU for years and was the chair of its parliamentary group, so they felt he was one of theirs. They were proud of his success and cheered him all the way to the platform. In his conversational way, he told them, 'I had a heart attack a few years ago.' He nodded in the direction of the FBU's general secretary, his old friend Matt Wrack, explaining that he had told Matt all about it. 'And I thought, OK, I'll retire quite soon. And then I'd sit at home watching the news on the telly and say, they should have taken my advice. And suddenly I've got the chance to do something about it, and I'm not letting that slip out of my hands.' A tax system that redistributed a greater proportion of the nation's wealth was top of his wish list.

Old friends were shocked to find that his new ruthlessness extended even to them. Jeremy Corbyn desperately wanted to be shadow Foreign Secretary and give a commitment to recognise Palestine as the first act of a new Labour government, but McDonnell explained that he feared his whole project would be hijacked by the Middle East, and Corbyn must have the Home Office brief instead.

Corbyn almost turned it down – he could not believe that his oldest friend in politics would deny him the thing he wanted most – but the smiling party leader left him in no doubt of the shocking truth: John would ditch him rather than let him have foreign affairs.

There was, however, a sense of relief when he appointed the able and experienced Mark Seddon as his strategy and communications chief. Son of an army officer, product of a private boarding school in Wiltshire, former communications adviser to the UN secretary general, clever, sophisticated, humorous and cosmopolitan: no more unlikely Bennite had been seen in politics since Tony Benn himself. Seddon, a left-winger who could talk happily with the *Daily Mail*'s political editor, made the right feel that McDonnell was serious about getting elected and reassured the left that he had not abandoned his principles.

There were fewer old Bennites in McDonnell's shadow Cabinet than most people had predicted. The new leader had smiled and wheedled and charmed, and people who had sworn never to serve under him meekly took middle-ranking positions. Just a few hardliners stayed aloof – nothing would get Chuka Umunna to take any of the posts he was offered. It was a difficult balancing act. McDonnell wanted to seem mainstream and unthreatening, but he also needed to hang on to the enthusiasm, the authentic feel, that his leadership had brought to Labour.

And in the first months of his leadership, it looked as though it was working. The enthusiasm among the young and the radical showed no sign of waning; Labour's membership was rocketing; and at the same time its leader was starting to look like a man the floating voter could just about imagine as Prime Minister. But the big test was fast approaching, and it was not at all certain that McDonnell's careful balancing act could survive it.

Conservative Prime Minister David Cameron had promised a referendum on whether to leave the European Union, and set the vote for 23 June 2016 – less than a year into McDonnell's leadership. In recent years, Labour had miraculously avoided the Euro wars that had nearly destroyed the Conservative Party. It had a settled policy of remaining in the EU, from which there were just a few dissenters. But the change of leadership had breathed new life into the moribund 'left Brexiters' – Lexiters for short – who looked back nostalgically to the 1975 referendum, when Tony Benn had stomped the country with his intoxicating vision of the socialist Britain he claimed could be created as long as the country was out of Europe. Under McDonnell, they wondered if the old message could be revived. He was, after all, an old Bennite.

Labour couldn't campaign for Leave – its policy forbade that – but surely, said Corbyn and his allies in the shadow Cabinet, the party didn't have to go all out for Remain. They could soft pedal on it. They could say, Europe is a non-issue, what people really want to talk about is jobs, and equality, and...

'No,' said the leader, firmly. 'You've got to deal with the issue in front of you.' And he quoted Harold Macmillan's famous line about what created the government's agenda: 'Events, dear boy, events.' The event was Brexit. That was what people were talking about. That was what Labour had to talk about. And it had to have a clear line.

Anyway, he said, what would happen to Labour's agenda outside the EU? 'We'd need a trade deal with the US so badly that we wouldn't be able to do anything that might offend American susceptibilities – which would include pretty well everything we'd want to do,' he told the shadow Cabinet. 'We've got to go out and campaign hard to remain.' He took on a punishing schedule of meetings where he argued passionately for the Remain case, and brushed aside with his shy, crooked smile the suggestion that he was contradicting what he had always stood for. Labour without a clear line on the big issue of the day would be swept aside, squeezed by both sides, he told them.

The other thing he knew he had to talk about was antisemitism. The left was used to racism being a problem of the right and was confused and resentful when it was suggested that the left itself might be racist. McDonnell knew a political cluster bomb when he saw one, and he made it clear early on that he understood how easily and imperceptibly criticism of Israel could morph into something that looked dreadfully like antisemitism.

He got a researcher to spend a week going through the cuttings for any hostages to fortune he might ever have given on this subject. This was a wise precaution. The *Daily Mail* had a researcher doing just that, in order to be able to raise a furore whenever it happened to be convenient. But the *Mail* was never able to 'reveal' that McDonnell had once tabled an early day motion in Parliament saying that Israel tried to suppress criticism 'with false accusations of antisemitism', for he had already revealed it himself.

At a long meeting with the Board of Deputies of British Jews – it was scheduled for just the morning but ran on all day – McDonnell exerted all the charm he could muster, exhibited contrition and humility, promised action on everything he was asked about, and solicited and won an invitation to visit Jerusalem's Hadassah Hospital, where Jews and Arabs were treated side by side.

Despite his efforts, the Brexit referendum went against him. The defeat was wafer thin – 50.5 per cent of the votes for Leave; 49.5 per cent for Remain. But in politics a defeat is a defeat. It doesn't much matter if it's by one vote or by millions.

Prime Minister David Cameron resigned and was replaced by Theresa May. After nine months in the job, May, buoyed by favourable opinion polls and believing that McDonnell could easily be painted as an extremist, asked Parliament to agree to a general election – a request that McDonnell could hardly turn down without looking as though he feared facing the electors. It was a piece of opportunism she was soon to regret. She ran a dreadful campaign while McDonnell ran a good one, and the healthy parliamentary majority bequeathed to her by David Cameron melted away under her horrified gaze. After the election, to stay in power at all, she had to do a grubby deal with the Democratic Unionist Party.

It was not a good background against which to try to negotiate a complicated treaty with the EU, but that was what she had to do. The parliamentary near-stalemate fuelled an immensely complicated and acrimonious debate about what leaving the EU actually meant – a subject, incredibly, to which neither the government nor the Leave campaign appeared to have given any thought at all before the referendum.

The government was in bad trouble. For Labour, this was an opportunity – so long as they knew what they wanted to do with it. Jeremy Corbyn once more argued that Brexit was a diversion, and Labour should be talking about it as little as possible. It was, however, also the hook upon which the Conservatives were impaled, and McDonnell thought that it was not in Labour's interests to help them off it by talking loudly of other things.

He steered the shadow Cabinet towards demanding a second referendum. There would be not two but three choices. You could vote for the best deal May could get; or you could vote for no deal; or you could vote to stay in the EU. McDonnell argued it in his best casual manner. If Britain were a company, he said, and the shareholders told the board to negotiate something, they would expect the board to report back for endorsement of what they had negotiated, not just impose it without consultation. The matter-of-fact nature of his argument disarmed his critics on the left; the capitalist flavour of the analogy pleasantly surprised the right.

For Corbyn, this was a betrayal. But there was worse to come. McDonnell further infuriated him by agreeing to ensure that his party adopted the International Holocaust Remembrance Alliance's definition of antisemitism. Sections of that definition seemed to limit what one could say about Israel. It led to Corbyn's resignation, and the breach of a forty-year friendship which has never healed. Even today, when Corbyn and McDonnell meet in the corridors of Westminster, they look the other way and pass by without speaking.

The *Guardian* columnist Seumas Milne revealed the rift in the shadow Cabinet in his newspaper, and insiders assumed that he did so with Corbyn's help and approval. Shadow Cabinet dissenters like Corbyn, wrote Milne, thought their leader was betraying his principles by caving in to 'a barrage of big-business-led scaremongering about the economic consequences of leaving the EU'. The leaders of the EU were the principal obstacles on the road to socialism, he wrote: 'They have given austerity and a shop-worn neoliberal economic model the force of treaty in the interests of Europe's banks and corporations.' And 'McDonnell's shameful capitulation to the Israel lobby' had come about because 'the left stands accused of antisemitism because of its opposition to Israel's military occupation and continuing dispossession of the Palestinians'.

McDonnell agreed to speak at the million-strong demonstration in London calling for a referendum on the deal Mrs May was negotiating. On his way to the platform, he ran into Milne, there to research a comment piece for *The Guardian*, who berated McDonnell for selling out to the middle class by speaking there. 'These aren't our people,' Milne told him. 'Look at them. They're not working-class; they're all middle-class. You can see them at north London dinner parties, can't you?' (Milne and Corbyn had a recently acquired but frequently articulated contempt for north London dinner parties.) 'Where did you have dinner last night, Seumas?' asked McDonnell. How McDonnell knew about the vegetarian gathering in Corbyn's Islington home, Milne never found out.

The last few weeks of May's premiership were dreadful. Political life, for government and opposition alike, was an unending stream of long, tortuous, acrimonious meetings in Brussels, in Downing Street, in the House of Commons, over increasingly arcane details of the Withdrawal Agreement. May failed to get a deal she could sell to the

House of Commons. Either it was too close to the EU for the Tory right, or it was too distant for all the other parties, and her slim majority meant she had to have one side or the other on board. She was turned out of 10 Downing Street by the Tory top brass, and the Conservative Party turned to the louche, shifty Old Etonian Boris Johnson to lead them. Johnson took one look at the opinion polls and started to try to tempt Labour into a general election.

But McDonnell could read polls too, and he was determined to have a referendum before an election. The only way to achieve that was to find the votes in Parliament to turn Johnson out; to put in a caretaker government whose limited task would be to organise a referendum on the deal May had negotiated; and then to call a general election.

If the Liberal Democrats, the Scottish Nationalists and the one Green MP all backed a motion of no confidence, and if he could keep the vast majority of Labour MPs on side, McDonnell was a very few votes short of throwing out the government – and he could get those from among the Remainers on the Conservative side.

The wily and massively experienced Chief Whip Nick Brown worked hard to get McDonnell his majority. At the last moment, a wobble from the inexperienced and excitable Liberal Democrat leader, Jo Swinson, almost derailed everything: she wanted to abandon a second referendum in favour of a general election, which, she seemed to think, could some-how be turned into a referendum on Brexit. Some frantic lobbying by her more experienced colleagues sorted that out.

But who was to lead the caretaker government? It should be the Leader of the Opposition, but some of the Conservatives whose support they needed were fearful of agreeing to serve under Prime Minister McDonnell. McDonnell immediately agreed that one of them could lead the govern-ment. On that understanding, the government was defeated by just one vote, and veteran Conservative MP Kenneth Clarke took the job he had sought ever since the days of Margaret Thatcher. He was, of course, expelled from the Conservative Party, and he led a Cabinet consisting mostly of Labour figures, but he didn't seem to mind. McDonnell was his Chancellor of the Exchequer, and the Cabinet set to work to organise the referendum.

McDonnell announced that he was following the example of Harold Wilson in 1976, to avoid splitting the party. Every Labour MP, including government ministers, was free to campaign and vote for any of the three options in the referendum. Second preferences counted, and if there was not a 50 per cent majority for any of the three alternatives, the option with the least votes would be eliminated and its second preferences redistributed between the other two.

Polls suggested the Remainers were going to win the referendum handsomely, and at the end of February 2020, they did just that. When the least popular choice – leaving under Mrs May's deal – was eliminated, there was a margin of 54 per cent to 46 per cent to Remain. Brexit was dead, and it was time to go to the country as promised.

But then the plan came unstuck.

A mystery virus, starting, it was believed, in the Chinese city of Wuhan, swept with frightening speed all through Asia and was making landfall in Europe. All the best scientific advice the government was getting indicated the need for an immediate lockdown.

The virus was passed on when people breathed near each other. So, the government needed to interfere in the lives of its citizens in ways that had never been seen before – preventing them from gathering in groups; keeping them, as far as possible, in their homes; making travel illegal; closing borders. It would not wait, the scientists told Clarke and McDonnell. They had to pull the shutters down now.

So they did; they acted fast and ruthlessly.

There were many who claimed this was an infringement too far. The Leader of the Opposition was one of them; Boris Johnson went about ostentatiously glad-handing folk, boasting of shaking their hands and presenting himself as the man who would restore liberty in these islands and get rid of 'socialist tyranny'. It was a powerful pitch with a general election due to be called any day – for the caretaker government had done its task, and it was now expected to fulfil its pledge to go to the country.

But the scientists looked at the logistics of a general election and told Prime Minister Clarke it was out of the question. Politicians knocking on doors for a month, meetings all over the country, millions of people pouring into polling stations – it was the superspreader of all super-spreaders, and it would make Britain the Covid capital of the world. Unless and until it could be done remotely – and there had been no preparation for that – the election had to be postponed.

So, the government was marooned in office. Desperate to go to the country, it looked as though it would have to stay put for months. The Prime Minister was coming up to his eightieth birthday, but, full of energy and enthusiasm, he made it clear that he was up for the task of leading the country through a national emergency.

This was McDonnell's moment. Always a believer in economic plan-ning, he was in his element. Having persuaded Clarke to go into a hard and early lockdown, he announced a huge package of measures to save businesses, to pay the wages of those whose jobs collapsed under them, to save threatened theatres, museums, art galleries. Resisting furious demands from the Conservatives to contract out the test-and-trace scheme to private companies, he gave the task to local councils.

It looked a lot like socialism, as the opposition benches never stopped saying. But when defended by an old Tory like Clarke, it did not seem so bad, and the criticisms fell flat.

Then the virus got Clarke. At his age, that was serious. It was touch-and-go for a while. He pulled through, but he was exhausted, and the after-effects of the illness were going to take months to clear. His doctor advised rest.

It was a national emergency, and after some hectic late-night tele-phone calls, all the parties in the caretaker coalition eventually agreed to serve under Prime Minister McDonnell. There was just no viable alternative. And he seemed such a nice, humble sort of chap.

The new Prime Minister was able immediately to announce measures that would have caused a revolution just a few weeks earlier. He nation-alised internet service providers and supplied free internet to every household in the land at public expense. He made travel on public trans-port illegal without special permission and commandeered the railways for moving essential supplies and personnel – food, medicines, doctors

– around the country as needed. Then he listened sympathetically to the cries of anguish from railway companies and agreed to bail them out – and to take the railways back into public ownership, so private owners would not have to bear the hideous costs of keeping virtually unused railways operating.

Just as a few months earlier McDonnell had taken inspiration from an earlier Labour Prime Minister, Harold Wilson, so now he went even further back and took his inspiration from Clement Attlee. He recalled that, in 1943, the government had announced its support for the Beveridge Report, for looking after its citizens 'from the cradle to the grave' and that the Attlee government had then proceeded to nationalise the railways, arguing that, in a national emergency, it would need to transport necessary items about the country and would not have time to negotiate terms with the boards of private companies. A huge hike in corporation tax and a clampdown on tax havens was to help pay for all this.

There was outrage, of course. The *Daily Mail*, the *Daily Express* and Boris Johnson invoked Stalin and Kim Jong-un, talked of tyranny and gulags and implied that the next step was to transport everyone's children to Siberia. But it was all done so fast, and with the Prime Minister's kindly and understated smile for everyone, that the warnings sounded simply hysterical.

'It's the spirit of the Blitz,' McDonnell told the nation. And it was, in more ways than one. For the Prime Minister was taking his courage and inspiration from what had been done during the Second World War. By 1941, measures that would have been denounced as socialist dictatorship before the war had become normal and acceptable. In a national emergency, as Churchill's wartime government had discovered, you cannot rely on the market; the government has to have its hands directly on the levers of the economy. So it was to be eighty years later, in 2021.

The UK's death rate, though high, was lower than in many other EU countries, and McDonnell ploughed what seemed like unimaginable sums of money into one of his old enemies, the pharmaceutical industry, to help it develop a vaccine.

2020 was a dreadful year for everyone, but by December there was a general view that if you had to have someone running things in dismal times, it might as well be John McDonnell, with his croaking voice, his lopsided smile and his air of understated competence.

Some time in 2021 or 2022, it will become safe to hold a general election, and it looks as though McDonnell will be installed for a full five-year term. The way the polls look right now, the Conservatives may be the biggest single party, but if the coalition of Labour, Liberals, Scot Nats, Tory Remainers and Greens can hold together, they will have a comfortable working majority. At the end of those five years, Britain will look very different.

Chapter 15

What if Britain had voted Remain in 2016?

Nathan Morley

Result

The clock struck ten. The polling station doors slammed shut. It had been an historic day as voters across the United Kingdom decided their destiny in an in–out referendum on the country's membership of the European Union.

It had been a brutal campaign: a Tory psychodrama, gloves off, knives out. Meanwhile, for Labour, their leader Jeremy Corbyn's tepid support for a Remain vote had left many in the party angry. Getting Labour voters in the cities to turn out in large numbers was hugely important for the Remain campaign.

Politicos up and down the land gathered around their television screens. The sense was of a Remain victory, albeit narrow. But Leave supporters thought they had caused an upset – or an earthquake, more likely.

At the Leave.EU rally, Nigel Farage claimed that it would be 'unfinished business' in the event of a narrow 52–48 vote to stay in the EU. You could just imagine the sighs at No. 10 – the issue was not going to go away. Even with a victory, the result might not be the decisive outcome they wanted to be able to put the issue to bed. The UKIP leader's campaign had been divisive, but it had appeared to galvanise many people who typically did not vote. So, the question remained: in what numbers had these people turned out to the polling stations?

The first results came in from the north-east, and predictably

Sunderland plumped for Leave. As the night progressed, it looked tight. The vote for Remain in Newcastle was a little uncomfortable; not quite the margin anticipated by Remain sources.

In Downing Street, the Prime Minister gathered with the Chancellor and his closest confidants. Whichever way the result went, how could their party recover? The Conservative Party had been ripped to shreds, with Leave-supporting ministers trashing their own government's immigration record and Remain-supporting ministers' economic bombshell warnings being attacked as 'Project Fear'. As the results gradually suggested that Remain had won, David Cameron pondered how he would respond to the result and the prospects for a 'unity reshuffle'.

Eventually, with all the counting concluded, the country opted for Remain, with 51.89 per cent against 48.11 per cent for Leave. A narrow result, but a decisive one.

Reaction

At 8 a.m. on Friday 24 June 2016, the Prime Minister addressed the nation. 'Going forward, our relationship with the European Union will never be the same. Leave voters, we hear you. We understand your frustrations. Your voice will be heard.' Strong words.

In adopting this tone, Cameron acknowledged the slimness of the result and wanted it to convey a message to other European countries: 'Let this be a warning to the institutions of the EU: this cannot be the end of reform. I know that this result was much closer than many anticipated at the beginning of the renegotiation process.' There was, of course, the need to bring the country and the government – and the party – back together. 'There has been a rigorous debate across the party. But now we must come back, back together, to govern for' – uttering the words from his victory speech at his general election count the previous year – 'One Nation, One United Kingdom.'

Quite. England had voted Leave by a whisker; Scotland strongly for Remain. Deeper regional divides had emerged: cities had delivered large votes for the status quo, but towns and villages had largely opted to rip up Britain's EU membership.

Cameron's response was certainly not a celebratory speech. He seemed to adopt the right approach. The question now was how his Brexiter colleagues in Parliament, on his own benches, would respond. Privately, of course, the PM was massively relieved. It is believed that he had planned to resign in the event of a vote to Leave; his credibility would have been shot. Instead, although far from partying at the victory, he was able to rejoice at his third national referendum victory, following those on the alternative vote and Scottish independence.

The reaction from the official Vote Leave campaign was largely conciliatory. Michael Gove, Boris Johnson and Labour MP Gisela Stuart conducted a short press conference, with the Tory duo putting particular – though brief – emphasis on the need to help bring the party back together.

But a small margin of defeat was not going to deter those for whom leaving the EU had been a lifetime's work; Leave.EU spearhead Nigel Farage called on David Cameron and George Osborne to resign. Elsewhere, there were rumours of Tory Eurosceptics whispering, 'This isn't over.' Conservative backbenchers from the influential European Research Group were considering their reaction; they remained furious at the way in which they had seen their leader use government machinery to convince the country, but what exactly could they do? Obviously, calling for a rerun of the vote would alarm the majority of the apolitical public, who had endured a hugely contentious campaign. While departure from the European Union remained the long-term goal, however, more immediately they could perhaps force a change in the leadership of their party.

Labour, meanwhile, had just about delivered the votes for Remain. Jeremy Corbyn remained in place, despite his backbenchers' unhappiness at his role in the campaign; a Leave vote was likely to have led to moves on his position. Now, sadly for the vast majority of the parliamentary party, they would need to wait for Corbyn to fail at the ballot box. Corbyn's allies assured the media that he had more campaigning energy in him; it was just that the Remain cause wasn't close to his heart. As Conservatives railed against Cameron, it was now Corbyn who found himself in a firmer leadership position, despite polls showing his huge unpopularity with the country.

Reshuffle

Predictably, the weekend's papers were awash with rumours of what would come next. Members of the ERG were briefing that they wanted Cameron to name a date when he'd stand down, echoing the way in which Tony Blair had found himself out of office in 2007, following his 2005 election victory. Iain Duncan Smith, having resigned from his Cabinet role just a few months before the referendum, wrote a seething piece in the *Sunday Telegraph*. Building on his resignation, in which he had referred to the now infamous 'we're all in this together' phrase to criticise the government, the former Tory leader now called the government's actions a 'disservice to democracy'. Eurosceptic ministers, sympathetic to the pleas of the ERG but bound by collective government responsibility, were not able to attach their name to such a call, but clearly they were encouraging their colleagues.

Other reports focused on how the PM would reshuffle his Cabinet team, and particularly on who might or might not be punished for their role in the referendum campaign. Sacking prominent Vote Leave advocates would risk creating Brexiter martyrs, who would use a backbench platform to do more damage. But would Leave supporters dare to turn down a promotion?

Putting aside Gove and Johnson, it was Penny Mordaunt's remarks that had been considered the most egregious by the Remain team in Downing Street. No. 10 considered that she had lied when she had claimed during the campaign that the UK would not be able to veto Turkey's accession to the European Union. Her statement that 'we're not going to be able to have a say' had kept the story in the headlines. She was followed closely by Priti Patel, who had written in the *Daily Telegraph* that she felt her party was unable to 'honour our own promises' in bringing net immigration down to the tens of thousands.

But despite all these words and barrages of headlines from his own ministers, Cameron didn't bite back as much as he could have done. He knew that he had to lead the party, as well as the country, after the bitter referendum campaign. So, on Monday 27 June, when he delivered a statement to the House of Commons on the result, it was about a 'time to heal' and to 'come together'.

Spotted close to Cameron on the front bench was Michael Gove. The Prime Minister and Gove had exchanged warmly worded texts following the vote, but the Cameron camp was clear that their working relationship would struggle to recover. Not only had Gove broken his promise to play only a small part in the campaign; he had then written an open letter to the PM, together with Boris Johnson, saying that his failure to cut immigration was 'corrosive of public trust'.

Loyal backbenchers made themselves vocal as the statement was delivered impeccably by their boss. He needed to legitimise the vote in the face of some of the Brexit camp's noises in the hours and days since the result. 'Last week saw one of the biggest democratic exercises in our history, with more than 33 million people from England, Scotland, Wales, Northern Ireland and Gibraltar all having their say. We should be proud of our democracy.' He built on his speech outside Downing Street on the Friday morning: 'We acknowledge that a large proportion of our country voted for change, and we get that.' He pledged to get the renegotiation implemented 'swiftly'.

While a few questions from his own side after the statement were helpful, Philip Davies asked: 'With Project Fear winning the referendum, will the Prime Minister now stop scaring the British people?' Anna Soubry was heard to mutter, 'Oh, bugger off.' The Tory wars were not over yet. Andrew Bridgen and Bernard Jenkin asked similarly snide questions. Cameron would have loved to inject in his responses comments such as, 'I await the arrival of millions of Turks,' but sensibly refrained. Boris Johnson, having taken a lead in the campaign, was not present in the House of Commons for the statement.

Some opposition MPs asked if the Prime Minister would sack Brexiter ministers. Some posed questions such as, 'Now Remain has won, would he remind his colleagues that the UK has a veto on Turkish accession?' Labour backbenchers were eager to add more fuel to the fires of the Tory wars.

An exhausted Downing Street wanted to conduct the unity reshuffle quickly after the vote, to help stamp Cameron's authority on the party and kill the constant rumours over who would get which job; waiting until after the summer recess wasn't an option. Cameron had spent most of the weekend on the phone to his inner circle, mulling over the finer details of his ideal reshuffle, as there simply hadn't been time to give it enough thought during the campaign.

Soon after the statement, the Prime Minister was due in Brussels for the European Council meeting with his counterparts around the Continent. It was decided that he would make the headline appointments and then resume naming the lower ranks of the ministerial team upon his return from the Belgian capital.

The biggest surprise was the appointment of David Gauke as Chancellor, while George Osborne moved to Foreign Secretary. Gauke was Osborne's choice and had been appreciated by the Treasury and No. 10 alike. Known for his eye for detail in his junior Treasury role, Gauke was often used to defend difficult government policies on the airwaves. Theresa May stayed at the Home Office. As she had been rather anonymous in the campaign, it is believed that the No. 10 team pondered moving her in order to achieve a Remain–Leave balance in the four great offices of state. Ultimately, though, they felt she deserved a platform to set up for the top job ahead of Boris Johnson; the reality was there were few, if any, Tory big beasts who could seriously challenge for the job apart from Boris. 'The Cameroons' didn't want to hand over the reins to Boris and were suspicious of his proximity to Gove during the campaign. Having flip-flopped over which way to go, the former Mayor of London, it was felt, had plumped for opportunism over pragmatism.

Boris himself went to the Ministry of Defence. Priti Patel and Penny Mordaunt remained in place in their junior roles, with Patel still in Cabinet attendance. Michael Gove also stayed in place in his role as Justice Secretary. Cameron had to make some moves to please Leave advocates: Andrea Leadsom was elevated to Transport Secretary from her junior position at Energy, and George Eustice was moved up a rank to become Secretary of State for the Environment.

Leave-supporting Conservatives expressed dissatisfaction at the reshuffle. Not only had Boris not been placed in one of the top offices of state (although as close as one can be, it was insisted) but the new Chancellor was also a Remainer, and the much-vilified Osborne remained at the top table. The now former Chancellor was their main enemy. Soon afterwards, Osborne's allies briefed that he had offered to sacrifice himself and go to the back benches, but Cameron had insisted that he remain at the top table.

On the opposite side of the House, discontent rumbled on in the Labour Party. Many Labour MPs remained agitated at their leader's few and ineffective campaign appearances. Alan Johnson, who had chaired the 'Labour In for Britain' campaign, described working with Corbyn as 'impossible' and issued a call for his colleagues 'to take back control of our party soon'.

A few months on

The economy continued to grow, with jobs and GDP figures looking steady. Investment decisions, put on hold by the uncertainty of the referendum, resumed favourably for Britain.

At the Ministry of Defence, the new Secretary of State, Boris Johnson, was settling in to the job. All the armed forces he met on his visits were thoroughly charmed. His Minister of State, Ben Wallace, a former army captain, was a huge asset in his departmental team. Of course, the real post Boris desired was the top job. The No. 10 team became frustrated that occasionally Johnson strayed off message, despite the absence of his weekly *Daily Telegraph* column (and of the lucrative cheque that had accompanied it). At a Conservative activists' Christmas dinner in the north-west, he was recorded as claiming that the MoD had been 'cash-starved' and that some people didn't really 'get it' on Defence. Was he frustrated at the Treasury push-back against his plans, or was it a more calculated remark? The *Daily Mail* naturally hoovered up the remarks and reinforced the impression that Johnson was the darling of the Tory foot soldiers. Perhaps David Cameron had accidentally given him the perfect role to appeal to the grassroots of the party.

Embarrassingly for Cameron, Jeremy Corbyn raised the issue of MoD funding at Prime Minister's Questions. It wasn't a subject you'd have expected the former Campaign for Nuclear Disarmament activist to use to attack the government. The PM fought back, jeering about Corbyn's anti-war stance, but it proved uncomfortable to have Boris firmly in the headlines again.

The Labour Party continued to define themselves as the party to roll back austerity. Shadow Chancellor John McDonnell used a speech to outline their economic policies, including reintroducing the 50p rate of income tax and abolishing past and future tuition fees. 'Working people voted to stay in Europe, allowing this Prime Minister to stay in his job. Now he must reward them.' Labour were keen to make the point that Cameron would probably have been out of office had enough Labour voters not turned out to back Remain. It gave Corbyn a little more confidence in his parliamentary exchanges, and he continued to push for the government to loosen the purse strings – something even some Conservative MPs had begun to ask for. Still, no Labour MP had made a move on the leadership.

Elsewhere on the opposition benches, the Liberal Democrat leader, Tim Farron, made the case for Britain to pursue a more active role in the EU: 'If we are always seen as the reluctant partner, always dragging our feet, what change can we ever achieve?' Farron wanted the Lib Dems to be seen as the only true pro-EU party.

As the SNP continued to dominate Scottish politics, Nicola Sturgeon sought to capitalise on divisions in London. 'The Tory Brexit boys of Westminster are more concerned with fighting each other than standing up for Scotland,' she claimed. Much as the independence debate had continued after the 2014 referendum in Scotland, the same thing was now taking place in the rest of the UK over Europe.

Meanwhile, George Osborne finally accepted that it wouldn't be worth standing for the leadership after his central referendum campaign role. From the Foreign Office, he continued his active engagement with countries like China and seemed distant from the domestic issues of the day. Many backbenchers felt that a Brexiter should have been in the Foreign Office; just below Osborne was the ardent Leave supporter, Dominic Raab, who had replaced Remain-voting David Lidington as Minister of State for Europe. Raab's legal background would, he hoped, help him to ensure that every letter of the renegotiation would be honoured by the other EU member states. But the union proved slow in delivering the reforms agreed in February 2016, helping UKIP to keep the Brexit debate alive.

Osborne approached Michael Gove to run for the leadership, but the Justice Secretary was looking in a different direction, having grown closer to Boris during the Brexit campaign. All these undercurrents and newspaper whispers weren't helpful to Cameron. His announcement, prior to the 2015 general election, that he would not seek a third term was proving unhelpful – not his desire not to go on and on itself, but his willingness to be open about it. And that was only exacerbated by the divisions over how the referendum campaign had been handled.

2017

Just before the first Monday back to Parliament in January 2017, a letter from forty Tory MPs to the PM asked him to name his departure date. It was a large number, and it made for an uncomfortable Sunday morning appearance on *The Andrew Marr Show*, though Cameron insisted that he was getting on with the job, pursuing social reforms and continuing the economic recovery. A few weeks later, however, after two defeats in the Commons, the Prime Minister eventually agreed to stand down after the May 2017 local elections.

Delivering his speech outside Downing Street and starting the official firing gun on the race for the top job, Cameron said, 'The country requires fresh leadership to take it forward.' After listing his achievements, he concluded: 'After nearly seven years in government, and in keeping with my words prior to the 2015 general election, I am not seeking a third term, and wish to give my successor the best chance possible at further years of Conservative governance.' The only reference to Europe came next: 'As we continue to push for reform in the European Union – as we always have – it will now be down to my successor to champion that.'

The speech came twelve months after the conclusion of the pre-referendum EU renegotiation in February 2016. It had been quite a year.

The referendum had strained many relationships, including that between Michael Gove and the Prime Minister. Gove was impressing in his portfolio, but it was now harder for him to win backing from No. 10 than it had been during his days at Education in the coalition. Justice, particularly in the coalition days, had always been an easy Whitehall department to target for cuts. Rightly, Cameron was aware of the problems of rising rates of reoffending and poor prison conditions, but shelling out money from the Treasury still remained a low priority. Reforms could have been another stick with which the right wing of his party could have hit him. It wouldn't take much for them to claim that he'd gone soft on crime and punishment.

Meanwhile, Labour was having troubles of its own. Despite government infighting, the party lagged significantly in the polls. Tom Watson had considered making a move on their hapless leader, but the resolute Labour grassroot support for Jeremy Corbyn continued to mean that an election was likely to be needed before Labour's parliamentary party could win such a challenge.

UKIP was enjoying a resurgence, with Nigel Farage going as far as claiming the referendum had been 'rigged', citing the leaflet sent to every household by the government. It was a gift when some European leaders were rumoured to be dragging their feet about putting the renegotiation into effect. Farage was as much a part of the national debate as he had been before the referendum, both through his speeches in the European Parliament and his frequent appearances in British media. The party was gaining a slicker social media operation; clips of David Cameron's post-referendum 'we hear you' speech were contrasted with the reality of little action since the vote.

Noticeably omitted from these clips, and from UKIP's role in the media, was the party's sole MP, Douglas Carswell. The Clacton MP was more resistant to the idea of an immediate referendum rerun, believing that arguing for another straight away gave credence to the 'loonies' perception many of the public held of his party. He kept in close contact with his Vote Leave colleagues, rather than the Leave.EU grouping of his party leader. Conservative MPs in Vote Leave expected to have a Brexiter in Downing Street shortly – a leader they believed would steer the country to an eventual Leave vote.

Tory leadership campaigns have always seemed to involve many promises of jobs and late-night deals in the corridors of the Palace of Westminster. The contest of 2017 was much the same. Having worked closely together during the referendum campaign, Boris and Gove knew they had to come to an arrangement. Boris was of course gung-ho for the role; as a child he'd had ambitions to be 'world king'. He had made efforts to get to know his parliamentary colleagues over recent months, and sessions in the Commons tea rooms led to lunches and evening dinners, with many job requests and offers. But a deal had to be reached with Gove. Allies of the Justice Secretary had leaked to the press that he was privately 'wrestling with doubts about the governing ability' of his Vote Leave ally and was 'considering a move'. They knew he would add intellectual clout to a campaign for the leadership by the Defence Secretary, but what did he want in exchange for his support? To be Chancellor, with added responsibility for Whitehall reform. 'The tentacles of the Treasury much more within government?' a slightly apprehensive Johnson asked. 'Well, you need Treasury backing to get anything done, and we have to reinvigorate far-reaching reform around Whitehall. It's too slow; too clunky. A lot of ministers are ministers for the sake of it. Not me.' A further demand came: he needed Dominic Cummings back by his side. Cummings, a special adviser to Gove as Education Secretary, had run the Vote Leave campaign in the Brexit referendum.

Boris Johnson agreed. He had to, for fear of splitting the vote of Brexit-supporting MPs in the parliamentary rounds. Now the duo – Johnson and Gove – were set.

The next big name to declare was Home Secretary Theresa May. Her style was the opposite of her main rival. She wasn't flashy, and she used that in her appeal to the many members of the parliamentary party who had often been suspicious of Boris. Remainers and Cameroons, angry at the Vote Leave stalwarts, rallied around May as the most credible 'stop Boris' candidate. Much of her support came from old allies who had been in Parliament for many years, such as Damian Green and Philip Hammond. While she had never been one to tour Westminster's tea rooms and bars, she was respected across the party.

Elsewhere, leadership candidate Priti Patel promised immediately to renegotiate Britain's EU membership once again, with a referendum within a year. But, like Sajid Javid, Liam Fox and Justine Greening, Patel did not survive the early rounds of the election. The final two were always certain: May and Johnson.

The pitch from the Home Secretary was centred around her experience in government and about 'moving on from our divisions'. She was very much the unity candidate. Naturally, she also tried to appeal to Leave-voting activists. Her responsibility for immigration at the Home Office allowed her to go in strong, almost trashing the record of the governments she had served. 'For too long as your Home Secretary, I have been hamstrung by European rules. I promise you, I know this area intimately, I have been in the room in those European Councils of Ministers, and I can achieve real change for Britain,' she said, going on to cite her opt-outs from many justice and home affairs measures in 2014.

On the question of a future referendum, Boris Johnson had to be careful. He knew that many of his enthusiastic supporters desired another. There would, of course, be future treaties in which he could push for reform, but an outright promise now would dominate his premiership and even legitimise the SNP's push for a second referendum on Scottish independence. May's position was that she would seek 'more reform, less division', and she refused throughout her campaign to commit to another vote on Europe.

UKIP leader Nigel Farage appeared on *Newsnight* to respond to Theresa May's speech, and he derided her: 'This is the Home Secretary who has overseen mass immigration, voted Remain to keep her job and been part of a government that brought back no reforms in their so-called renegotiation.' It was looking clear that Farage would thrive if May won the leadership, just as he had thrived post-referendum with Cameron at the helm.

In the end, Johnson settled on a 'never say never' position. 'What I've found in politics is never to rule things out. We have to consider if the vote in 2016 receives the reform it deserves, but, like we always have, Britain reserves the right to leave, the right to determine our own future as a sovereign nation.' Wanting a firmer commitment, and increasingly spooked by the re-emerging UKIP threat, activists asked him to name a date by which he would commit to a future vote. 'Clearly, when we write the next Conservative manifesto, we will need to address whether the reforms we have made so far in the EU are enough and whether a referendum will need to be included.' Naturally, Boris wanted to please people. The European issue would continue to dominate British politics.

Early June
Prime Minister Boris Johnson was settling into his new office. He had truly swept the board with a far-reaching reshuffle and an ambitious speech on the steps of Downing Street. He had won an impressive 61 per cent in the final vote against Theresa May, who had fought a strong but uneventful campaign.

A divided Tory Party had enjoyed a mixed bag of results in the local elections the month before, although a mayoral victory in the West Midlands was considered a triumph. Labour was still suffering from divisions, with their leader failing to convince a sceptical public, who had seemingly exhausted themselves of politics after the previous year's referendum mudslinging, but they were starting from a high base, defending the gains made the last time these seats had been fought, in 2013. The insurgent UKIP were the big winners of the night, benefiting from a preoccupied Conservative Party and from Corbyn. The Liberal Democrats made modest gains in traditional Conservative areas disgruntled at the party's continuing battles over Brexit.

Politics felt stagnant. The government was unable to govern

meaningfully as it struggled to recover from the referendum infighting. The Conservatives seemed unable to find a vision beyond deficit control and fiscal prudence. There were splits between those eager to move on from the EU debate and those who hadn't lost sight of their Brexit dream, all within the constraints of a tiny majority.

But this suited the incoming PM. He was able to announce that 'it's time to boost Britain' and 'time for Barnsley, Bognor and Boston to boom' (all towns that had voted heavily for Leave), with promises of new infrastructure, technology and hospitals. It was now the main faces of Vote Leave at the heart of government. Austerity would be eased. Chancellor Gove, although more fiscally conservative than his Downing Street neighbour, was ready to aid the reset, not least because it made it more difficult for Corbyn and McDonnell to get a hearing for their policies of increased investment.

Autumn ballot

It was time, though, for a general election to deliver a real chance for change and to capitalise on a divided Labour Party. The narrow parliamentary majority won in 2015 seemed a lifetime ago.

The Fixed-Term Parliaments Act made things a little more complex to get the country back to the polls. Ultimately, however, Labour agreed to back a general election, delivering the required two-thirds-plus Commons vote in favour of the motion; since Corbyn had repeatedly called the new PM 'unelected' and 'lacking legitimacy', he had little choice. During the Tory leadership battle, Boris had been reticent about calling a general election, but his inner circle later privately admitted they had always planned to go to the country.

Opinion polls consistently predicted an increased Conservative majority. There was, though, a brief surge for Labour in some seats, where their 'Remain Means Remain' message cut through. This phrase spoke to voters who were tired of the Tories continuing to bang on about Europe just a short time after a referendum had been held supposedly to settle the issue. In turning the tables on 2015, when the Conservatives talked of a potential 'coalition of chaos' under Labour, the Labour campaign pitched a message of 'more chaos, more uncertainty and European neverendums under the Tories'.

But in opting for a heavily pro-European message – as pushed by the shadow Cabinet – Labour repelled some of their Leave-voting constituencies and target seats in the Midlands and the north. 2016 had seen the lifelong Eurosceptic Jeremy Corbyn campaign for Britain to stay part of the EU, a cause for which he appeared ambivalent and uncomfortable. And now, he looked much the same. But Brexit dominated the election, and Corbyn could not avoid the choice; his party had persuaded him that a pro-EU line would be successful in many of the metropolitan seats David Cameron had recently won. It was more Bristol North West than Bolton West.

The Labour strategy left little room for the Liberal Democrats to gain traction. Since the referendum, their direction had been to emphasise the need to move on and engage positively in the EU. The target voter most susceptive to their message was the pro-European Cameron supporter who had liked the Conservative–Lib Dem coalition government. Sadly for Tim Farron, it was all too easy for the Conservatives to squeeze the Lib Dem vote with fears of letting in a Corbyn government.

On the campaign trail, Labour were far more at home talking about 'Tory cuts'. But with the new Conservative administration openly reversing the more austere fiscal policies of George Osborne, Corbyn's anti-austerity message did not receive the cut-through he had hoped.

UKIP's vote was effectively squeezed by Boris. Although the party had enjoyed a boost in the polls during the period before David Cameron eventually stood down, Nigel Farage did not stand for Parliament; he claimed that he wanted to focus on his role leading UKIP in the European Parliament. However, the bigger story came when Douglas Carswell announced that he would stand down from his seat and endorse the Conservatives. It was quite a U-turn from his defection just three years before. Furious, Farage claimed the party had been 'used'. It all came back to the bitter battle between Vote Leave and Leave.EU, when the former – with Carswell part of it – had secured the official campaign nomination.

In Scotland, voters found themselves back at the polls after successive years of referendums and parliamentary elections. The SNP continued to angle for a second vote on independence, and the unionist vote split. Conservative gains under Ruth Davidson at the 2016 Scottish Parliament polls were difficult to replicate in this UK election, as Boris Johnson did not prove attractive to Scottish voters. In fact, talk of another Europe vote and constant grievance from Leave voters in England only gave succour to Scottish Nationalists seeking to overturn their 2014 referendum result. Labour had hopes of small gains from a starting point of just one seat as their railing at 'Tory cuts' gained a little traction.

Election result

Polling day came, and Boris swept the board: Conservatives 367 (thirty-seven net gains); Labour 199 (thirty-three losses); Liberal Democrats nine (one gain); SNP fifty-two (four losses). There were some extraordinary Tory gains, with seats like Mansfield and Stoke South going blue; a mix of Corbyn's perceived lack of patriotism and the Vote Leave messaging from Boris meant that many traditional Labour voters had been repelled from their usual party.

The Tories would stay in power and the battle over the UK's future in Europe would resume. Could it have been so different after all?

Chapter 16

What if Jeremy Corbyn had stood down in late 2017?

Philip Cowley

From the moment Jeremy Corbyn became Labour leader in September 2015, his position came under almost constant attack – and not just from his party's opponents. Elected with close to 60 per cent of the vote, his overwhelming support among Labour's membership was not shared within either the Parliamentary Labour Party or the party's professional staff. The Corbyn team's own analysis identified just twenty MPs who could be described as his core supporters, and Corbyn backers within the party establishment were even more of a besieged minority. He faced unremitting hostility from much of the right and centre of the party. The strength of his grassroots support meant that a formal leadership challenge in 2016 was batted away easily enough, but more damaging were the constant attempts to undermine him and force him out: a vote of no confidence from his MPs, resignations, rumours, leaks, personal attacks. Much of the Corbyn team's time and energy was taken up negotiating compromises between the various factions within the shadow Cabinet and other sections of the party – never very successfully.

In April 2017, when Theresa May unexpectedly called an election, the widespread assumption was that Labour was heading for a devastating defeat. Opinion polls put the Conservatives twenty or so percentage points ahead, and Labour's initial internal polling had the party crashing to just 157 seats. Even some of the MPs who publicly backed Corbyn had so little confidence in the outcome that they privately lobbied for extra resources to help defend their own nominally safe constituencies. Many of Corbyn's critics hoped that from the impending electoral catastrophe would come salvation and that the result would be bad enough to end his leadership.

It didn't happen like that. Instead, the Conservative election campaign imploded, while Labour's poll ratings climbed inexorably, week after week, as polling day approached. Corbyn's campaign rallies drew huge crowds, where he was rapturously received. When the votes were counted, he had led the Labour Party from what had seemed like certain slaughter to close to Downing Street. The Conservative majority in the Commons was wiped out, and Theresa May clung on to power only thanks to a deal with the DUP. Fewer than 1,000 people voting differently, spread across just eight constituencies, could have put him in No. 10.

In 2016, the prospect of Prime Minister Corbyn was used as the title for another volume of political counterfactuals, full of other things that never happened. Yet now it might. The prospect of a Corbyn premiership was no longer a joke.

True, Labour had not actually won the 2017 election in the pedantic, old-fashioned sense of getting more seats or votes than the other lot. But it had won the campaign and, some Corbynites claimed, the argument. And anyway, by late 2017 Labour was ahead in the opinion polls. The election had elevated Corbyn as it had diminished May. The Conservative government – which at the election had promised 'strong and stable leadership' – was delivering neither; May remained Prime Minister, but it was clear she couldn't last long. By contrast, Corbyn's position in the party was now dominant; his supporters seemed vindicated in their belief that his personality, along with a more left-of-centre manifesto, would prove popular with the electorate. Many of his internal critics had based so much of their critique on Corbyn's supposed unpopularity that they found themselves undone by the election result. Corbyn's team were now able to reshape the party in their own image. A clear-out of senior staff at Labour HQ began – most jumping before they were pushed – and the left consolidated its position on the National Executive Committee. Before the election, the left's hold on the Labour Party had been tentative and contingent; it was now firmly in charge.

When Corbyn appeared at Glastonbury in June 2017, he spoke from the Pyramid Stage to tens of thousands of people, many of them chanting his name. The event's organiser, Michael Eavis, asked one of the leader's aides when he would be Prime Minister. The answer: by Christmas.

Which made Corbyn's decision to resign as party leader – announced in December 2017, on a day when an opinion poll put Labour eight per-centage points ahead of the Conservatives – all the more surprising.

~

As was his way, Corbyn had come to the decision slowly, rationally and calmly; and then, having made it, he was unwavering.

For all the certainty among his supporters, he had a more sceptical view of the future. For one thing, he was certain that Theresa May had fought her last election as Conservative leader. However long she might cling on for, there was no way Conservative MPs would be willing to march behind her banner again. So next time – whenever that was, and he suspected it would be sooner rather than later – he would be facing someone else. Since almost anyone would be a more effective campaigner than May had been (and he really did mean almost anyone), the next election would be a tougher fight.

And in 2017, many voters had been discovering Corbyn for the first time. They had been told constantly that he was the devil incarnate; some crazed Marxist ready to nationalise their children. Yet when they had actually seen him during the campaign, he had seemed normal and reasonable – less a threat to the nation, more a friendly, caring uncle. Next time, there would be far less chance to impress afresh.

Then, there were the attacks on him, especially the claims about antisemitism. All attacks on his integrity riled him – he knew he was one of the good guys; it was the other lot who were the bastards – but this one really got under his skin. But even through the red mist, he could still see that this issue wasn't going to go away. If anything, it would probably get worse. He was aware of other things he'd done in the past, things that had yet to come out, that his opponents were bound to discover. It was all grossly unfair how perfectly reasonable things – support for a mural here, a wreath-laying ceremony there – could be painted to make him look bad. But he knew how they would twist such things.

What if he stayed on and Labour won the next election? Deep down, he wasn't even sure he'd be a good Prime Minister. One of his closest aides had once described him as a political activist who happened to be an MP; someone who was happier out of the office or Westminster, campaigning. Corbyn didn't demur. The happiest weeks of his time as Labour leader had been the election campaign. He wasn't sure that a political activist who happened to be Prime Minister would be that much better a fit. He was aware of that famous quote from Mario Cuomo: 'You campaign in poetry. You govern in prose.' Corbyn loved poetry.

But more important – much more important – was what would happen if he stayed on and Labour lost. As leader and the (almost) triumphant victor of 2017, he was significant and influential. If he lost, he would, almost overnight, lose all that. The hold of the left would be diminished. He could see how many would-be successors were positioning themselves already. Many of them were not Corbynites, even if they said the right things and pretended to have signed up to his agenda. If he stayed, there would be no guarantee that his successor would be a true believer.

At various points, in his first two years as leader, he had considered standing down, only to be persuaded out of it for the good of the cause. Previously, he had needed to stay on because there was no guarantee that a left-wing candidate – or at least someone who Corbyn would consider to be a proper left-wing candidate – would make it onto the ballot. The rules had required candidates to secure nominations from 15 per cent of the PLP, a hurdle Corbyn himself had cleared only narrowly in 2015, when he had been lent nominations by MPs willing to 'broaden the debate' but who had no intention of voting for him. 'I don't know why everyone is panicking,' said one of those who nominated him and then spent the next two years regretting it, 'He isn't going to win.' After what transpired in 2015, there was no way MPs were going to do that again. Had he stepped down before the 2017 election, the PLP would have ensured that no left-of-centre candidate was anywhere near the ballot.

But that argument no longer held. For one thing, there had been an influx of Labour left MPs in the election; one of the consequences of a snap election in which everyone assumed Labour would get hammered had been a laxity about candidate selection, resulting in all sorts of people being selected for what were assumed to be unwinnable seats only now to find themselves as MPs. But anyway, after the election the Corbyn-dominant party had changed the rules: the new hurdle was 10 per cent of the PLP, and the left could clear that easily.

So, it was now guaranteed that a candidate from the left would make it onto the ballot, and while there was always uncertainty about the way elections could go (he was, after all, living proof of that himself), he would be able to throw his weight – as a leader at the peak of his power – behind the chosen candidate. He couldn't quite guarantee who would win, but it was pretty close. A new Labour leader, from and of the left but without any of the baggage Corbyn knew he had gathered during his lengthy career as a backbencher, would be better able to take the fight on. Corbynism without Corbyn, they called it.

That Labour had begun to poll well made his decision more impor-tant, not less. If there was a chance of Labour winning the next election, it was crucial not to be a drag on the party. To do that, having come this close, would be unforgivable.

He could see how it could all go to your head: the adoration, the cheering crowds. Before his elevation, he had often been the support act as a speaker, third or fourth on the bill: reliable, fairly predictable but usually not the one people had actually come to hear. Slightly to his surprise, he'd enjoyed being top billing. But the party, and perhaps more than that the project – the cause – was more important than anyone's ego.

Having previously had to fight day by day to cling on to the leader-ship, Corbyn could now pick his own departure date. When he had first been elected leader, as he walked from the room where he had been told the result, he turned to his long-term ally, John McDonnell, put his arm around him and said: 'It's bigger even than we thought it would be, John. Think what we can do.' What he could do now was to secure the party for the left, maximising its chances of winning the next election.

~

Who would it be? Here things got trickier. Even Corbyn could see that there was not exactly an embarrassment of riches surrounding him on the front bench. There were plenty of would-be candidates but no obvious successor. If McDonnell wanted it, it would be hard to deny him, although there was a growing mood within the party that the next leader ought to be a woman, given that no woman had ever been elected to the party's top spot.[1] This might help the candidacies of Rebecca Long-Bailey or Angela Rayner, both of whom he could see standing. Clive Lewis didn't have his sex on his side, but he would be the party's first black leader and that too would be something to celebrate. The claims of Emily Thornberry, his constituency neighbour and shadow Foreign Secretary, were trickier. She had done sterling work for the party at the last election and had stood in for him at Prime Minister's Questions, where she had performed well. But she was no natural Corbynite, and there had to be a risk that she would unite those on the left who thought she was with those on the right who hoped she wasn't.

The issue of his successor was the thing which gave Corbyn most pause. Perhaps it would be better to hang on, waiting until there was an obvious successor – maybe even one of the 2017 intake? But time wasn't on his side or theirs. The government could collapse at any point; there might be an election within a year or two. All of his possible successors had flaws, but then – and with his usual modesty he could see this – so did he. What mattered was that they might be better able to build on what he had achieved and take the fight to the Tories. So, he would take soundings, decide and then – once he had backed one of the candidates publicly – the others would know they had no chance and would swing behind the anointed one. Earlier that year, he'd seen some bookmakers' odds that had put Keir Starmer as the favourite to replace him; it was obviously important to prevent that.

~

There are at least two, maybe even three, counterfactuals lurking above.

The first one, mentioned in passing, is the claim about Labour getting close to office in 2017. This has become a key part of the left's narrative about what happened between 2015 and 2017; it allows supporters of Jeremy Corbyn to argue that they could have won in 2017 had it not been for the criticism and sniping that Corbyn suffered from the right of the party in the first two years of his leadership. It is true insofar as it goes, although – as so often with counterfactuals – what seems simple enough initially soon turns out to be much more complicated.

It is certainly true that it would not have required many votes to have changed hands for the 2017 outcome to be different. In the eight most marginal Conservative-held seats after the election, just 944 votes changing hands would have resulted in five seats going Labour; two to the Liberal Democrats; one to the SNP. This would have produced a sufficiently large anti-Conservative block that Theresa May would not have been able to construct a majority, even with the support of the DUP.

You will see different versions of these numbers. Some add up the size of the majorities that needed to have changed; some look at the number of people who needed to have changed their mind (which is half the former); some focus just on the most marginal seats where Labour was challenging; some focus on the most marginal Conservative-held seats. It doesn't really matter; however you calculate it, it's all small fry in the context of an election in which 30 million people voted.

This wouldn't have been enough to give Labour a majority in the Commons – they were still a long way from that – but it would almost certainly have been enough to have prevented Theresa May continuing as Prime Minister, and it might then have been enough to put Jeremy Corbyn in, heading a minority Labour government. Given the lack of a Commons majority, it would probably not have turned out to be a government marked by stability or longevity, but it would have been a government nonetheless.

The first problem with these sorts of claims is that while this might have been enough to create an anti-Conservative block in the Commons, it is not inevitable that this would then have led to Corbyn entering No. 10. The Liberal Democrats in particular (and maybe even some on the right of the PLP) would have been in a particularly painful quandary.

Another possible outcome would have been a second general election, the result of which would have been anyone's guess.

The second (and bigger) problem is that two can play at this game. For if Labour were under 1,000 votes away from blocking the Conservatives, the Conservatives were a mere fifty-one votes away from a Commons majority of their own. May would end election night in 2017 just seven seats short of a Commons majority – and there were four constituencies that the Conservatives lost with majorities of between just twenty and thirty votes. Just fifty-one people voting differently in those four seats would have been enough to give her a majority.

At best, all these sorts of calculations do is show you how close the 2017 election turned out to be. But there are much bigger problems with this sort of political what-if than just a handful of votes here or there.

For example, let's assume that the disunity in 2015–17 hurt Labour's poll ratings (which seems a fair assumption). Had Labour been more united, it might well have polled better. But if it had polled better, there might not have been a 2017 election in the first place. Would Theresa May, who was decidedly sceptical about the arguments for an election when she was twenty or so percentage points ahead in the polls, have been willing to go for it had the gap been smaller? It's doubtful.

And even if there had been an election, it would have been fought in an entirely different context. With Labour polling better, the campaign would have been fought on the basis that they were realistic challengers for government, rather than the election being a shoo-in for the Tories. This would have had all sorts of consequences. There almost certainly wouldn't have been any risky announcements about social care, for example, which we know badly hurt the Conservatives in the campaign.

And while Labour did extremely well in the election to fight back to within a few percentage points of the Conservatives, had they been polling better in the first place, it is likely that their campaign fightback would have been less dramatic. Much of Labour's improvement during the campaign came from former Labour supporters who had become disenchanted with the party; these people presumably wouldn't have left Labour to begin with but for the events of 2015–17.

So maybe. But maybe not.

The second counterfactual above is the core of the chapter: the idea that after getting so close in 2017, Jeremy Corbyn might have stood down voluntarily and by so doing ensured that the leadership of the Labour Party passed to someone who might have done better at the subsequent election.

The first section of text all happened pretty much as described (although it was Corbyn himself who made the claim to Michael Eavis at Glastonbury about becoming Prime Minister by Christmas – or at least Eavis says he did). The next section of text didn't happen, obviously, although all the things that the hypothetical Jeremy Corbyn thinks might come to pass did: the election did come sooner rather than later; he faced a tougher opponent in 2019 than in 2017; he failed to repeat the barnstorming campaigning of 2017 (Labour's poll ratings barely moved during the 2019 campaign, unlike their rise in 2017); allegations against him over antisemitism only intensified after 2017; and having lost in 2019, the party did not then choose a Corbynite successor, electing Sir Keir Starmer instead, comfortably defeating the left's Rebecca Long-Bailey and showing once again that when the chips are down, the desire to have a female party leader maybe isn't quite as strong as it seems when the question is being discussed in the abstract.

Is there any evidence that Corbyn considered standing down after 2017? None. But had he done so, it does seem highly likely that if there had been a leadership campaign in late 2017, it would have been won by a Corbyn-backed candidate. By standing down at a time of his choosing, Corbyn would have been that rare thing: a political leader who steps down of their own volition. He would have disproved Enoch Powell's dictum that all political lives end in failure (at least, if we set aside 2017). He would have retired at the height of his powers and would now be remembered as someone who almost led Labour to victory – and few organisations rate glorious failure as highly as the Labour Party – rather than as someone who led them to their greatest defeat since 1935.

What happens after that, however, is much harder to predict. In part, it depends on which candidate emerges from the left to take the leadership and one's view of how competent and electorally appealing they would have been. There was no evident successor. Of the obvious potential candidates, none were without problems or drawbacks, and all would have faced their own challenges. Yet it seems at least plausible that, whoever they were, an alternative leader from the left may have been better able to navigate some of the tricky issues that lay ahead. They would, for example, almost certainly have been better able to deal with the issue of antisemitism. Everyone close to Corbyn admits that he was simply unable to engage properly with the issue because the nature of the attacks so upset him. A new leader might have been more able to take it on. No doubt they would have been attacked for other things – such is the nature of political competition – but these alternate attacks might have been less insidious, less emotional, more easily parried. And maybe an alternative leader would have dealt with them better. As leader of the Labour Party, John McDonnell, say, would certainly have come with plenty of baggage from his time as a backbencher – much of it baggage similar to Corbyn's – but he always seemed more capable at deflecting such attacks.

An alternative leader may also have been better able to deal with one of the other key issues that helped derail Labour: the fallout from the attempted assassination of Sergei Skripal, a former Russian military officer, in Salisbury in 2018. Corbyn's hesitation to believe that the Russian government were involved – at one point suggesting that they be sent samples of the nerve agent that was used to test – was widely criticised. Even some of those close to Corbyn say that this helped reignite all the doubts about the leader among both the PLP and the wider public. It is at least plausible that a different leader (perhaps with different advisers) would have avoided such an obvious bear trap.

Harder to navigate, however, would have been Labour's Brexit position. Here the details of the would-be alternate leader matter even more, because the various candidates would have taken different positions. Yet although the details may have differed, the basic outcome might not have done. No leader would have been able to avoid or overcome the essential electoral fact that Labour supporters were badly split over Brexit:

a majority having voted Remain but with a significant minority – and too large a minority to ignore – having voted Leave. In the event, after a lot of prevarication, Corbyn's Labour ended up fighting on a policy of a second referendum – albeit with some caveats and qualifications – and by so doing managed to alienate many of its Leave-voting supporters.

Following defeat in 2019, plenty of people have argued that this was a costly electoral position. They are able to argue this because it manifestly was a costly electoral position. What is less obvious is whether any alternate position would have been less costly. There is, therefore, an implicit third what-if lurking here: what would have happened if Corbyn had stood down and his successor had been firmer in rejecting the calls for a second referendum (or indeed, if Corbyn himself had done so)? But the idea that this was an easy route to electoral sunlit uplands is a pretty simple-minded analysis. In such a situation, Labour were at risk of haemorrhaging Remain voters to the Lib Dems – an outcome which also leads to the Conservatives gaining dozens of seats in 2019, because even if the Conservative vote in a seat doesn't rise, if the Labour vote falls beneath it, the Conservatives take the seat. Three months before the 2019 election, and prior to its second referendum policy shift, Labour's own internal analysis showed that for every Leave voter the party was losing, they were also losing three Remainers. This put the party on track to fall to 138 MPs.

Adopting a second referendum was a disastrous policy for Labour; rejecting a second referendum may have been even worse. The result may have been different in form – with different seats changing hands – but probably not in its overall outcome.

There may still have been some advantages to a change of leader, though, even with Brexit considered. The leadership contest might have forced the new leader to articulate their Brexit position, and then, having won on that manifesto, the policy would have been given some legitimacy. The former scenario would have meant Labour going into the election with longer to articulate and explain its position (Labour's actual 2019 position was adopted only months before the election); the latter might have avoided some of the intra-party rowing that took place as Labour struggled to agree a position. And maybe the lengthy parliamentary battles over Brexit in the House of Commons would have played out differently under a different leader. A less divisive figure than Corbyn may have been better able to hold the PLP together through the Brexit votes, and build cross-party coalitions, in a way Corbyn struggled to. This, though, must all be considered pretty marginal. The simple truth is that there was, in electoral terms, no good position for Labour over Brexit after 2016.

The likely outcome is that Labour would still lose the 2019 election, even under another leader from the left (and, for the avoidance of doubt, almost certainly under any leader). Corbyn standing down probably doesn't change that. But perhaps they wouldn't have lost quite so badly. Maybe the defeat wouldn't discredit and demoralise the left in quite the way that 2019 did. Maybe the new leader would get to stay on for a second election – if, say, the Conservative majority were narrower[2] – or perhaps another leader from the left would be chosen. Or maybe not. Perhaps it is just as likely that a McDonnell- or a Rayner-led party would go down to basically the same sort of defeat as did Corbyn's. A demoralised left would then lose a leadership contest in early 2020 to a more centrist figure – like, say, Sir Keir Starmer.

Perhaps, sometimes, what-ifs don't matter all that much.

Notes

1   Indeed, it was worse than that. At the time our hypothetical Corbyn is pondering his decision, every Labour leadership contest to have taken place and in which a woman had stood (1994, 2010, 2015) had seen female candidates come below every single male rival. In any Conservative vote in which female candidates were participating (1975, 1989, 1990, 2016), the opposite held. This trend ceased to be true for the Conservatives in 2019, yet it still holds for Labour.

2   See Chapter 19 for Josh Bartholomew's 'What if Boris Johnson had won the 2019 election with only a small majority?'

Chapter 17

What if Theresa May had passed her Brexit deal at the third attempt? (1)

Teddy Robertson

As night fell on Brussels, Jean-Claude Juncker stepped into the lift running up the European Commission's headquarters, his left sock squelching in rainwater that had seeped through a hole in his shoe. '320 votes to 308!' he declared breathlessly, for the fifth time that evening.

'321,' his assistant corrected him as they wrestled with a soaked EU-branded umbrella.

'I never thought she'd manage it,' Juncker said, as the lift reached the cavernous corridor that led to his office.

'They're calling her Britain's own Mrs Merkel,' said the assistant. 'I just saw it on the evening paper review.'

Juncker raised an eyebrow. 'I thought they loathed Merkel over there. I wonder why they're saying that?'

'I'm not quite sure, Mr President. I would guess that the British press got bored of comparing her to Margaret Thatcher. And Merkel has, after all, run Germany for nearly fifteen years without a hiccup.'

'I'm not sure we'd all agree with that, *jeune homme*,' said the President. 'But anyway – in we go.'

The assistant pushed open Juncker's office door and feigned surprise as the office erupted in cheers. Seemingly everyone in the commission had arrived to celebrate Theresa May's victory in the House of Commons.

Their relief was understandable: Brussels – with Mrs May's help, of course – had got Brexit done. At the third time of trying, the Withdrawal Agreement had been heaved over the line. Admittedly, the majority it mustered was unimpressive. Lamentable, even. But it was just enough to move things on.

This breakthrough had stunned Mrs May's political rivals, with their respective parties collapsing into ugly recriminations. What mattered for now was that Brexit – or at least its first stage – was over.

President Juncker saw that the glass table at which he received guests was groaning under the weight of some fifteen bottles of what appeared to be English sparkling wine. 'Where the hell did all this come from?' he asked incredulously.

'A gift from the British,' said Martin Selmayr, the President's right-hand man, as he knocked back his fifth glass of the evening. 'Do you remember Steve Baker and his gang? It was sent in a hamper with a rather charming card.'

'Ah, the British... gallant even in defeat,' chuckled Juncker. 'I'll read it later – but first, it's time for a drink.' He poured a tall glass from one of the open bottles and took a deep gulp.

'Don't tell anyone I said this, Martin, but it's actually pretty good.'

Martin smiled. 'Don't enjoy it too much, sir.'

Half an hour later, Juncker was standing on his desk, sparkling wine bottle in one hand and his arms spread out like a surfer riding a choppy wave as his guests stared up in admiration. 'Thank you all for coming,' he said. 'As you are aware, Mrs May has finally delivered what was promised, and a celebration is in order. It's a special moment for the British Prime Minister, but it is a towering victory for Europe. I think it is fair to say that we outmatched those, er, dastardly Brits at every turn.'

'Hear, hear,' cried one of the guests in the best British accent they could muster.

'I know you're all exhausted, so I am keeping my comments uncharacteristically brief. However, my assistant has something he would like to show us.' Juncker pretended to peer around the room in puzzlement. 'Now, where has he got to?'

Right on cue, the assistant threw open the office door and triumphantly crossed the threshold in a pair of leopard-print high heels. A grey wig wobbled atop his head as he offered the guests a steely glare and pursed lips glistening with dark-red lipstick. He strode up to the desk, kicked away the wine bottles with gusto and climbed on top. The room exploded in laughter.

'We stand together, and together we have a great future,' the assistant declared in a theatrical British accent, gripping an invisible lectern. 'The Withdrawal Agreement has passed, and so I will continue in this job, which has been the honour of my life to hold.'

At this point, the assistant pretended to fight back tears. 'I do so with enormous and enduring gratitude,' he said, his voice quivering, 'to serve the country I love.' And with that, he did an about turn and hopped off the table.

'*Merveilleux*!' cried Juncker. 'A formidable impression of her victory speech! Strange to watch, though, wasn't it? Felt like a resignation speech that had been hastily rewritten.'

'I have no doubt it was,' said the assistant. 'From a resignation speech, I mean. I expect even she was surprised when the deal went through.'

~

After her own comparatively sober celebrations in Westminster, the Prime Minister braced for the enormous backlash that she had expected to follow the passage of the Withdrawal Agreement. The week that followed was dominated by feverish analysis across the airwaves and in the newspapers, as people tried to piece together how May had triumphed against the odds.

Many pundits chalked it up to what was called 'Brexhaustion'. It was true that many backbenchers had decided in the end to help the deal go through Parliament because they were simply worn down. For too many months, they had sloughed through wall-to-wall Brexit coverage, Brexit votes in Parliament and rehashed arguments over Brexit in every pub across the nation. There was a growing sense that the public, despite the shortcomings of the deal, just wanted the government to get on with it. Or, as one pro-May Tory MP said to colleagues: 'I just don't think voters are going to riot over the Common External Tariff.'

The theory proved popular and was encouraged by the Prime

Minister's allies, who painted a picture of their boss showing her steel by grinding down her opposition. In their eyes, she was driven by a fierce belief in the rightness of her cause and a burning desire to fulfil her democratic duty; after taking on the Eurocrats and toughing out more humiliation than any of her predecessors, the 'bloody difficult woman' had delivered.

But the truth, as tends to be the case in the cut-throat world of Westminster, was not quite so simple and rosy. Much of the whispers centred around the government's Chief Whip, Julian Smith, who was credited with playing a key role in winning over the stragglers. No one was entirely sure what dark arts Smith had managed to conjure up. But even his critics acknowledged in private that he had 'found his inner Francis Urquhart', in tribute to the Machiavellian Chief Whip immortalised in *House of Cards*.

Chris Grayling may also have had a hand in May's unlikely victory. Not long before the vote, the Transport Secretary signed off a raft of infrastructure projects in seats across the nation, from new bridges to road-widening schemes and railway electrification. Some academics noticed that these projects tended to fall in the seats of Tory and Labour MPs who had backed the deal, but the government insisted it was part of their mission to 'turbocharge the Northern Powerhouse and level up the UK'.

Certainly, the change in parliamentary behaviour was remarkable. Philip Davies, the man who had at first snubbed the Chief Whip on camera, was far from the only Tory Brexiter to come on side. Even the hardiest members of the European Research Group bowed to the pressure, with self-described 'Brexit hardman' Steve Baker admitting that he had decided – after a long night of reflection and prayer – that it was best to see the deal pass 'for the greater good'. He explained his thinking at length to the ERG brethren, at times seeming on the point of tears in lamenting how corrosive the debate had become.

In a sorrowful, resigned voice, he argued that it was time to put the country first by securing its liberty from the EU, however imperfect the deal might be. He warned that persisting any longer risked plunging the nation's future, and Brexit with it, into jeopardy – which millions of Leave voters would not forgive. He rounded off with a baleful *cri de coeur* to his colleagues: 'I know many in this room have joined me in standing up as modern-day Spartans ... but we must remember what happened at Thermopylae: they were all cut down in the end.' He was heard in sympathetic silence, as dozens of his colleagues began to realise that they too would need to come round to the deal.

Then, the unthinkable happened. The Democratic Unionist Party, the most implacable of all May's opponents, underwent a dramatic change of heart. Some were beginning to suspect that many Tory Brexiters, if forced to choose between Brexit and the union, would opt for the former. The hated backstop – the compromise that would keep all of the UK tied to EU rules to resolve the Irish border conundrum – was very bad indeed for Brexit, the DUP acknowledged. But was it so very bad for the union, considering that it would avoid a trade border between Great Britain and Northern Ireland? Was this messy arrangement the lesser of what Ian Paisley might have described as two thundering, clamouring evils? And, if the chance arose for Tory Brexiters to scrap the backstop for something else – something that would set up an NI–GB trade border – well, the mere prospect made some in the DUP shudder.

Others in the DUP were outraged by this school of thought but recognised that Brexit uncertainty was starting to wear thin on voters in their constituencies – even those Unionists who supported leaving the EU. Conversely, they did not wish to look weak in front of Sinn Féin. The Irish Nationalist party was breathing down the DUP's neck in at least one key electoral battleground: Emma Little-Pengelly's seat of Belfast South. Even Belfast North, the backyard of the DUP's Westminster chief Nigel Dodds, was in danger.

Given the staunchly held views of his colleagues, Dodds knew that the only passable compromise was to accept that this vote was a matter of conscience, allowing the party's ten MPs to make up their own minds. Some supported May's Bill, with Little-Pengelly leading a few of her colleagues in arguing it was the fairest Brexit for the whole United Kingdom. Others abstained, most notably Sammy Wilson – who complained privately that he would not dignify this 'betrayal of the union' and stayed at home.

Without any DUP ire over the deal, the ERG was left to weigh up its provisions carefully. Their legal eagles, including the prominent Eurosceptic Sir Bill Cash, pored over the detail throughout the night and concluded that the constraints inherent in the deal were 'tolerable'. Sir Bill added a wry, handwritten addendum to the conclusion that was circulated around Brexiter MPs: 'This all could be circumnavigated by a subsequent Prime Minister with the right instincts.'

And so, the rebels fell on their swords – or at least pretended to do so – as they lacked any convincing excuse to mount serious opposition to the agreement. Cynical commentators suggested later that the prospect of ermine cloaks may have helped some of the more hardline Eurosceptics to cross the line.

May also had unexpected help in passing the deal from a Labour politician. Lisa Nandy, one of Labour's pragmatists, had championed an amendment which was designed to make the deal just about acceptable to the party by insisting that Parliament had a say over the trade negotiations that would follow. The wording had been artfully phrased in co-operation with her colleague, Stoke MP Gareth Snell, to sound tough enough to reassure colleagues on their side of the Commons, while loose enough to encourage government whips to accept it. Once the Speaker, John Bercow, picked the amendment, it had little trouble mustering enough support among MPs – with every side seeing in it what they wanted. As a result, more Labour MPs were able to swing behind the deal, including Gloria De Piero and Caroline Flint – even the old Bennite Eurosceptic Dennis Skinner, the Beast of Bolsover, was able to give the deal his stamp of approval.

However, the ploy went down like a lead balloon at Labour HQ. Nandy was deemed to be a leading light of this 'Red Tory coup' and was summarily stripped of the whip before the week was over. Jeremy Corbyn maintained a publicly beatific silence about this move, but his socialist Svengali, Seumas Milne, was seen in Portcullis House muttering into the ears of journalists about 'uncomradely conduct'. Onlookers were in no doubt that he was hell bent on vengeance, as Labour greybeards chalked it up as their party's equivalent of the blue-on-blue Maastricht rebellion of the 1990s.

As dramatic as such internecine warfare was, it lacked the high-stakes drama of the previous few months, which the media had gorged upon with endless questions about whether the UK was in a fit state to deliver on its own referendum. Some journalists tried to whip up interest about the potential mayhem the bruised egos on the Tory and DUP benches could make, but it was too late.

After failing to stop the deal at the pivotal vote, the scale of potential opposition ebbed away, given that the principle had been agreed: Brexit was going to happen under the terms of this deal. Any attempts by MPs to tinker with the deal in the later legislative stages were too easily dismissed by ministers, who reminded the Commons that it had agreed 'to get Brexit done'. The issues they raised, such as the size of the so-called Divorce Bill or the shape of the Irish backstop, were too easily tarred as niche complaints or, in a twist of irony, Brexit-delaying quibbles.

As the weeks drew on, the main testament to May's success came from the near-disappearance of the B-word from the newspapers. The only exception was a handful of troublesome and highly speculative articles about trade deals in the business pages. With the UK now set for a two-year transition period, during which a fiendishly complicated trade agreement had to be hammered out, much of the human drama evaporated from the story.

This state of affairs gave May the breathing space to proceed, after a colossal delay, with her domestic political agenda. 'If you took Brexit out of the equation,' one veteran Tory backbencher was fond of telling colleagues, 'you've got a rip-roaring proper Conservative agenda in that Prime Minister. She's rock hard on immigration, sensible on trade and – this is the key bit – all her talk about tackling "burning injustices" helps us steal votes from the Commies.'

In the weeks that followed Mrs May's triumph in Parliament, however, her closest advisers immediately undertook a more daunting task: repairing her reputation. The bitter months of embarrassment, strife and humiliation at the hands of Brussels had left more than a few dents in the so-called New Iron Lady. Tacked to the wall of the Prime Minister's office was a front page from the *Daily Mail*, depicting Mrs May as a high-heeled guardian of Britain, standing triumphantly on the cliffs of Dover. It was perhaps the happiest day for her media team since she had become Prime Minister. But now, May having emerged with many battle scars from Britain's biggest diplomatic challenge since the Cold War, there was little hope of recapturing that same image.

In the end, it was the *Daily Mail* that struck their inspiration again, with an editorial published after the so-called MV3 vote. It was the same piece that had caught the attention of Mr Juncker's assistant in Brussels; it called on the Prime Minister to become 'Britain's own Mrs Merkel'.

'Mrs May drew on her inner Iron Lady to see off EU negotiators and bring home a deal which, despite its flaws, bears many of the fruits of Brexit,' wrote the editorial's anonymous author. 'Now that those short negotiations are behind her, and a vaster array of trade deals beckons her to the United States and beyond, it is time for a change in tack.' The piece went on to cite Angela Merkel, the German Chancellor, as an unlikely new role model for Mrs May, noting favourably her steely resolve, popularity and, above all, reputation for stability. For it was stability, the piece argued, that Britain's exhausted electorate now desired more than anything else.

The editorial went down a storm at May HQ and was quickly canni-balised as their own new media strategy. It was one of those typical cases of a newspaper doing a more effective job at promoting a Prime Minister than her own media team.

A bevy of advisers was discreetly packed off to Germany to find out how Mrs Merkel had managed to stay in power for so many years, seeing off countless new rivals and quelling rebellions in her CDU party. And a consultancy firm was hired, at eye-watering expense, to explore ways in which Mrs May could subtly channel the speech patterns and mannerisms of the German leader. It was noted excitably among her team that the two women already shared much in common, both being daughters of vicars. They were both stern pragmatists; unshowy leaders who preferred to get on with the job and let actions speak louder than words. With such an overlap, May's team said it was not just easy but logical for Theresa to embrace her inner Merkel.

At one point, a junior member of the comms team was overheard wondering why Theresa May couldn't simply be Theresa May. But they were promptly laughed out of the room.

~

Seizing her moment to capitalise on the disarray among her critics, especially given Labour's internal crisis, Mrs May pounced and declared a snap general election in June 2019. To everyone's surprise – even her own – the Prime Minister returned with a respectable majority of fifty seats. The brief, frenetic campaign had zeroed in on the fact that Theresa, as voters were invited to call her, had 'got Brexit done'. Critics pointed out that Brexit was nowhere near done, and that the hardest negotiations were still to follow, but the main platform for that criticism – Labour – was still mired in its own disputes.

The fatal blow was dealt when May purloined a clutch of left-wing economic policies from Mr Corbyn, including plans for an 'NHS of care workers', capturing swathes of the red northern heartlands.

At this stage, all seemed to be going extraordinarily well for the Prime Minister, with an end to the Brexit chaos and a thumping election victory under her belt. Her first move was a daring reshuffle, which showed no mercy to the leading Brexiters who had resigned from her Cabinet in the early days, by leaving them out in the cold. Of course, that was not how she billed it – on the contrary, she was treating a sickly party with bitter medicine that would save the party as a whole.

Those who had advocated what they considered a 'sensible Brexit' – a close trading relationship with Europe that ceded some aspects of sovereignty – were brought on board. Among them was Rory Stewart, rewarded for his tireless work selling the Withdrawal Agreement even though his ministerial brief – prisons – had had little to do with Brexit. He was granted his lifelong dream of becoming Foreign Secretary. Various lesser-known Eurosceptics who had beefed up the majority backing May's deal at the last minute were rewarded by being shuffled into junior ministerial postings. The promising young Housing Minister, Rishi Sunak, was bumped up to be Communities Secretary, becoming one of the most senior members of the Cabinet to have fought for Brexit at the referendum.

But the biggest spoils went to May's most loyal acolytes. Julian Smith was brought out of the shadows as Chief Whip and made Justice Secretary. As for the Chancellor role, that one was an easy choice for May – David Gauke was a safe bet after his years working his way up the Treasury ladder.

Less fortunate was Boris Johnson, who chose to bide his time outside government and explore his options. When the deal passed, he was struck by the eerie sensation of watching history veer off course.

~

As the transition period drew to a close, there was one hiccup: a brief spasm of media interest in Northern Ireland, as some papers reported warnings of loyalist violence. There was even some speculation about loyalist attacks on EU buildings in Dublin, though this did not come to fruition and nor did mass riots.

Businesses – on both sides of the Unionist and Nationalist divide – were relieved that the status quo was being preserved. They knew all too well that a hard border between north and south would be a nightmare for trade – not just because of customs checks but also because of health checks on food and animal products. The same type of disruption would be unleashed on any east–west border, though some businesses had calculated that that would be less severe.

The backstop also came as a relief for many of Northern Ireland's Nationalists, who viewed a hard border with the south as a symbol of British oppression; a return to the bad old days of checkpoints and frontier guards.

And then there was the issue of independent trade policy – and the prize of a US–UK free trade agreement. After all, taking back control of trade policy meant facing down demands from some of the UK's closest allies, particularly the United States.

Embarrassed by photographs of her previous visit to the White House, which had depicted a frail Mrs May walking hand-in-hand with President Donald Trump, the Prime Minister's handlers wanted this time to project an aura of confidence and poise. The 'Mrs Merkel' strategy once again came into play, with the Prime Minister urged to emulate the German leader's firm, unemotive, crystal-clear messaging. There would be no more mystical catchphrases such as 'red, white and blue Brexit'. As for maintaining a steely exterior of determination, no coaching sessions were required – that came naturally to Britain's second female Prime Minister.

In public, the talks seemed to be going very well indeed. The first impression conjured up by Mrs May's bold new style was striking. One photograph of Mr Trump visibly wincing as his hand was locked in Mrs May's iron grip went viral and was splashed across newspapers on both sides of the Atlantic. The image of the 'strong and stable' leader was beginning to solidify into something more than just a catchphrase.

Here, the Prime Minister's supporters claimed, stood a woman who should not be underestimated and who would battle for Britain's interests until the very end. Some, who disapproved of the continental Merkel comparison, dubbed her the Brexit Boudicca, battling for her plucky people, the true heir to Thatcher.

But behind closed doors, it was clear that the power dynamic between Britain and the United States was the very opposite of that suggested by the photograph. The US side was quite happy to allow Mrs May to appear as the more formidable negotiator in public, as it hardly dented their superpower status. But in the backrooms, as the two sides went over the details of the trade deal, it was made very clear who was boss. Britain, the American negotiators made clear, would have to rethink its fundamental red line in refusing to compromise on food standards if a trade pact was to go ahead.

The British had good reason to be wary of allowing cheap imports of America's notorious chlorinated chicken and hormone-treated beef. It was deeply unpopular in focus groups, while the National Farmers' Union (NFU) had made clear that such produce would undercut

British farmers up and down the country. This wariness was informed by painful political experience; Chancellor Gauke remembered, as a junior Treasury minister, how cross the working people of Britain had become when he'd had to push tax hikes on pasties and caravans. Back then, provoking the bakers of Britain into marching down Whitehall was no small feat, and it came as the finishing blow amidst mounting backbench dissent before a hasty government U-turn. Many years on, the Chancellor knew it could get ugly if the NFU was provoked into leading rural Britain in a march on Whitehall.

But the Americans were unsympathetic. 'It doesn't matter how you spin it,' one White House negotiator warned his British counterparts in the early stages of the talks. 'There is no way that this deal will get through Congress if you guys don't go with us on the food standards stuff.' He was referring to America's powerful farming lobby, which wields huge power over the legislative system and which would never accept a trade agreement that didn't stand to benefit them. As creative as the British could be in search of compromise, the Americans were only interested in whatever might see their produce enter new markets.

Labour eventually caught wind of the Americans' demands on food standards, and for a short while the party was united in condemnation of 'Frankenstein' beef and chicken being forced onto British dinner plates by the Tories. In a strange twist of fate, the transition period so despised by Tory Brexiters shielded their party from much of Labour's criticism; two years, the Tories argued, was a very long time indeed to iron out the wrinkles, and so Britons had nothing to worry about. In the meantime, May's colleagues clung to their hopes that the US would come round in the end.

But, unfortunately for May, it was not to be. Within two years, Mr Trump would be out of office and replaced by Joe Biden – a man who made no secret of his wariness towards the British state. The hallowed US–UK free trade agreement vanished from the White House agenda as if it were a cigarette end tossed from a speeding Mustang.

Then, despite Brexit triumphs, promising trade talks with Japan and a raft of popular domestic policies, May's political Ragnarök approached: coronavirus.

By March, cases had sprung up in every region and nation of the United Kingdom, feeding a growing public clamour for action. While the Prime Minister had a carefully cultivated reputation for prudence, that did not mean she was unwilling to take action when her mind was set on it. True to her political instincts as a former Home Secretary, she went for a big, bold, sweeping move: all forthcoming flights into the UK were banned, with anyone who had landed in the past twenty-four hours ordered to go into a fortnight-long quarantine. Meanwhile, external flights out of the UK's main airports were immediately cancelled. If anyone wanted to leave the UK, there was no guarantee that they would be able to return with any ease.

The backlash came immediately, as libertarian critics muttered about May's Stasi-like policies. But she made no apology for taking action that she believed would protect the public.

As the days went by, some pundits said that the steadily rising number of Covid-19 cases suggested that May needed to take further action. And sure enough, it was decided on the first Saturday of March that she would address the nation. To the surprise of few and the fury of a vocal minority, a national lockdown was imposed. She levelled with the British people about the threat, evoking the Blitz spirit with a twist: 'Keep calm and carry on... following the rules.'

Those rules were unprecedentedly draconian, and Mrs May gave no suggestion that they would be relaxed until vaccines were developed. The most notorious edicts were instituted in law, rather than fudged as mere 'advice'. They included a ban on sitting down for a rest while exercising outdoors. This led to uncomfortable scenes for the government, as breathless joggers across the country were fined for taking a moment's pause on a park bench.

Travel in and out of the country was cancelled by train and plane, with the only permitted international traffic being commercial freight. As the year dragged on, a few British families, desperate to ski on the European mainland, were caught trying to stow away on a cargo ship crossing over the Channel.

The 'cargo-gate' scandal capped off a year of increasingly sinister authoritarianism in the eyes of Mrs May's Conservative colleagues, as concerns mounted about whether she was letting power go to her head. Some ruefully argued they had seen this coming, pointing to her controversial decision years before to send vans round the country telling immigrants to 'go home'. One former May ally, who had worked with her back in the Home Office, uttered a cutting jibe at a Zoom-powered lunch with Westminster's lobby correspondents that 'we have gone from go home to never leave home'.

The resolve Mrs May had shown in shutting down the country early was initially met with strong support from the public, despite the libertarian complaints. But it soon emerged that she had few plans of restoring any freedoms until the virus had been completely eradicated. Any suggestions from her inner circle, such as winding down the 'park bench law' or opening up gyms to support public health, were dismissed as reckless.

By the end of the year, her party and the nation saw her less as the grand Merkel-esque mother of the nation uniting her people and more as a harsh Nurse Ratched-like figure: unsympathetic and all too happy to deny people their freedom. And all the while, the silent scourge of Covid-19 raged on. Any attempt by the public to mount a peaceful protest was ruthlessly suppressed, with baton-wielding police stationed around Speakers' Corner and Trafalgar Square to break up gatherings of any size.

Some names came to renewed prominence in this environment. Nigel Farage, who had segued effortlessly from Brexit campaigner to US talk show host, was fined £300 for having a pint of bitter with some friends on a park bench. The experience sent him hurtling back into national politics with a new anti-lockdown party, to the lament of the Tories.

By the summer of 2021, the vaccines had been squeezed into millions of arms, the dust had settled and the nation was moving on. And one balmy Thursday evening, a small group of backbenchers slipped into the Red Lion. They had booked the room upstairs for a private gathering to ensure no one could eavesdrop on their conversations as they slowly and methodically drew up their plans against Britain's second female Prime Minister.

While it was true, they all agreed, that May was 'a tough old bird' and 'a steady pair of hands in a crisis', Britain was now entering a new phase altogether. It was one in which Brexit, compared to the carnage of the coronavirus pandemic, no longer felt quite so important. That game had been won, and the people had received what they voted for.

They were now emerging from a phase where the country was exhausted once more, having sloughed through four years of grit under a stern Prime Minister. Britain, surely, was crying out for a more animated style of leadership, they reasoned.

'Well,' said one grey-suited backbencher as the terms of the rebellion were laid out. 'Let's have a chat with our new leader, shall we? That's him coming up the stairs, I think.'

All the grey heads spun around in the evening gloom. They saw the outline of a figure ascending the stairwell: a brooding fellow, broad-shouldered and stooping a little, with an anarchic mass of straw-coloured hair.

Chapter 18

What if Theresa May had passed her Brexit deal at the third attempt? (2)

Noah Keate

Theresa May walked into Committee Room 14. It was full of Conservative MPs. Covering every part of the parliamentary party, the internal divisions couldn't have been starker. The whips banged on their desks, presenting an illusion of widespread support that was, in reality, long gone. The mood inside the room was uncomfortable. It perfectly reflected the politics of the day: febrile, divided, full of anger.

Why? Brexit, of course. 29 March 2019 was only two days away. The scheduled date on which Britain was meant to leave the European Union; it should have provided closure. But Parliament had decided otherwise – including many Conservative MPs. On 15 January, a date that felt like a century ago, her government had gone down to the largest ever parliamentary defeat in history as the Withdrawal Agreement was rejected by 230 votes. It was a bitter blow only rectified by Parliament voting its confidence in the government the following day.

Barely a fortnight before the committee room meeting, Parliament had again rejected the Withdrawal Agreement, this time by 149 votes. Not even a late-night dash to Strasbourg had been enough to persuade MPs. It hadn't been helped by Geoffrey Cox, May's booming Attorney General, arguing that the UK might remain in the Irish backstop indefinitely. He sat in the committee room glumly, his eyes darting away from the Prime Minister.

Theresa May knew that 29 March was her last realistic chance to ratify the Withdrawal Agreement. A third rejection would eliminate any authority she still had. Last December, the Conservative Party had held a vote of confidence in her leadership. While she'd won the vote, by 200 votes to 117, the victory had been dampened by her needing to promise not to lead the Conservatives into the next election. Today felt like another of those moments. A dramatic statement was needed.

'The Prime Minister,' spoke Sir Graham Brady, the chair of the 1922, the most powerful committee that had toppled Conservative Party leaders past and, perhaps, present.

'Colleagues, we face a serious choice. The Withdrawal Agreement will return to Parliament on 29 March – the day we should have left the European Union.' May paused for silence, looking at the group to recognise their responsibility. 'That day is the opportunity to deliver on the Brexit referendum. This relies on your votes. The deal is the best one to ensure that we leave in an orderly fashion. Fail to back it, and the UK will be forced into European elections in May, with no end of political consequences for our democracy.'

The questions came thick and fast.

'What about the backstop?'

This had been a major point of contention ever since the Withdrawal Agreement had been finalised the previous November. Aiming to preserve peace and trade on the island of Ireland, the backstop guaranteed that, if a new UK–EU trade agreement could not be agreed by the end of December 2020, the whole country would remain aligned to key EU rules.

'Neither side benefits from the backstop coming into force. As a government, we want to use Brexit to trade freely across the world. That's what Liam has being working on.' Dr Liam Fox, the International Trade Secretary, gave the Prime Minister a nod of recognition. 'And the EU has no reason to want the backstop either. Look at what it gives us: unfettered economic access without freedom of movement. The deadline of December 2020 will ensure a decision is made.'

'Prime Minister, shouldn't we just leave without a deal?'

While she assumed the MP was part of the Eurosceptic European Research Group (ERG), she didn't recognise the voice. They all merged into one. It was, of course, unwise to think like that; the decision of every single MP was crucial.

'That is possible on 12 April if this agreement fails. It is the very opposite of leaving smoothly. To leave without any agreement would be a diplomatic failure and cause immense economic difficulties.' The Prime Minister heard groans erupting, but, as she had done throughout her premiership, she carried on. 'Besides, given the arithmetic, MPs would do everything to stop that. If you don't vote for this deal, Brexit may never happen. What a failure that would be!'

'Prime Minister, with the greatest of respect, you have failed.' Theresa May recognised the voice immediately. Steve Baker, MP for Wycombe and ERG deputy chairman, had been instrumental in trying to topple her, repeatedly voting against her agreement. 'You failed to win a majority in 2017, your deal disrespects Brexit and Parliament voted against it twice. Isn't it time you resigned?'

Shouts of outrage and hissing filled the room. Once again, the Prime Minister hushed the protests and regained order.

'Thank you, Steve, for your consistently honest questioning.' Provoking a short amount of laughter, May regretted her inability to express her affable self. 'Over the past few weeks, it has become clear that a renewed change of direction is necessary, not least as Brexit continues to dominate the country's conversation. I can therefore announce that I will not lead the UK in the next stage of Brexit negotiations after we have left.'

For a moment, there was only silence. The Prime Minister waited to let her remarks settle before carrying on:

I am prepared to leave this job earlier than I intended in order to do what is right for our country and our party. What is right? Delivering on the referendum. Ensuring that we leave the European Union. Maintaining stability through the transition period. Ending freedom of movement to have control over our borders. Ending the European Court of Justice's jurisdiction, for control over our laws. Trade negotiations, to ensure the backstop is never used. That is taking back

What if ...

control. That is what we want. We just need to vote for it on Friday
29 March. Then you will have control, with a new leader in place.

There was substantial, though not overwhelming, applause. May could
even spot some of her supporters becoming emotional. She deeply
regretted the end of her domestic agenda. But she recognised that her
time in Downing Street would always have been dominated by Brexit.

Her speech began to change the minds of MPs who were more open
to persuasion. Among them was Marcus Fysh (Yeovil), a long-time
Eurosceptic; he immensely disliked May's Withdrawal Agreement, but
the prospect of no Brexit at all made him reconsider. Similarly, James
Duddridge (Rochford & Southend East) hated the backstop but found the
Prime Minister's argument about ensuring it was never used persuasive.
The fact that leading Brexiters Jacob Rees-Mogg and Boris Johnson now
planned to back the agreement also made him see it differently. Julian
Lewis (New Forest East) was encouraged by May's imminent departure;
a Brexiter could then ensure that the new trade agreement delivered
Brexit.

In sacrificing her political career, the Prime Minister looked set to
perform the impossible. The question was whether Parliament agreed.

~

The debate on the Withdrawal Agreement on 29 March was honest and
frank, though tense. MPs were aware of the frustrations in the country
caused by their failure to pass a deal. Enraged by the deadlock, Nigel
Farage held a protest outside Parliament.

May sat in the Commons listening to backbenchers' speeches. How
they voted was far more important than the opposition front benches, all
of whom had whipped their MPs to vote against the agreement. While
the Prime Minister knew that support for the agreement in her party
had grown since she conceded her departure, she was aware there would
always be some rebels who would never back any agreement. Their
attachment to leaving without any deal was too much. Labour votes
from MPs in Leave seats were vital.

'Today I will vote for this agreement. Not because it is perfect, far from it, but because it provides the country and my constituents with certainty. It allows government and Parliament to focus on essential domestic matters,' said Labour MP Ruth Smeeth (Stoke-on-Trent North), whose constituency had voted heavily to Leave.

'This deal provides stability for businesses and voters. By backing it, Parliament would show itself acting pragmatically on the wishes of voters,' argued Labour's Gloria De Piero (Ashfield), who, despite supporting Remain, was aware of the electoral costs of refusing to back Brexit. May began to feel there was a real possibility of success; both Smeeth and De Piero had previously voted against the Bill.

Finally, the debate drew to a close. The whips gave the result: 'The ayes to the right – 316. The noes to the left – 314.' It had passed. Her agreement, by the skin of its teeth, had been approved. May felt an elation she hadn't enjoyed since becoming Prime Minister. The cheers from her front bench and back bench alike represented a unity not seen for years. She could only hope that this would be repeated across the country, regardless of how people had voted in the referendum – though that seemed unlikely given the cries of 'shame' from the opposition benches.

May indicated to the Speaker that she wished to make a point of order. It was time to take control.

> Mr Speaker, it is fantastic that Parliament has passed this Withdrawal Agreement that will allow the UK to leave the European Union on 22 May in a smooth and orderly fashion. Though passing the agreement by a small margin, this House has respected the referendum result and shown that when voters make decisions they are acted upon. This government and the country will now move forward to forge a new relationship with the world as well tackling burning injustices at home.

Subsequent points of order from the opposition leaders were all negative. It shouldn't have been surprising. The Liberal Democrats had continued to campaign for Remain after the referendum verdict was announced.

The entire purpose of Change UK – The Independent Group, which consisted of pro-Remain former Labour and Conservative MPs, had been to prevent Brexit from happening. They had failed.

Ian Blackford, the Scottish National Party's Westminster leader, shouted:

> Be in no doubt, Mr Speaker, Scotland does not want to leave! This agreement takes Scotland out of the EU against its will and will decimate our economy. The case for independence has only got stronger. We in the SNP will do whatever we can to ensure Scotland rejoins the EU as a free, independent nation.

May was not surprised. Brexit would obviously endanger the union. She was aware that Blackford wouldn't have been so blunt unless Nicola Sturgeon, the Scottish First Minister, had approved his remarks.

The most crucial comments came from the Democratic Unionist Party's Westminster leader, Nigel Dodds. Currently in a confidence and supply arrangement with the Conservatives, their ten MPs had voted against the agreement once again:

> We in the DUP deeply regret that this Withdrawal Agreement has passed. That the backstop remains fails to offer protection and freedom to the people of Northern Ireland. We hereby suspend our confidence and supply arrangement with the Conservative Party. In any future Budget or no confidence vote, our party will abstain. It is only because of who the Leader of the Opposition is that our party won't vote against the government.

Dodds sat down, maintaining eye contact with May. How ironic that the survival of her government would come down to the fact that the alternative was that friend of Sinn Féin, Jeremy Corbyn.

Using her political instinct, May acted spontaneously. 'Mr Speaker, although the Withdrawal Agreement vote was extremely close, this

Parliament has endorsed the government's flagship policy. We believe this vindicates our agenda for office.'

This generated one of the biggest cheers. It was one May herself was tempted to join. 'However, this government's stability is clearly more fragile if it cannot command the support of a majority of members. We will therefore make time for a debate on a motion of no confidence in this government if the Leader of the Opposition tables it.' Given that the vote of confidence back in January had given May strength after her weakness, she felt she had no option but to act decisively.

Jeremy Corbyn remained sitting, unresponsive. His folded arms reflected his relaxed approach towards Brexit taking place at all. Following the silence, Theresa May decided to cherish the moment, asking for another point of order.

'And that, Mr Speaker, tells you everything anyone needs to know about this Leader of the Opposition: constantly voting against legislation, unable to control antisemitism in his own party and always in the knowledge he can't win a vote in Parliament.' The cheers gave the Prime Minister an adrenaline rush she hadn't enjoyed for a long time. Overriding all that was the knowledge that she, her party and the country had seized a democratic victory when it had looked so close to disappearing.

~

The Brexit discussions didn't come to an end on 30 March. Parliament's approval for the UK's departure would never remove strong differences of opinion – but on the whole, the reaction was one of relief. Carolyn Fairbairn, director-general of the Confederation of British Industry, stated that businesses would appreciate the 'stability this agreement provides, giving them time to plan for Britain's post-Brexit future'. Minette Batters, president of the National Farmers' Union, said she was 'looking forward to working with government on future agricultural policy to ensure farmers are represented'. Even Frances O'Grady, general secretary of the Trades Union Congress, was not overly harsh, remarking that while she was 'disappointed, the country needs to focus on ensuring that workers' rights are not sacrificed'.

The collective sigh of relief among journalists that Brexit had been resolved meant that attention immediately turned to May's departure, and to her likely replacement. But her priorities were elsewhere. The local elections were on her mind. Though they appeared trivial compared to the UK's exit from the EU, the Prime Minister recognised their value. As a young party worker, May had always taken her turn delivering leaflets, and the situation was no different now. Journeying across the country to defend Conservative councils, she made the election about the councillors rather than herself. It was the very opposite of a victory tour; whenever the media photographed her, she emphasised the location rather than her political future. In turn this encouraged likely leadership contenders, such as Michael Gove and Rory Stewart, to look even more active in the campaign.

Labour's momentum was falling away. Corbyn's leadership – consistently voting against Brexit and failing to tackle antisemitism – was hurting their appeal. The arguments they made about austerity didn't have the same traction as in 2017. Both the Liberal Democrats and Change UK had lost their key message. Although Lib Dem leader Vince Cable tried to motivate his party members, the party's previous determination over Brexit was gone.

Nigel Farage had formed the Brexit Party assuming that May's Withdrawal Agreement would fail, forcing the UK to take part in the European elections. Now that was redundant, his campaigning faltered. 'While the Brexit Party is bitterly disappointed that this agreement passed Parliament, we're greatly relieved that a second referendum has been prevented.' Asked whether he was leaving politics, Farage quickly dismissed the question:

> Far from it. Brexit doesn't stop now; there's still a trade agreement to be negotiated. Whether she likes it or not Mrs May will soon leave Downing Street. Her successor must be aware that Brexiters haven't vanished. We learned from that mistake when Brexit was almost

stopped altogether. We will hold their feet to the fire. The government must make sure that the backstop is never used, and they must negotiate a Canada-style relationship with the EU. If it looks like Brexit will only be delivered in name only, we will be there to make sure Brexit means Brexit.

In the days after the UK's departure was confirmed, US President Donald Trump tweeted that a UK–US trade deal was 'far less likely' and that 'suing the EU is always the answer'. Despite the subsequent media furore, the polling impact was minimal. The Conservatives enjoyed a nine-point lead over Labour, with a YouGov poll showing that 57 per cent of people were either pleased or very pleased that Brexit was finally happening.

Election night was a time for celebration, with the Conservatives gaining 450 seats and several councils, including Ashfield, Stoke-on-Trent, North Devon and Ryedale. Opposition parties all lost ground. For a party to make such gains nine years into government was a huge victory. The atmosphere was reminiscent of the 2017 local elections before the doomed general election. It was obvious that Brexit's imminence had pleased the public; their voting was an expression of relief that the government had done what they had asked.

The Prime Minister could tell that the voters weren't fed up with her. At door after door, her party's campaigners had found an appreciation that Brexit was finally being done. Though concerns were of course raised about matters such as health and education, voters believed that the Conservatives were the best party to deal with them. May realised that the Westminster animosity didn't match the reality in the country. These brilliant results gave her the mandate to carry on her agenda alongside negotiating a post-Brexit trade agreement. Maybe she didn't need to leave just yet.

Besides, what could the Conservative Party do? She had won a leadership vote of no confidence the previous December and had until 12 December 2019 before she could be challenged again.

The morning after the local elections, May gave a speech outlining her domestic agenda. She aimed to tackle the 'burning injustices' she had spoken about in Downing Street when she had first become Prime Minister. She wanted to show how the state could help people help themselves. Her only regret was that it had taken nearly three years for this to start.

Her speech was vastly overshadowed, however, by the remarks of Nicola Sturgeon. As the leader of the Scottish National Party, her aspiration for independence through a second referendum was well known. She had kept quiet since the Withdrawal Agreement had passed, issuing only a statement of regret. That, however, was about to change. Broadcasters were lucky that Sturgeon's speech began just after May's ended. It was damning.

> What last night's council elections show is that England and Scotland are on two separate paths. England voted to leave the European Union and has rewarded the Conservatives handsomely for doing so. Scotland did not want to leave the European Union. Just as our country keeps receiving Tory governments we didn't vote for, so we are now seeing the full consequence of Tory policies we didn't want. The time, mandate and motivation for separation has never been stronger. If my party is successful in winning a majority of seats in the next Scottish Parliament elections, I will apply for a Section 30 Order allowing an independence referendum to be held. It has become an absolute necessity.

Sturgeon's words came as a surprise. Ever since the SNP had lost a third of their Westminster seats in 2017, they had avoided raising the question of a second referendum. Now the UK's departure was confirmed, alongside the Conservative victory in the local elections, they had the excuse they needed. Few could blame them for trying. Even though the Conservatives were ahead in the polls nationally, in Scotland, the SNP polling lead had grown ever since the Withdrawal Agreement had passed. The future began to look rather less rosy than it had done.

And it was gradually dawning on Conservative MPs that Theresa

May had deceived them. Many of them had voted for the Withdrawal Agreement on its third appearance not because they supported its contents but because it hastened her departure. Now showing no signs of leaving, she had been wholly dishonourable. Despite her immunity from another vote of confidence in her leadership until December, the letters of no confidence to 1922 Committee chairman Sir Graham Brady continued to arrive.

Prospective candidates acted like the leadership election was already taking place. Former Foreign Secretary Boris Johnson announced that he would 'of course' stand when a vacancy arose, believing that he could bring together the party and the country. The International Development Secretary, Rory Stewart, and former Work and Pensions Secretary, Esther McVey, also announced their candidacies. The Prime Minister's chances of pushing through her domestic agenda looked less and less likely.

EU departure day, 22 May, arrived with Theresa May still in office. Although parties were organised to celebrate the occasion, the day itself was anti-climactic. Remainers wished it wasn't happening, while staunch Brexiters felt that their version of Brexit would have been better; their fears over the backstop remained strong. Across Europe, any sadness about the UK's departure was secondary to final campaigning for the European Parliament elections. 11 p.m., the exact moment of departure, came and went with little fuss. A new era in Britain's future had begun.

It would transform the Prime Minister's future. The following morning, she received a call from Brady asking to see her in person. As the representative of all the Conservative MPs, he was one of the few people whose requests would always be answered in the affirmative.

Brady's face was ashen. May knew what was coming.

'Prime Minister, the 1922 Executive Committee have met. We all agreed that your position is rapidly becoming untenable, and this reflects the mood of the parliamentary party. Many have spoken of the betrayal they feel from you going back on your promise to step down, not least when your deal passed by such a narrow margin.'

May wasn't going to give up immediately. 'But what about the local elections? We performed brilliantly. I've got a whole domestic agenda to implement.'

'Prime Minister, with the greatest of respect, those local elections were a Brexit surge any party leader would have seen. The success wasn't predominantly down to you. In any event, the executive has decided that, should you fail to announce your date of departure within twenty-four hours, we will reconvene to decide whether to change the rules on a no confidence vote. My assessment is that you would not survive such a vote.'

The Prime Minister knew the game was up. It was better to leave with dignity, on her terms, than to be abruptly forced out of office. She nodded to Brady, aware that she would need to let the Queen know of her intentions.

At 10 a.m. on 24 May, Theresa May announced that her resignation as leader of the Conservative Party would take effect on 7 June.

While it will always be a matter of personal regret that I was unable to implement more of my domestic agenda for the country, our nation and Parliament can look proudly on having delivered the result of the referendum. The United Kingdom can now chart its new journey as a free and independent country.

The battle to find her successor was on.

~

The leadership contest took place more quickly than anyone had expected. With the relief that Britain had finally left the EU, several MPs felt liberated to seek power. Needing to win over the parliamentary party first, every candidate tried to please everyone. Some stood no chance of winning; their candidacy was entirely for self-promotion.

Numerous Cabinet members stood, including Michael Gove, Matt Hancock, Andrea Leadsom and Sajid Javid, as well as former ministers like Dominic Raab. Even the Chancellor, Philip Hammond, stood, arguing that his position in government made him the most competent candidate. Though initially tempted to stand, Steve Baker backed Boris Johnson, who was gaining widespread attention.

However, it was Liz Truss's campaign, promoting a free trade agenda, that got off to the best start, with the rising stars Rishi Sunak, Oliver Dowden and Robert Jenrick all endorsing her vision.

Naturally, the numerous rounds of the election made tactical voting inevitable. After the first round saw Leadsom, McVey and Hammond all eliminated, Matt Hancock withdrew to back Liz Truss. Initially a Remainer, she had become a full-throated Brexiter since the referendum, using her position as Chief Secretary to the Treasury to promote the cause of economic freedom.

Truss's, Johnson's and Stewart's were the campaigns gaining momentum. Stewart had engaged in numerous 'Rory walks', where he would spontaneously speak to members of the public. While it gained traction on Twitter, it was unclear whether Conservative MPs were impressed.

With Sajid Javid losing the next round and backing Truss, the tide was turning. It was precisely because Truss appealed to Remainers and Leavers, social liberals and conservatives, that her campaign was so far so well. However, although by the third round Truss had received enough votes to be sure of coming in the last two to face the Conservative membership, victory was not guaranteed. With a defeated Dominic Raab backing Michael Gove, Truss could face a Brexiter who would use her Remainer status against her.

She wanted to face Rory Stewart in the membership vote. Agreeing to every interview, his popularity was far greater outside the Conservative Party than within. But in second place in the latest round was Boris Johnson, and he was bound to win the party membership – they loved him. With a few votes to spare, Truss discreetly encouraged some of her supporters to vote tactically in the next round.

It worked. Johnson lost by one vote to Stewart and was knocked out. This came as an immense surprise. That he would eventually become Prime Minister was a foregone conclusion; his rivalry with David Cameron and his annual leader-like speeches at Conservative conferences had always given the impression that he was destined for the top job. Why had he fallen?

As allies would later admit, there were many reasons to explain his defeat. His performance as Foreign Secretary had been poor, damaging the UK's reputation. Throughout his time as an MP, he had failed to spend time making alliances. Though presenting a confident demeanour, not least in his *Daily Telegraph* columns, in person he was far shyer. While Conservative MPs knew that he could win – he had triumphed twice in London as mayor – he seemed an unnecessary risk. They were far ahead in the polls and had just performed strongly in the local elections, while it was unclear whether Johnson really appealed outside the M25. His band of supporters was not large enough.

Boris Johnson imagined life in an alternative universe, had May's deal not passed. What if Article 50 had been extended? What if the European elections had taken place, to the benefit of an insurgent Brexit Party and the Liberal Democrats alike? It was one column idea among many he could never construct.

Liz Truss was delighted. She would now face either Michael Gove or Rory Stewart. Though Gove was a tougher opponent, she doubted whether the membership would endorse him. And Johnson had never forgotten what Gove had done to him in 2016 – first supporting Johnson's leadership campaign before ditching him and running himself; that was far worse than any manoeuvrings by Liz Truss. Johnson still had enough support to swing votes against Gove. And Gove's chances were not helped by a biography alleging cocaine use. Whatever Truss's or Stewart's flaws, Gove couldn't be trusted. It was perhaps this factor, above all, that cost the Environment Secretary his place in the final contest.

The debates between Stewart and Truss were firm but cordial. They expressed their disagreements respectfully. Stewart continued his walks in different parts of the country, but they were losing their novelty value. He gave the impression of wishing that Britain had voted Remain, seeing Brexit as a problem to manage rather than an opportunity to embrace. His endorsements from both *The Guardian* and Nigel Farage's new Reform Party hardly helped his case, with the latter arguing that Stewart 'would be the biggest vote generator for our party since Ed Miliband'.

Truss conducted a dynamic and optimistic campaign, creating memorable 'Liz for Leader' and 'Leave with Liz' merchandise. She spoke time and again about the benefits the new trade agreements would bring the UK. She championed freedom at home with friendly relations abroad, arguing that the UK should re-establish its Commonwealth links.

On 23 July, Truss won with over 62 per cent of the vote. The size of her victory was undoubtedly down both to her dynamic ideas and to her opponent. On winning, Truss said:

> The choice facing Britain is stark. More of the same or a new, bold future? My government will offer the latter. Now we have left the European Union, our country's opportunities know no bounds. Enterprise, freedom and Conservative values are here to stay. Whatever your background, it is our one United Kingdom where everyone can succeed.

The day was Liz Truss's. From tomorrow – 24 July 2019 – it would be the country's too.

~

Liz Truss's premiership got off to a brisk start. She wanted to be a Prime Minister with energy, who commanded respect and loyalty. To gain support from the parliamentary party and the country, she appointed a number of her leadership rivals to key positions. Michael Gove became Chancellor, while Rory Stewart was appointed Defence Secretary; whatever their differences, Truss and Stewart were united in agreement on defence. Dominic Raab became Foreign Secretary, Priti Patel was Home Secretary and Jeremy Hunt returned to his favourite position as Health Secretary.

Truss needed to prove her Brexiter credentials. Eurosceptic backbenchers were deeply unhappy that the choice of leader had been between two Remainers – and Farage's new Reform Party could never be underestimated. Truss knew that the issue would shoot back up the agenda as the transition period ended. Steve Baker, who had consistently voted against the Withdrawal Agreement, was appointed International Trade Secretary, while Suella Braverman became Education Secretary, Esther McVey ran Local Government and Jacob Rees-Mogg was Environment Secretary.

The most important appointment was Boris Johnson. Though regretting his leadership failure, he gladly accepted being made Minister for the Cabinet Office. It gave him significant influence in government and mirrored his time as London mayor in City Hall. The challenges were, of course, far bigger.

Truss's first few weeks in office couldn't have bought more favourable press coverage. Headline after headline touted her as the new Iron Lady, with polling showing the Conservatives 12 per cent ahead of Labour. Many of her senior advisers urged her to call an election in her honeymoon period. After all, she was running a minority government.

Truss resisted. Winter was approaching, the public was fed up with repeated votes – one of the reasons she had opposed another referendum – and, most importantly, it looked too opportunistic. Although her advisers tried to convince her to run a campaign based on giving her a strong hand in Parliament to help negotiate a trade agreement with Brussels, in reality Parliament wasn't proving a problem. It had passed the Withdrawal Agreement, albeit by a small margin, and the DUP would abstain on any Budget votes, giving her an effective majority. The Prime Minister wanted to avoid the trap Theresa May had fallen into in 2017, calling a snap election for no strong reason.

In any case, under the Fixed-Term Parliaments Act, two thirds of all MPs had to back an early election and few of the opposition parties would. Labour and the Liberal Democrats still hadn't recovered from Brexit and the local elections, and the SNP was concentrating on the 2021 Scottish Parliament elections, which were just around the corner.

The Prime Minister spent her first weeks in office travelling the country meeting people. From fishing in Scotland to manufacturing in Sunderland, she wanted to reinforce her determination to achieve national renewal outside the European Union. She took the time to visit the Irish border, making it clear that technology would ensure the backstop was never enforced.

While people were pleased to see her, reality obviously needed to match the rhetoric. No Queen's Speech had taken place since June 2017. In September 2019, parliamentarians were recalled to Westminster a week early to allow the government to outline its agenda and test its support. Failure to pass the Queen's Speech would make an election inevitable.

The government's main proposals included strengthening Britain's 5G network, investing in transport infrastructure, increasing educational freedom and reducing individuals' tax burdens. It was the return of a Thatcherite economic agenda; Brexit and the EU were hardly mentioned. David Frost, the long-term Eurosceptic who had replaced Olly Robbins as the Prime Minister's Europe adviser leading the negotiations with Brussels, was fully aligned with Truss's future vision: Britain open for business.

Despite a new occupant in Downing Street, Jeremy Corbyn's attacks remained the same: 'Mr Speaker, this Queen's Speech provides no protection for workers and fails to deal with the Irish border. Isn't it time the Prime Minister admitted the UK should join the customs union?'

Although Truss easily batted away Corbyn's remarks, mentioning his association with Sinn Féin and support for Irish unification, she knew that he'd hit on an underlying truth. Negotiations had not been going to plan. Although the Queen's Speech passed the Commons, Truss was beginning to realise that being Prime Minister was very different to travelling across the country giving speeches.

Frost had been unable to find a technological solution that would prevent the Irish backstop coming into effect. Truss tried to accelerate the negotiations on a comprehensive free trade agreement in discreet meetings with EU negotiator Michel Barnier, French President Emmanuel Macron and German Chancellor Angela Merkel, but no solution was found.

The joy of Conservative Party conference provided a brief distraction from the Prime Minister's woes in Brussels. Walking on stage to the iconic sound of 'Land of Hope and Glory', the Prime Minister spoke about patriotism throughout history. Looking ahead to future trade deals, she aimed to match economic liberalism with respect for her nation's traditions. Her speech was well received, praised by journalists and going down well in the polls. Putting her vision of optimism into practice seemed to be working. Jacob Rees-Mogg offered support mechanisms for British farmers; Jeremy Hunt was increasing the scope for private contractors in the NHS; and Priti Patel was aiming to raise police numbers. A prime ministerial trip to Australia and New Zealand gave Truss a chance to start reconnecting with the Commonwealth, building links she had always felt had been weakened with Britain inside the European Union.

Despite the problems over Europe, a Christmas opinion poll showed the Conservatives ten points ahead. Truss reached the end of 2019 content with her first five months in power.

~

The New Year, however, did not start well. EU negotiators were refusing to move on to matters like fishing rights until the problem of the Irish border had been solved.

Truss decided to take matters into her own hands. A bold move was needed to shock the Europeans – something that Theresa May had never managed. Truss entrusted Boris Johnson with introducing an External Market Bill, which, regardless of the outcome of the negotiations, would allow the UK to trade however it wished. 'This Bill is a final resort should a trade deal not be reached,' he argued. 'It ensures that the UK can fulfil its freedom as an independent, self-governing nation outside the European Union.'

Justified as an insurance policy for the UK, the Bill created a vast international uproar; there was widespread condemnation at the UK being seen to defy the terms of the Withdrawal Agreement. Parliament began to flex its muscles again, and the Bill only passed with an amendment from Bob Neill and Hilary Benn requiring parliamentary approval before any of the Bill's powers were used. Truss realised that pursuing a full, unfettered Brexit was impossible in this House of Commons.

The case for a general election was now overwhelming. Parliament had shown itself as obstructive, and this was obvious to voters; the divisions received widespread coverage. The Conservatives still led in the polls by 8 per cent; that Labour was gradually increasing its support only reinforced the case for an election now rather than later. The Liberal Democrats would support an early election; under their new leader, Jo Swinson, they were forging a post-Brexit vision based on the closest possible relationship with the EU. The final argument for an election was the gradual growth in support for the Reform Party, using the media to campaign for a harder Brexit and socially conservative values. An election now would catch Farage's party unawares. Scotland was a problem, with the thirteen Conservative seats under threat from the nationalist surge, but Truss thought the Scottish Conservatives under Ruth Davidson's strong leadership stood a chance as the leading Unionist party.

Like the Withdrawal Agreement, a trade deal with the EU would need parliamentary approval. Truss pictured the campaign: a Conservative majority would deliver economic freedom instead of permanent European alignment; bold innovation against tired, failed ideologies. The Conservatives would become the full Brexit party, using their reinforced mandate for economic liberalisation.

She thought the best time to announce the election was 17 February, the Monday after Valentine's Day. Her aim was to hold the vote on 7 May, allowing for a long campaign to distinguish the Conservatives as the best party and capitalising on longer, warmer days as spring turned into summer. Over the next few weeks, before announcing the election, Truss would try always to make clear the benefits of what a strong Conservative government could do in power.

On Thursday 30 January, the Prime Minister walked to her daily morning briefing and spotted Cabinet Secretary Mark Sedwill holding her briefing notes. 'Good morning, Mark!' She spoke positively, happy with her forthcoming decision to announce an election. 'What's on today's agenda?'

'Good morning, Prime Minister.' He handed over the documents with a serious demeanour. 'There's something quite important for you: a new virus, a new coronavirus, specifically.'

'Thanks, Mark.' Truss had already heard about the new virus in the Chinese city of Wuhan. But it was a problem on the other side of the world. 'I doubt it will cause us much trouble.'

Chapter 19

What if Boris Johnson had won the 2019 election with only a small majority?

Josh Bartholomew

12 December 2019, CCHQ

After seven long, enervating weeks, the staffers at CCHQ were feeling the tension as the clock ticked towards 10 p.m. on election day. The opinion polls pointed their way, but that had also been the case in 2017, and Boris Johnson's steady lead had dwindled as the campaign went on.

The clock struck ten, and the characterful timbre of Huw Edwards's voice diffused through the Conservative Party's silent headquarters. The silence lasted only moments, though – soon, CCHQ was a scene of jamboree and jubilation as the prediction of a 24-seat Conservative majority was broadcast to the nation.

The one man declining to join in the celebrations was Isaac Levido, the party's canny campaign director. His face was a contradictory combination of fatigue and relief, but also the glum realisation that the 'Get Brexit Done' slogan had been unable to resonate with the northern voters that the party had been so keen to represent. Although Jeremy Corbyn's personal leadership had proved far less popular than in 2017, the bonds of years of Labour allegiance were too strong to be broken by a single issue. The Red Wall remained intact, though 'Get Brexit Done' had chipped its brickwork.

Meanwhile, at Labour's Millbank headquarters, the scene was funereal. It was a stark contrast to the shocked celebrations of 2017, when

Labour had defied the odds to deny Theresa May an overall majority. Corbyn, and Corbynism, had now been repudiated by the electorate, though not as strongly as some had prophesised. The silver lining – that Labour had managed to hold much of the Red Wall – came as little consolation to the staffers who had devoted themselves to 'the project', much as it had in 2010, when Gordon Brown's success in maintaining support in Scotland was dwarfed by failures elsewhere.

Party	Vote share (%)	Seats	Change from 2017
Conservative	42	337	+16
Labour	35	233	-29
Liberal Democrat	12	15	+3
SNP	3	41	+13
Green	3	1	–
Plaid Cymru	2	4	–
DUP	0.9	8	-2
SDLP	0.7	3	+3
Sinn Féin	0.7	7	–
Alliance	0.7	1	+1

13 December 2019, BBC, *One O'Clock News*

Boris Johnson insisted that his mandate to execute Brexit was 'irrefutable and indisputable' in his victory speech after last night's election result. The Prime Minister's Conservative Party won a 24-seat majority in the polls, allowing Mr Johnson to carry out his Brexit pledge. The Prime Minister was speaking only minutes after Jeremy Corbyn appeared on TV, promising to step down after 'a period of reflection for the party'.

Speaking to Conservative members at the Queen Elizabeth II Centre in London, Mr Johnson said the election win means he will finally be able to carry out his Brexit deal:

'My friends, for too long, we have been obstructed by the intransigent, obstreperous Remainers in Parliament. For too long, our Brexit-voting friends have been ignored. For too long, the intelligent will of the many has been blocked by the noisy resistance of the few,' the Prime Minister said, in a nod to Jeremy Corbyn's famed slogan.

> But as I speak to you this morning, after the most successful Conservative campaign since 1987, I say to you that these days are now gone. We have been granted an unequivocal, irrefutable, indisputable mandate to Get Brexit Done. And that is what we will do. No ifs, no buts, no maybes – we will leave the European Union by 31 January, and this One Nation Conservative government will oversee the greatest change in a generation.

Analysis, BBC political correspondent

This was a stoic, triumphant speech from the Prime Minister, who will have been delighted to secure a solid mandate and another five years in Downing Street. While the Conservatives did not manage to break down Labour's Red Wall, as many had predicted they would, Johnson's victory is a triumph for the Conservative Party and sets the platform for a full term in power.

It isn't all positive for the Prime Minister, though – having been unable to win the thumping majority most had thought possible, he will need to be adept in managing his party to avoid going down the route of John Major's 1992 government. Much as Theresa May was, he could well find himself at the whim of the more radical members of his back benches.

For the Labour Party, it is another dismal day. They have now endured four consecutive election defeats, and the halcyon days of New Labour's successful electioneering seem a lifetime ago. With Jeremy Corbyn's admission that he will step down by February, a fierce fight will be under way to become his successor. As is so often the case with the Labour Party, the next couple of months promise to be ridden with passionate infighting and factionalism.

27 February 2020, Keir Starmer elected Labour leader

Labour leadership election results, first round: Keir Starmer 44 per cent; Rebecca Long-Bailey 20 per cent; Laura Pidcock 19 per cent; Lisa Nandy 17 per cent.

Second round, after eliminating Nandy and transferring her votes: Keir Starmer 55 per cent; Rebecca Long-Bailey 24 per cent; Laura Pidcock 21 per cent.

Despite the defeat of Corbynism in 2019, its roots remained intact, and two of his closest acolytes launched a bid to replace him: Rebecca Long-Bailey and Laura Pidcock. Although 'the project' remained partially popular within the party, Long-Bailey and Pidcock had each refused to step aside for one another in the name of ideology; Brown and Blair this was not.

It meant the Corbynite vote was largely split, although it would not have been enough to topple Starmer, whose confident intellect was enough to impress, though not dazzle, the party faithful. Besides, Corbyn's personal weakness was the greatest reason for Labour's loss the previous December; appointing a new leader in his mould was not in the interests of the membership.

Much as it had been in 1983, the Labour Party was keen to appoint a leader of exactly the opposite type to the predecessor. Just as Neil Kinnock had been a steadying hand after Michael Foot's utopian inspiration, Keir Starmer was a figure of stable erudition who contrasted well with the chaotic leadership of Jeremy Corbyn.

28 March 2020

Only months after Boris Johnson's triumphal address to Conservative members, a dark cloud had fallen over the Prime Minister and the country. Having passed his Withdrawal Agreement in late December 2019, Johnson expected that he would be remembered as the leader to oversee Britain's exit from the European Union. Instead, he was faced with the greatest crisis of a generation. The freedom-loving Prime Minister was forced to strip his citizens of their most basic liberties, imploring them to 'stay at home'. Despite concerns from the libertarian wing of his party, the Coronavirus Act 2020, which gave the government powers not seen since the 1940s, passed Parliament with ease due to the support of the Labour Party and their newly elected leader, Keir Starmer, despite his concerns over the delay in locking down.

31 March 2020, *The Times*

Boris Johnson's decision to wait two weeks before following scientific advice to lock down will likely lead to thousands of extra deaths, a leaked government document has claimed.

Despite the SAGE committee's recommendation on 14 March that a lockdown was the only way to control the exponential spread of infection in England, the Prime Minister was reportedly reluctant to reduce his subjects' liberty in such a fashion, and so he held off until backlash from the opposition became impossible to ignore.

Keir Starmer, Leader of the Opposition, said: 'Boris Johnson's delay in impos- ing these restrictions is a display of negligence, and must be answered for by the government. The Labour Party demands that the Prime Minister begins to explain his carelessness. Until he does so, we will refuse to support the government in any further Covid restrictions.'

Facing severe opposition from both sides – the libertarian wing of his own party and the Labour Party – Johnson was locked in an inescapably difficult position. Public opinion was turning against him, too. Far from the 'rally round the flag' effect in the polls that many had predicted, the bewilderingly high rate of infection had seen the Tories' poll advantage subside dramatically. Where before they had held a sixteen-point lead over a Labour Party still recovering from its fourth consecutive election defeat, their lead had fallen to only two points in the wake of a strong public backlash to Johnson's reluctance to impose lockdown.

It was a sombre mood within Johnson's inner circle. With public sup- port declining so quickly and a Labour Party willing to strike, a sense of reality was beginning to overwhelm the Prime Minister and his advisers. But they had a plan.

If they were to invite Labour for coalition negotiations, they could make the opposition complicit in the crisis by association. There was the added bonus that it would be likely to encourage a show of national unity, much as the wartime coalition had in 1940. The key questions, alas, were similar to those faced by the Conservatives in 1940: would Labour agree to enter coalition? And would they agree to serve under Boris Johnson? The latter was not even a question that Johnson had considered, but Starmer would have the opportunity to answer it the next day.

1 April 2020, Cabinet Office

The next day, the Leader of the Opposition was invited to the Cabinet Office by the Cabinet Secretary, Sir Mark Sedwill. The senior civil servant was asked by the Prime Minister to leave the room, though, when negotiations began.

Johnson, keen to set the agenda as ever, tried to initiate some introductory terms of agreement, but Starmer interjected before he could begin. 'Prime Minister, thank you for inviting us down here, but I'm sure you'll appreciate that there are some crucial questions surrounding your leadership that we must discuss first,' the lawyerly leader said.

The statement shocked Johnson. He struggled to hide his consternation over the realisation that he might have to step down not even a year after winning the job he had sought since he was a child. Seeing the Prime Minister's discomfort, Starmer broke the silence again. 'We think a new government calls for a new leader. We firmly believe that it's in the national interest.'

It was not the response Johnson had expected. Having approached a Labour Party that had spent the past ten years in opposition, he and his closest advisers had thought their proposal would be accepted without a second glance.

Johnson, still stunned, managed to muster up the words to explain that he would need to speak to his advisers and closest political confidants, and the two leaders went their separate ways.

2 April 2020, Cabinet Office

The Labour team returned the next day unsure of what to expect. Starmer and his advisers knew that Johnson was extremely unlikely to accept their proposal; rather, it was simply a case of drawing out as many concessions as possible.

Johnson opened the meeting: 'Well, Sir Keir, thank you for joining us once again, but I'm afraid I have bad news. Your idea of replacing me simply won't wash. I'm afraid this is a take-it-or-leave-it offer.'

Starmer's team had planned for this scenario and quickly went into negotiation mode, recalling the spirit of Lord Mandelson in 2010. Recognising that the Labour left would take some persuading, Johnson was willing to accede to all but the most brazen of demands. By the end of the meeting, Labour had picked up a vault of coalition policies: additional financial support for those who were infected and forced to isolate; a promise of pay rises for nurses by the end of the parliament; a commitment to a cross-party vaccine task force. It was a platform Starmer found agreeable.

Starmer would become Deputy Prime Minister, with three of his shadow Cabinet appointed to a coalition Covid response group of nine: Starmer, Lisa Nandy, Anneliese Dodds and Jonathan Ashworth would sit alongside Johnson, Matt Hancock, Dominic Raab, Michael Gove and Rishi Sunak.

4 April 2020, *The Times*

The new coalition government was last night plunged into chaos as the Prime Minister and his closest advisers all tested positive for coronavirus, as well as the Health Secretary, Matt Hancock. It is understood that Keir Starmer, Johnson's Deputy Prime Minister, will deputise in his absence and run the government.

A senior government source said there were concerns in the administration over Starmer's ability to lead so soon after entering Downing Street. 'One wonders whether the government would have been better placed with a more experienced politician in charge. I can only imagine how Gove, Raab and Sunak feel about being overshadowed so quickly,' a source said.

This development comes after Richard Burgon, secretary of the Socialist Campaign Group, criticised Starmer for his decision to enter coalition. 'Keir Starmer's decision to go into coalition with the Tories is an abominable, treacherous moment in our party's history,' the MP for Leeds East said. 'He claimed he was trying to follow in the footsteps of Harold Wilson, but clearly he is paying homage to Ramsay MacDonald. In years to come, the Labour movement will remember his betrayal. Agreeing to serve under a criminally negligent Prime Minister betrays all the values of the Labour Party and shows that Starmer is willing to write off the ideology of our movement just to gain power.'

In only three days, Keir Starmer has gone from Leader of the Opposition to Deputy Prime Minister to running the government. It remains to be seen whether Johnson will suffer badly from the virus or not, but the real test is facing Keir Starmer: has he got what it takes to manage the greatest crisis in a generation?

8 April 2020

The Prime Minister's condition was quickly deteriorating. Since coming down with the virus, he had been largely bed-bound and unable to concentrate on government business, but he was now struggling to breathe. There remained little option other than to admit him to St Thomas' Hospital.

Starmer, meanwhile, was excelling in the forensic detail of running the government's Covid response. Where Johnson had been unable to grasp the gravity of key statistics, Starmer could swiftly identify the issues, the solutions and where the government should focus its dwindling resources.

Starmer's capability was coming across to the public too. Though Johnson's personal ratings had seen a slight uptick since he caught the virus, Starmer's public image was steadily improving.

11 April 2020, BBC

The Prime Minister was last night moved into an intensive care ward as he continues to battle with Covid-19.

The reality of his condition is being closely guarded by Downing Street, but an official statement said that it had 'worsened' in recent days. The Queen has been kept informed about Mr Johnson's health by No. 10, according to Buckingham Palace.

An official Downing Street statement said: 'The Prime Minister has been under the care of doctors at St Thomas' Hospital in London, after being admitted with persistent symptoms of coronavirus. Over the course of the past three days, the condition of the Prime Minister has worsened, and, on the advice of his medical team, he has been moved to the intensive care unit at the hospital.'

Keir Starmer, the Deputy Prime Minister who is currently in charge of the government, said: 'This is a hugely worrying development. I, and the rest of the country, will be hoping against hope for a quick recovery.'

14 April 2020

Though the Prime Minister's condition had stabilised, Starmer was continuing to excel. His approval ratings were continuing to improve steadily as his calm handling of the crisis proved a stark alternative to Johnson's boosterish optimism – a quality the public did not appreciate as hospitals reached capacity and numbers of deaths soared.

All was not well within the Conservative ranks, though. Gove and Sunak, who had taken it upon themselves to lead the party in Johnson's absence, were unhappy that Starmer had taken advantage of the Prime Minister's illness. They were continually briefing against Starmer; he was accused in the press of political opportunism, and falsified rumours that he was willing to continue serving under Johnson after the Covid crisis were proliferated to turn Starmer's back benches against him.

It had little effect. For all the criticism he had attracted after the coalition negotiations, Starmer's insistence on becoming Deputy Prime Minister was paying off handsomely. Neither Gove nor Sunak had any constitutional route to leading the government, for all their Machiavellian moves.

Days later, as Johnson recovered and left hospital, it became clear that the public saw no reason for Starmer to relinquish his role just yet. Besides, it was not a question that needed answering: Johnson was recuperating at Chequers with his partner, Carrie Symonds.

16 April 2020, meeting between Starmer, Gove and Sunak

Starmer: Thanks to you both for joining me – there are a few things I want to discuss after recent events. I've been in this game long enough to know that it's you two who are providing the newspapers with untrue gossip, and it needs to stop.

Gove: I mean, with respect, Deputy Prime Minister, you haven't been in this game very long at all.

Starmer: I've been in it long enough to know that I have to be wary of you, Michael.

Sunak: Could you provide us with some proof of this, Deputy Prime Minister?

Starmer: I'm not looking for an argument; I'm here to tell you that it needs to stop. This crisis is difficult enough without your childish games. If it goes any further, I'll have to take it to the Prime Minister.

Gove: Well, I certainly thank you for that input, Deputy Prime Minister. I'm sure the Prime Minister would very much appreciate that.

Sunak: Is that everything?

22 April 2020

As the days passed, Johnson gradually recovered from his illness and returned to Downing Street revitalised and with a renewed sense of purpose around the gravity of the Covid situation. Having, by his own admission, come close to death, he was well aware of the dismal reality of the UK's fight. He vowed to be careful as the UK sought a return to normality; he was insistent on avoiding another lockdown.

Having locked down earlier than the UK, other countries were beginning to open up again. To Johnson's and his backbenchers' great frustration, government scientific advisers were warning that it would be months before the virus was at a low enough level for the UK to do the same. The Prime Minister was paying the price for his early indecisiveness.

Within Downing Street, few were more thankful for the Prime Minister's return than Gove and Sunak. Starmer's Stakhanovite approach to the crisis had left little room for politicking, and Gove and Sunak had paid a heavy price. By the time Johnson returned, Gove in particular was being left out of government meetings.

Starmer was quietly happy to return to being Deputy Prime Minister in role as well as in name. He had safely navigated a real test of his leadership; Johnson would have to make the difficult decisions on the easing of lockdown, not Starmer.

Although he may have been pleased that Johnson had relieved him of taking charge of the government, however, the public were not. They had rallied round Starmer as their nominal Prime Minister; the Labour Party had drawn level in voting intention. With innumerable challenges still to come for the Prime Minister, it was a lofty position for Labour to find itself in given where it had started, and one that they had not at all expected four months before.

24 May 2020, *The Guardian*

Boris Johnson said that the coming months will be 'times of joy' for the UK as he announced his plan to lift lockdown restrictions in an address to the nation last night.

Johnson, who caught the virus himself six weeks ago, had previously vowed to be cautious in easing restrictions, but Labour insiders say that the Prime Minister had gone against scientific advice in his address. 'Discussions over the easing of lockdown have brought about a fractious split inside the government,' a source said. 'Keir Starmer is very much on the side of caution – he wants to avoid another lockdown at all costs – but Johnson is under significant pressure from his backbenchers and Rishi Sunak, who is extremely concerned about the economic difficulty that will stem from lockdown being extended.'

It is the first real sign of discord between Johnson and Starmer, whose management of the crisis has been fairly harmonious up to this point.

26 May 2020

Johnson's decision was met with glee on the rebellious Tory back benches. Despite scientists' fears of a second wave, the Prime Minister had vowed to open the hospitality industry by July and promised that the country would have moved past Covid by the end of the year.

Johnson had avoided what would have been a mutinous split in his party – but he had opened one in the Labour Party. Starmer had opposed Johnson's plan, but his parliamentary party was fearful that, as a result of their complicity in the easing of lockdown, they would face political consequences down the line.

Johnson's acquiescence to his backbenchers meant that the lifting of lockdown passed easily, but not without a 123-strong rebellion within the Labour Party. With over half of his MPs opposing the government,

Starmer was in a worrying position: stick with the Conservatives and risk hugely damaging splits within his party, or leave the government and risk potential public backlash for putting party before country.

There was one other option, favoured by most of his front bench: stay in the government but try to oust Johnson. The difficulty for Starmer was that this was wholly unprecedented. Lloyd George may have forced Asquith out in 1916, but they were from the same party. For Starmer to remove Johnson would be constitutionally concerning, at best. He would most likely require an election to do so.

However, given the disintegration of public trust in the Prime Minister, it was no surprise that the public were far more cautious in their approach to easing restrictions than the government. This played into Labour's hands.

27 May 2020, meeting of Labour ministers

Starmer, pensive as ever, consulted his closest ministers on the best path to follow. Although the likes of Angela Rayner, Nick Thomas-Symonds and Rachel Reeves were not on the Covid committee, they had still been in the coalition's wider Cabinet.

Rayner: In my view, you've got to go for the kill. Screw the Tories. If you don't, we'll pay the price further down the line.

Thomas-Symonds: But Angela, that's seriously constitutionally damaging. I don't know how you could sell that to the public.

Rayner: You wouldn't need to. They already want it.

Nandy: In fairness, I don't think it's possible to say that. We need an election.

Reeves: But how can we have an election in the middle of a crisis this big? We'd never live it down with the electorate. Besides, if we were governing on our own, we'd probably bear the brunt of the second wave that is undoubtedly coming.

Starmer: Thanks, Rachel. Anneliese, what do you think?

Dodds: I'm not really sure, to be honest with you, Keir. I think there are useful arguments on both sides.

Starmer: Right, thanks for that...

31 May 2020

The coalition trundled on. Starmer could not find the will to force Johnson from office, especially so soon after his illness. Besides, an election was not a desirable outcome for anyone, with infection numbers still high and the threat of a second wave in the winter.

The Labour Party was not best pleased. Johnson's position at the helm of the government was so imperilled that his poor personal polling was beginning to affect Starmer's party, who were seen as culpable by association.

3 June 2020, meeting between Johnson and Starmer

Amidst growing pressure from his party, Starmer visited Downing Street to raise personal concerns over the speed at which Johnson was planning to ease restrictions.

'I'm concerned, Prime Minister, if I'm honest. I really don't think it's possible that we've extinguished Covid in the way that you claim. I'm losing the support of my party, and that is really damaging for the government,' said Starmer.

Johnson retorted in his typically cavalier manner.

'Well, Keir, yes, that is certainly a concern. But what I would say is that there is a theory that we could just squash this disease. We've built up so much immunity that Covid possibly will never return. And on that second point about your party; I think you should assess whether you actually support this government. If you are not willing to support our plan, perhaps there is no place for the Labour Party in government any more. The British people are sick of their liberties being limited by this wretched disease, and your party seems intent on ensuring that this hell continues.'

Starmer, now with his tail between his legs, initially nodded along but was so incensed by Johnson's last remark that he offered his own riposte: 'Well, let me tell you, Prime Minister, if your plan goes as badly as we think it will, Labour will no longer be in government with you.' Not normally a man accustomed to such a hostile tone, Starmer looked almost as shocked as Johnson and left the room quickly.

4 July 2020, *The Guardian*

75,000 dead, but Johnson marks VC day by declaring freedom for all.

The Prime Minister today claimed that coronavirus had been 'destroyed by the Herculean effort of the British people' as the incidence of the virus fell to its lowest rate since March. Despite the highest death toll in Europe, Johnson relaxed most social distancing restrictions, opening up all the hospitality sector. The only remaining restrictions surround face coverings, which must still be worn on public transport, and mass gatherings, which have been limited to 10,000 people.

Mark Harper, chair of the Covid Recovery Group (CRG), is thought to have played a crucial role in forcing the Prime Minister's hand. A Downing Street source said: 'Had it not been for the knowledge that he would face a significant challenge from his back benches, the Prime Minister would likely have been more cautious, especially given his personal experience with the virus.'

Harper and Johnson are rumoured to have met in Downing Street before the Prime Minister released his plan for easing lockdown in May. The support of Harper and the CRG may become all the more important in the coming months, given the divisions within the coalition government that have developed since Johnson released his roadmap out of the crisis. The Deputy Prime Minister and Labour leader, Keir Starmer, has reportedly been edged out of crucial government business after expressing his fears over the roadmap.

A leading government scientist expressed concern over the rate of easing: 'It is simply impossible to say that we have beaten this virus. We saw an enormous second wave with the influenza pandemic in 1918; the likelihood of a second wave of coronavirus is extremely high.'

25 July 2020

A matter of weeks after lifting restrictions, Johnson's plan appeared to be going as badly as the scientists had predicted. Infection rates were growing rapidly, as were hospitalisations. It was only a matter of time before hospitals started to be overwhelmed again.

For Starmer, it was the final straw. Having lost most of his influence in government, he was now being partly blamed for its disastrous approach. That evening, he visited Johnson in Downing Street and informed him of his decision to withdraw from coalition.

26 July 2020, Keir Starmer speech to the Parliamentary Labour Party
'Thank you for joining me today. I won't keep you long, but I'm sure you will be happy to hear me say that I have decided to formally withdraw the Labour Party from the coalition government.

'Although the opportunity to serve in government was a welcome one for our party, I cannot support the Prime Minister in his approach to coronavirus. He has pandered to the extremist wings of his party; I believe that it is no longer in the national interest for Boris Johnson to be this country's Prime Minister.

'As soon as Parliament returns from recess, I will be submitting a vote of no confidence in the government.'

2 September 2020, *The Times*
Johnson vows to battle on after scraping through no confidence vote.

The government last night won a vote of no confidence by only four, preventing the calling of an early election. The vote, forced by Leader of the Opposition Keir Starmer, finished 327 to 323 after ten of Boris Johnson's MPs rebelled against his leadership.

Johnson, who has faced severe public opposition after adopting a controversial 'herd immunity' strategy to combat coronavirus, was reported to be 'highly concerned' about the risk of becoming the first Conservative Prime Minister since Stanley Baldwin in 1924 to lose a vote of confidence in his leadership.

5 April 2022, Boris Johnson speech to the nation
'My friends, we have just come through the greatest challenge this nation has faced for decades. Thousands have tragically died, and our economy had suffered the biggest downturn in a generation. Yet I have never been more convinced of the indefatigable British spirit; this crisis will be remembered in history for the strength of the British people more than anything else.

'And one of the greatest lessons you can learn from history is that a crisis is perfect timing to stop, take stock and re-evaluate priorities. Having done so at great length over the past weeks, I have decided that it is time to give you – the Great British people – the chance to decide who you wish to see you through the recovery from this wretched virus. I have gained authority from Her Majesty the Queen to call a general election on 8 May.'

6 April 2022, YouGov opinion polling

Johnson's manoeuvre shocked Starmer and his advisers, who had expected that the Prime Minister would battle through to the end of the parliament in 2024, even as his political capital began to wane. It was a large gamble, especially given the deadlock in the opinion polls. But then again, for Johnson – the perennial political chancer – gambling had produced handsome rewards before, and he hoped it could do so again. Our latest polling shows: Conservatives 40 per cent; Labour 39 per cent; Liberal Democrats 9 per cent; Scottish National Party 5 per cent. This election is too close to call…

Chapter 20

What if the UK's Covid response had been led by a woman?

Richard Brooks and Amanda Chetwynd-Cowieson

August 2021

Theresa caught her breath. She stopped at the top of a small ridge and turned round, expecting Philip, as he always was, to be a short distance behind her. When the television cameras were on the couple, they had to walk side by side at a frustratingly slow pace, but out here in the seclusion of Gornergrat, she could stretch her legs. Philip didn't mind; he never did.

She turned, shielding her eyes from the sun to look at her husband of forty-one years next month, and smiled. Even in her darkest moments, she found the fresh air and isolation of Zermatt to be rejuvenating. Now, on the precipice of her greatest political triumph, it was exhilarating.

The irony wasn't lost on her. The most (in)famous trip she took here was back in July 2017, when she had decided to call that snap general election. Look at how that ended. What a nightmare. But now, in the summer of 2021, she was ready to go again. There were whisperings about another vote – there always were – but no one knew, not really. They thought she would wait until summer 2022, when things would be properly 'back to normal', but she knew better. Don't let things drift; strike while the iron is still hot. She had learned that the hard way.

And why not? There was no serious opposition to her in the party any more. The raucous briefing wars that had characterised those horrible two years from 2017 to 2019 had quietened to the sound of a whimper. Even Boris Johnson, the bane of multiple Conservative leaders' existence, wasn't making much of an impact with his silly Covid Recovery Group and his increasingly inconsequential *Telegraph* articles. He didn't have the numbers, and he knew it. All of those weak, weak men now pledged fealty to her and no one else.

They had always underestimated her; the old grey men in their dark suits and those Bullingdon boys. Boring they called her – boring! Too safe, too cautious. Yes, she had a grasp of her policy brief, but people didn't want that in their politicians any more, did they? They wanted 'personality' and the ability to 'energise'. Until, of course, boring began to sound rather excellent, thank you very much. It's all fun and games when it's trade agreements and interparty warfare, but when the proverbial hits the fan, you want a woman in charge.

And speaking of interparty warfare, she noted with some satisfaction that she was currently polling fifteen points ahead of what was left of Jeremy Corbyn's Labour Party. How that man managed to stay as leader after losing control of so many of his MPs, and after that damning Equality and Human Rights Commission report essentially called him and his party institutionally racist, she'd never know.

You'd never see that sort of thing with the Conservative Party – why, she was the first Prime Minister to choose a BAME Chancellor of the Exchequer! And the rank and file loved Sajid Javid.

The last time she had seen Corbyn, a couple of months ago in Parliament, he had looked genuinely quite ill. Although, that might have been because a significant minority of his MPs were voting with the government, not with him. God bless Lisa Nandy and David Lammy.

Clearly Corbyn didn't want to carry on, and she assumed he was only being forced to because Seumas, Karie and Len knew that when he went the whole house of cards would fall down. Despite her sly remarks in Parliament to the contrary, she knew most Labour members didn't want him to continue. She, on the other hand, very much did.

She almost felt sorry for Corbyn, repeatedly attacking AstraZeneca and the rest of 'Big Pharma' at the beginning of the pandemic, despite the fact that it was clear they would be the ones getting the country out of this; producing the vaccines in record-breaking time; saving thousands of lives at home and abroad. The flip to then demanding that the MHRA approve Russia's Sputnik vaccine was a bizarre move, even for him. Amber Rudd, her deputy and Home Secretary, had particularly enjoyed tormenting him about that one at PMQs.

As Philip finally started to draw level with Theresa on the ridge in Gornergrat, she knew that she didn't need to worry about opposition parties for a long while yet. Even Nicola Sturgeon, a constant thorn in her side for so many years, no longer looked invincible. The spring of 2021 had seen her prevaricate on Covid restrictions north of the border and struggle to answer questions about her role in the Alex Salmond affair. As a consequence, and perhaps most damningly for her political project, the SNP's poor performance in the Scottish elections meant they were short of a majority at Holyrood, undercutting their argument for a second independence referendum. Her long-running Scottish Conservative leader, Ruth Davidson, continued to make inroads, and the sharks had already begun to circle.

Theresa had far grander designs these days. She bestrode the world – alongside fellow members of her 'squad', Harris, Ardern and Merkel – like a colossus. Like Gordon Brown and the financial crash, her premiership would be defined by her assured response to a crisis both at home and abroad; it wasn't a comparison she usually encouraged, but on this occasion she was happy to oblige. Her vaccine programme had broadly gone off without a glitch; the comparisons with Trump had been entirely favourable; and the UK's economy looked to be bouncing back as well as could be expected. Even von der Leyen, a horrid woman who had started off her reign even more arrogantly than Juncker, had seen the way the political tides were shifting and jumped on board.

All the challenges that had stood before her – uncontrollable back-benchers, a resurgent Labour Party, Scottish independence and the European Union – had been conquered. Life, for now, was good.

She thought back to those dark days of 2019.

Everything had changed.

March 2019

She remembered crowded meetings, with heated tempers coming from all corners; MPs from *her own party* jumping at the opportunity to trash her live on *Peston*; the constant shouting of that man with the sodding loudhailer outside Parliament. The stress of the 2019 Brexit saga felt like a different lifetime compared to the eerily empty corridors of Westminster she had grown used to throughout the pandemic. And there were very few Conservative MPs who went on TV to criticise her now.

After years of painful political machinations, it had only taken one afternoon for her to outmanoeuvre her challengers, decisively proving them all wrong, again. It was the morning of the dreaded 1922 Committee meeting. Her director of communications, Robbie Gibb, was uncharacteristically silent as he sat in her office, reading and rereading the speech that she was to give that evening. It was sad that it had come to this, but she was to offer to stand down ahead of the next stage of Brexit talks if they finally gave in and passed her Brexit Bill. Even though she had made her choice, she couldn't help but run through the options in her head, just one more time.

She knew that one of the reasons why she was so reluctant to go was because her replacement would likely be Boris. She admonished herself for being so churlish, but she could be honest to Philip and Robbie that it bothered her. She had tried everything else: offered those Labour rebels much more than a Conservative Prime Minister should have had to; piled pressure on them when that failed. Her luck had run out.

They'll be gone at the next general election either way, she thought.

By that point, the numbers were so close that she had almost hourly calls from MPs, begging her to give it one more try. *It wasn't her they needed to call*, she wanted to scream. But that was when good fortune knocked on her door – or, indeed, Caroline Flint did.

Without waiting for an answer, the Labour MP for Don Valley had barged straight in. Rude. Out of breath. 'We've got them!' she exclaimed. 'They're in. Seventeen in total. They're in!'

Everything happened so quickly after that. Bercow, finally caving in and allowing another vote on 29 March, of all days. The man was always desperate for drama. She watched triumphantly as one after another, seventeen Labour MPs made clear that they would vote for the deal, Withdrawal Agreement, Political Declaration and all. Flint had come through, though it had taken her long enough. Driven by a mix of vocal constituent anger, loathing towards Corbyn or, like Kate Hoey, much deeper ideological reasons, they certainly made for an unusual grouping. But she'd only had to make minor concessions in the end, which made no difference to her final goal. Pass the deal this year, in full, and get Brexit done.

Oh, the pained expressions on John McDonnell's and Tom Watson's faces. She knew then that it was over. And so did everyone else. The second that Julian Smith, her ever-reliable Chief Whip, started recording the new names, the previously coy Tories saw the way the wind was changing and realised that the time for abstaining was truly over. The vote count took longer than normal; the tension in the chamber palpable. She could faintly hear the man with the megaphone. She twitched the speech she was holding. She had waited a long time to give this and intended to savour every single victorious word.

316 for. 314 against.

The sound in the chamber was unlike anything she had heard before. Speed was key here. Stand up tall. Deliver the speech – finally – and watch Labour implode. Stare down the ERG. They couldn't exactly ask for another vote, or for a different one. The tweet doing the rounds was by the BBC's Laura Kuenssberg, gleefully explaining, 'This vote is a first, in that well over half of the House will be furious it passed. And yet it somehow did.'

It was over the course of the next month that Theresa first considered calling an early election. She knew that Boris, Baker and the Brexiters were regrouping, waiting for another moment to strike, even as they pledged their loyalty while talking to Kay Burley on the green. They would find another reason to try to oust her; that was obvious. But even they knew they had missed their moment. She was safe for this year.

With some notable exceptions, she was riding high on the praise from her party. Philip Hammond, for his part, knew that his time was up.

He had told her privately that when she next reshuffled, he would like to step down as Chancellor. The idea of actually delivering Brexit was one he could not consider. She would soon happily oblige. Others were, perhaps, taking it too far, with Rishi Sunak's interview for *The Spectator* a bit sycophantic even for her taste. Angling for a promotion from his role as a junior minister, as ever.

'Watch out for that one,' Ken Clarke had told her, only half joking. But it had genuinely pleased her to see some of the more sensible members of the party return to the fold. Rory Stewart, Antoinette Sandbach, Sam Gyimah – all friends and colleagues who were to play pivotal roles in the fight against Covid but who had been pushed to breaking point by Boris, Michael Gove and the other 'Spartans' in the Brexit debate.

Labour was having an awful time of it. The lack of retribution for the seventeen MPs who'd voted for her deal had finally pushed the party's Remainiac wing over the edge. The press said they had lost over 100,000 members in the week since the vote after their calls for the rebels to be expelled had been ignored. Clearly, Corbyn and McDonnell were at odds; their conflicting comments to the media were excruciating, if satisfying, to watch. The posturing of what felt like every single Labour MP to take over the leadership was welcome, in a way. Not only had Labour helped pass her deal; they seemed even more determined to implode than they had before.

The six-month transition period was to end, appropriately, on 31 December. Theresa was confident that 2020 was going to be a fantastic year for Britain.

January 2020

It started on New Year's Day. She loathed the enforced festivities of the season and the constant carousel of parties and fundraisers. Rubbing shoulders with the not-so-great and the less-than-good trying to hawk her a new bit of fintech or introduce her to someone 'mutually beneficial'. She used to look forward to 1 January: a sign of new beginnings and for the graft to begin again.

Mark Sedwill, her understated national security adviser, told her that the World Health Organization's China office had been informed of a pneumonia-like virus in Wuhan, with an unknown cause. She immediately felt uneasy, knowing that he wouldn't be alerting her unless he thought it had the potential to escalate. Despite her public protestations of continuing George Osborne's 'golden era' of UK–China relations, she had never fully trusted Xi Jinping or the communist country. She knew this made her antiquated in the eyes of the media elite.

So, something to keep an eye on, but she was ensconced in No. 10, busy reshuffling her Cabinet and making plans for the year ahead. 2020 was to be a year of new beginnings, with a post-Brexit domestic agenda to finally deliver – and that meant new personnel. A Cabinet that reflected modern Britain, to her mind. Sajid to Chancellor; Amber back as Home Secretary now that Windrush was finally out of the headlines; Penny staying at Defence; and Matt Hancock at Health. She was particularly pleased with Copeland's new MP, Trudy Harrison, at Education. A non-university graduate in a role that had historically been too dominated by the alumni of the Oxford Union.

And she enjoyed the fact that despite the overarching conclusion that 2017 'hadn't worked', she could still point to fresh faces and 'non-traditional' Conservative backgrounds on her front bench. She hadn't founded Women2Win for nothing. As she told Philip, with the necessity of Brexit compromises over, it was time to put principles into practice. No more prevaricating; decisiveness was the order of the day. And with women making up half her Cabinet, and only a third having been to Oxbridge, she felt confident that they were presenting a new face of the party to the nation.

So, she asked Sedwill to ensure that a daily Wuhan update was part of her morning briefing and to monitor the situation together with Hancock. But she didn't think too much more of it in early January. It was during another round of protracted negotiations with the DUP's Nigel Dodds that she was told Wuhan was 'going into lockdown'.

The briefings from Sedwill and Hancock continued to be inconclusive, but clearly there was a major problem. Coronavirus cases were beginning to be found in other countries, including Japan and Thailand.

It was obvious to everyone that Xi Jinping and the Wuhan authorities were more focused on reputational damage limitation than any actual limitation of the next SARS.

On 24 January, she attended the first COBRA meeting on the new virus. Chris Whitty, the softly spoken chief medical officer, was clear. There was no 'good' option, merely a choice between the 'least worst scenarios'. They should work on the assumption that without a firm idea of how many people were arriving from China each day, it was a case of *when* the first cases would be found in the UK, not *if* they would be.

That happened just five days after the COBRA meeting, on 29 January, when the UK's first case of coronavirus was found in York. The day after that, WHO declared a global health emergency.

She thought that, at worst, several thousand people who had been to the region would get it, and that the number of British-born nationals who would die from it would be incredibly small. But it was clear that firm action had to be taken, and soon.

The job of Prime Minister is particularly lonely at times of crisis. As her government stood on the edge of an unprecedented emergency, Theresa felt that isolation more acutely than ever. She wished that Fiona and Nick were allowed to be by her side; they'd know what she should do.

Maybe 2020 wasn't going to be so fantastic after all, she thought grimly.

February 2020

She was happy to shut down the borders. Her critics suggested that she was almost too happy to do so, and they might have been right, with numerous political cartoons suggesting she would bring back the 'Go Home' vans. The Prime Minister's patriotic duty was the protection and security of her people; she made no bones about it. The radical left and those citizens of nowhere might protest otherwise, but she felt that the voters understood. Frankly, she was relieved to be leading when her expertise was most needed. On Brexit and on the economy, she had been second-guessing herself. No longer. It was also an opportunity to show proof of concept for some of the things Dave had blocked her from doing as Home Secretary. She just needed the right time.

And SAGE handed that to her. At their meeting on 3 February – their third on the virus so far – it was agreed that travel restrictions from China alone would be of minimal effectiveness. People were sly and would go to great lengths to get around restrictions when they had a target country in mind, as she knew only too well. So, to buy the NHS the extra month it would need to prepare, she would have to think bigger.

In the upstairs flat at No. 10, it took her and Amber less than ten minutes to agree: from Monday 10 February, the United Kingdom would ban all flights from countries with recorded cases of coronavirus. There was a tricky trilateral with Arlene Foster and Leo Varadkar to check that the island of Ireland was in lockstep too – as well ensuring that the DUP wouldn't oppose the measures in the Commons. Fortunately, New Zealand's leader, Jacinda Ardern, had already gone a step further, closing borders and enforcing a fourteen-day quarantine for new arrivals. The business implications were very different for the two countries, but it helped make Theresa look less like a 'panicking, over-protective mother hen' or whatever it was Mark Francois had called her. Businesses would just have to deal with it, and her Business Secretary, Greg Clark, would just have to deal with them. Thankfully, nothing lowered the blood pressure quite like spending prolonged time with Greg.

The week after, in mid-February (the same day that the UK's closest neighbour, France, announced the first death from the newly named Covid-19), she gave her first Covid-related speech to a packed Commons. The mood was low and the chamber quiet, only punctuated by previously innocuous coughs and the immediate recoiling of the MP's closest neighbours. Fear and confusion hung over Westminster like smog.

'We are asking everyone in this country to limit their travel, and if they have been to the affected areas, to isolate and submit themselves for a coronavirus test as soon as possible,' she urged.

Deep breath, shoulders back, look up. Now for the big finish.

'We may have to go further and faster, soon. But we will do so as one

United Kingdom and as one people. This may well be one of the greatest tests our country has ever faced. We will meet it, head on.'

In a rare show of unity, all sides of the House and all parts of her party supported her. Inviting Sturgeon, Drakeford and Foster into COBRA meetings with her had helped, as had her briefings to the various metro mayors in England. They couldn't disagree if they had been in the room where the decision was made, could they? There were some off-the-record briefings, of course, but at this point that was white noise to her.

The real problems started when she made the decision in late February to cancel all major sporting events. She knew that it would be unpopular with both the public and Parliament, but she was not prepared for the level of vitriol some of her male colleagues threw at her. She got Jeremy Wright at DCMS to make the announcement that Cheltenham and all other major sporting events were postponed indefinitely. But the backlash on her was furious and not helped by 'allies of Jeremy' making clear their reluctance to enforce such a 'radical pre-emptive decision'.

She would have thought that the horrific images beaming into everyone's living rooms from northern Italy would have given people pause for thought. Apparently not. The furore only started to calm down when Liverpool's manager, Jürgen Klopp, whose side were meant to be playing Atlético Madrid at Anfield the following month, came out in support of her decision. Quite how people had expected the Spanish fans to be allowed to come to Liverpool given that they weren't even allowed to go to matches in their own country was unfathomable to her. But it seemed that people needed to hear it from the manager – and a man, to boot – before they piped down.

Trudy wasn't having a much better time of it at Education. Pushed into a corner at the most recent Education Select Committee, she'd made the mistake of referring to pubs and bars as second-order priorities compared to children's education. She was right, of course, but she incurred the wrath of the hospitality industry, their expensive PR agencies and a large proportion of her fellow Tory MPs.

To cap all this off, earlier in February, Theresa had made the difficult decision to cancel her constituency engagements and encouraged others to do the same. For this, she was roundly mocked by her colleagues. A particularly biting quote (off the record, of course) in the London Playbook suggested, 'Where I'm from, we're not afraid to shake hands with the people who voted for us.' This was allegedly accompanied by some actual chest thumping. Alison McGovern had told her this was toxic masculinity 101. Theresa didn't quite know what that meant, but it sounded about right.

March 2020
She regretted David Davis's resignation – she had always liked him, despite herself. But it was always going to end this way. Now that the Brexit drama had been overtaken, she didn't need his particular set of talents on the front bench anyway, so his resignation – accompanied by a holier-than-thou letter, telling her he was stepping down due to 'significant and irrevocable concerns about this government's civil liberties policies' – was probably best for all involved.

David was at the vanguard of a group of idealistic Conservative MPs who couldn't seem to get their heads around the fact that in times of emergency, the government steps forward, not back. Strong and stable leadership, some might say. The received wisdom from many of her own MPs, and even a handful of her scientific advisers, was that she had 'gone too soon'. The British people wouldn't stand a long lockdown, they told her. She found unlikely allies in Rory Stewart, Nicola Sturgeon and Diane Abbott, which naturally made her incredibly nervous.

With an irritatingly small majority dependent upon the DUP, she knew that she was in a dangerous place. She was about to announce the single biggest expansion of the state into the public's lives by a British Prime Minister since the Second World War. Just seven Conservative MPs holding her hostage could derail her plan, wasting precious time.

The only consolation was Corbyn. He had clearly lost all perspective on the situation. There really was no other explanation for it. Attacking the government during a national crisis was not exactly a vote winner at the best of times, but alongside his undermining of support for AstraZeneca was his equally strident apologism for China. While unhelpful to her in one respect, his stubbornness and overtly partisan attitude had its benefits. His attacks on the government's lockdown policies, and his hesitancy in calling out Xi Jinping, often put him on the same side as Boris Johnson. Labour Party members could forgive many things but not that.

It was this, she assumed, that drove Lisa Nandy to reach out. Maybe her calculation was that showing leadership at a time of national crisis, on policy areas which Labour members supported, would endear her to them at some point in the future. Or, because of her Brexit stance, perhaps she considered her chances of being a frontbench Labour politician to be over anyway, so she didn't care any more. Certainly, there was an appeal to others who joined her, like David Lammy, to just stick it to the current Labour leadership.

Either way, Theresa didn't mind. Passing longer-term Covid-19 restrictions was going to be as difficult as it was important; she needed every vote she could get. Her backbenchers would be the first to go, and if she wasn't careful, the DUP too. And the support of Labour MPs at odds with the leadership wasn't exactly a bad look for her in the future.

In exchange for her support and that of around fifty of her fellow Labour MPs, Lisa drove a hard bargain. On top of the furlough scheme and small-business support that Sajid was already set to announce, they demanded a £20 uptick in universal credit for a year; an independent commission into the disproportionate effect that Covid was having on disadvantaged communities; and specific efforts to support women in the workplace and at home.

'Why do I get a distinct feeling that we've just been mugged,' muttered Robbie after the second and more tempestuous meeting. Theresa's team and Lisa, Caroline Flint and the TUC's Frances O'Grady had been gathering in secret for weeks, and tempers were running hot. No matter. The deal was done and her measures guaranteed. The Labour MPs were taking a massive risk with them as well, she reminded her staff, as she washed her hands for the eighth time that day.

On Monday 10 March, she got her spokesperson, James Slack, to brief that she would be hosting an unprecedented press conference the day after. Peston had texted James back immediately to ask for more information, but she told James to ignore him. She couldn't risk confused details leaking out before the event itself.

The measures got final sign-off the morning of the press conference with Sajid, Amber and Hancock. They were ready; the room was all set up. She personally got James Slack to check the sturdiness of the NHS plaques on their podiums before the cameras were allowed in. Despite the severity of the occasion, she allowed herself a brief moment of appreciation for the Downing Street press room. Stately, not too fancy, did the job. Much like her, she believed. Neither were going anywhere any time soon.

'Good afternoon everybody, and thank you for coming,' she said to the ten socially distanced journalists in front of her. 'I have just chaired a meeting of the government's emergency committee, including ministers from Scotland, Wales and Northern Ireland.' A cough would be particularly disastrous during this speech, she thought.

Deep breath before the more controversial parts.

If you have symptoms – either a new and continuous cough or a high temperature – you must stay at home. We do not yet fully know how this disease is spread, and therefore we are asking everyone, where possible, to limit human and physical contact. I know', she paused for effect, 'that it is a very British thing to stop and talk to your neighbours or to shake hands with people you meet. But sadly, now is the time to stop doing that.

As well as this, we will be extending our ban on major public events, such as sporting fixtures, until at least June. I know this is disappointing for many. As we've said over the past couple of weeks, the scientific advice is that banning such events will have a significant effect on the spread of the virus.

On to the grand finale.

I am afraid to confirm that we will – I repeat – *will* be closing schools
for the next three weeks, at least. While I am aware that this is a
significant challenge to young people and their families, not to do so
would cause more harm than good at this time. I hope to allow schools
to return after the Easter holidays, and the Secretary of State will be
announcing support in the coming days for those who will have to
undertake some form of home schooling.

The next section of her speech had taken the longest to write. It was the
part she and the Labour rebels felt most strongly about:

For those who feel unsafe staying in their homes because of a partner's
or a family member's domestic violence, I want to be clear. The stay-
at-home rule does not apply to you. You can travel if you need to, and
I am announcing an additional £200 million of funding for women's
refuges to be able to support this. For pregnant women, specific measures will be announced in the coming days to make sure that during
your medical appointments and when giving birth, you are not alone.

'Well done,' said Sajid, waiting in the wings offstage.

'Thank you,' she replied, 'but that was the easy bit.' She knew greater
troubles were to come, likely beginning tomorrow with Sajid's own
moment in the limelight: his first Budget as Chancellor of the Exchequer.

Bizarrely, some corners of the press seemed more interested in the fact
that she was wearing a jacket she had worn just the previous week, rather
than the fact she was announcing the almost complete shutdown of the
UK economy. Well, that was one thing Sajid wouldn't have to worry
about, she thought wryly.

As it happened, Sajid's speech was nearly derailed by the news that
Italy was shutting down its whole hospitality and retail industries. They
knew that the scenes from their European neighbours meant urgent
action was even more important, and the grim reality seemed finally to
be permeating into the heads of Conservative MPs.

Javid had only taken over as Chancellor two months before, and now he was announcing one of the biggest interventions in British history outside wartime. The stakes couldn't be higher. Nor the situation odder, with Sajid giving his speech to a half-empty chamber. But as he finished, the markets rallied and political journalists tweeted their positive reviews. His measures were popular and his performance assured. £20 billion of extra Covid support and more than double that in social programmes, recognising that Covid-19 could exacerbate the burning injustices of the country. Lisa got her universal credit uplift, and Conservative MPs got their tax breaks for small businesses.

Theresa's and Sajid's announcements brought the country dramatically to a halt, as intended. London Marathon cancelled; care homes locked down; local and mayoral elections delayed: it all happened so fast. But while the crisis gathered pace, the government broadly looked like it was in control.

But a week that had, politically speaking, started well, was destined not to end that way.

Nadine Dorries had tested positive for Covid on 11 March. This was concerning enough, as it meant a minister in Theresa's own government was the first high-profile case in the UK. But worse yet, Nadine had kept her diagnosis secret and had continued coming to work. Bad enough in any circumstances, but particularly so when Theresa was expecting Members of Parliament to lead by example. Nadine was meant to have been a nurse, wasn't she?

Theresa knew there was a certain degree of scepticism within the Conservative Party about the seriousness of the virus, but this was surely a whole new level? Nadine's whip was suspended – which was called an 'over-reaction' and 'reopening old wounds' by Mark Francois. It begged the question what Francois and company thought was an appropriate reaction to putting the safety of Commons staff at risk.

April 2020

The Dorries Affair was one of the reasons why Theresa spent early April fighting her backbenchers as well as the virus. Her calls for post-Brexit unity had clearly fallen on deaf ears. And her personal appearance was under continuous scrutiny, with even Gove getting caught by a BBC camera commenting about her hair looking 'frazzled'. As she told him later: 'Of course it's messy, Michael; I've closed the bloody hairdressers.'

She went on the offensive, creating a series of cross-party MP working groups for different areas affected by the pandemic – on the face of it to advise ministers but in reality to help ensure support for her measures. Jeremy Hunt was to chair a new Covid-19 health group, made up of MPs from clinical backgrounds, including Rosena Allin-Khan, Paul Williams and Maria Miller. Justine Greening chaired its education counterpart, which included former teachers Emma Hardy and Steph Peacock. A rod for her own back, perhaps, but the polls showed that the public were overwhelmingly supportive, even if Hancock was not. The education group was already clamouring for free laptops and improved broadband access for under-privileged children, with the health group focusing on mental health support. The tensions between Hunt and Hancock were as predictable as they were irritating, but she was clear: leave the infighting to Labour. Now was the time for pragmatism, not public spats.

Some colleagues had other priorities. Liam Fox continued his personal private protest of lobbying the Prime Minister for a sped-up relaunch of Premier League Football.

'The people need it, Prime Minister.'

To which she curtly replied: 'No, the men would like it; there's plenty of other things to be getting on with.'

It seemed that others were indeed getting on with their own plans. Boris had been caught going round to his father's for a dinner party, despite the lockdown rules stating that you could not mix between households. A video taken by a neighbour of him skulking out of his back garden was trending on Twitter – not a good look. The *Daily Mirror*'s headline of 'One Rule for Them, Another for Us', was particularly piercing, she thought. Thankfully, she didn't have to make excuses for him any more and simply chastised him in an answer to one of Pippa Crerar's questions at a press conference.

She understood that people were 'longing for a summer of freedom', as Boris had opined. But the situation across Europe and the numbers coming from the NHS were worsening. She was personally pleased with her tart response: 'That unfortunately means – for the foreseeable future – no pubs, no travelling and no dinner parties. Lockdown means lockdown.'

May 2020, Sky News

'A typically pessimistic speech this evening, as we've come to expect from the Prime Minister. And here with a response to her most recent press conference, we have – via video call of course – deputy chair of the Covid Recovery Group Steve Baker, and backbench Labour MP and sometime supporter of Theresa May David Lammy.'

Adam Boulton turned to Baker's screen first: 'Mr Baker, let's start with you. What did you make of the Prime Minister's press conference this evening? Do you agree with Ken Clarke's assessment that "If there was ever a time to be a bloody difficult woman, this is it"?'

'Well, frankly, Adam, I'm stunned.' Twenty years of forced indignation meant he had his performance close to an art form. 'What we heard from the Prime Minister this evening was nothing short of a surrender. We may as well go to Wuhan and fly a white flag if that is going to be our attitude. Cases are going down, deaths are going down and the British public are clear: while we must take sensible precautions, our civil liberties must be returned to us. We have to learn to live with this virus; not live in fear of it.'

'OK...' Boulton hesitated, before moving on. 'And to you, David Lammy. What did you think? Alongside other Labour MPs, such as Lisa Nandy, you have been an on-and-off supporter of the Prime Minister these past few months. Can she continue to rely on your vote?'

Lammy was not happy. 'The Prime Minister may have won plaudits for her response to the original outbreak of Covid, but I'm afraid she appears to be spending more time recently listening to hard-right MPs like Steve here than to the British public. I am, of course, happy to work with anyone to deliver for my constituents, but unfortunately tonight we saw more of the old Theresa May; the one who delivered the hostile environment to the immigrants who are currently holding together our NHS. The same Theresa May who was the architect of the Windrush scandal and brought the disgraced Amber Rudd back into the centre of government; the Theresa May who oversaw the tragedy of Grenfell and did nothing to…'

Adam interrupted. 'I'm sorry, David, we're going to have to stop you there. We have a breaking story we'd like to share with our viewers.'

He turned in his chair, to view his colleague on another screen. A wry smile threatened to escape his lips. 'So, Beth, breaking news out of Durham this evening, am I right?'

His colleague responded quickly, tweaking her earpiece. 'That's right, Adam. Many of the wider public might not know too much about Dominic Cummings, leader of the Brexit campaign, on–off adviser to Michael Gove and popularised in the critically acclaimed Channel 4 drama *Brexit: The Uncivil War*…'

Chapter 21

What if Rebecca Long-Bailey had won the Labour leadership contest in April 2020?

Paul Richards

The result, when it came, was no great surprise.

After a protracted Labour leadership contest fought against the familiar backdrop of electoral defeat but also on the untrodden ground of a global pandemic, the results played out how the candidates, the pundits and the media had expected. For the first time in the party's 120 years, on 4 April 2020, the winner of Labour's leadership contest was announced not in a central London conference venue but online. With 490,731 votes cast on a 62.58 per cent turnout, the three candidates secured the following shares of the votes: Lisa Nandy 22 per cent; Keir Starmer 27 per cent; but the winner, with 51 per cent on the first ballot, was Rebecca Long-Bailey.

Rebecca Long-Bailey, then aged forty, had first been elected to Parliament just five years earlier, after a career as a solicitor. She was the first woman to be elected leader of the Labour Party. Her achievement was all the more remarkable when one considered that she had only joined the party in 2010, as it was leaving office, and she had spent the previous thirteen years, while Labour was in government – the whole of her adult life up to that point – without filling in a membership form.

As the analysts and commentators pored over the results, two things were clear. First, that the endorsement of outgoing leader Jeremy Corbyn and the funding of Unite, Communication Workers Union and the activists' group Momentum had been decisive factors in Long-Bailey's victory. Len McCluskey, then general secretary of Unite, tweeted within minutes of the result: 'It was Unite wot won it.' Long-Bailey's senior campaign team were being hailed within minutes of the result. 'Political titans,' said one observer. 'Strategic geniuses,' said another. Those members of the campaign team would soon take up well-paid positions within the new Leader of the Opposition's Office (LOTO) at Westminster.

Long-Bailey's appeal to the old-time religion of the Labour left, coupled with a futuristic vision of a high-tech, post-carbon economy, had created a winning coalition of support. The Green New Deal proved to be the elusive 'big idea', like Wilson's white heat of technology, which could appeal to trade unionists and trendy Guardianistas alike.

The second clear meaning of the result was that the managerial 'moderate' wing of the Labour Party had failed yet again to inject much enthusiasm into the hearts of Labour members, most of whom had joined after 2015. The political heirs to Attlee, Wilson, Blair and Brown showed little of their predecessors' campaigning flair or political guile. None of the candidates offered more than an anaemic version of what had gone before, proffered without much passion or conviction. By failing to coalesce around a single candidate, the Labour moderates had split their vote in two. Just as Jeremy Corbyn had seen off Yvette Cooper, Andy Burnham and Liz Kendall in 2015, so Long-Bailey had pulled off a similar feat in 2020. The centre-left, moderate part of the Labour Party, once intellectually hegemonic and electorally invincible, had been divided and defeated yet again.

When it came to the deputy leader position, Long-Bailey had established an informal ticket with her friend, flatmate and fellow MP Angela Rayner. Rayner, the tough, no-nonsense working-class trade unionist, seemed to present the perfect counterbalance to the Cheshire solicitor. However, during the campaign, significant support had started to drift away from Rayner and land on Richard Burgon, the MP for Leeds East. The endorsement of John McDonnell had signalled that Burgon, not Rayner, was the continuity Corbyn candidate. Several trade unions, like the Bakers, Food and Allied Workers Union, the Fire Brigades Union and ASLEF followed suit. In the end, Richard Burgon was elected as deputy leader of the Labour Party.

Burgon had first come to the political world's attention as an entry on p. 549 of Tony Benn's *Diaries* in 1999, when the sixteen-year-old Burgon had showed Mr Benn his home-made T-shirt with the slogan 'Socialism is the Flame of Anger and the Flame of Hope'. Since that important moment, Burgon had got his degree from St John's, Cambridge, and won a safe seat, before joining Jeremy Corbyn's shadow Cabinet. His platform for deputy leader was to become Labour's campaigner-in-chief, like a British Bernie Sanders. But his real pitch was as the true Corbynite candidate. As Burgon repeated endlessly at the various hustings, he was the only candidate to have supported Corbyn in both leadership contests. If elected, he pledged to visit every seat Labour had lost in 2019 within the first month of his tenure.

That meant Burgon spent the whole of July 2020, once the first lockdown was over, touring the sixty seats Corbyn's Labour had lost the previous December – on most days visiting more than one constituency to hit his ambitious self-imposed target.

His tour started in Kensington in west London and progressed to Peterborough, Ipswich and Lincoln, through the West and East Midlands to the former steel- and coal-mining towns and villages of Yorkshire and the north-east, to the Lancashire towns of Blackpool, Bolton, Bury and Burnley, across North Wales from Wrexham to Delyn, and on to Scotland: Kirkcaldy and Cowdenbeath, Midlothian, Rutherglen & Hamilton West and Glasgow North East.

These were parliamentary seats that had been Labour since the days of Harold Wilson or Clement Attlee or even Keir Hardie; seats where workers came from mills and docks and shipyards and foundries and forges to elect Labour MPs decade after decade; seats where the union, the chapel and the co-op framed the existence of millions: all seats that had deserted Labour under Jeremy Corbyn. Burgon's tour, coinciding with the spread of Covid-19, was conducted among socially distanced, mask-wearing groups of Labour activists drawn from all parts of the socialist movement, to allow Burgon to engage with a broad spectrum of opinion.

Long-Bailey's first act was to announce a new position within the Labour Party constitution: President for Life. This position, largely ceremonial, would be in the gift of the National Executive Committee. 'There is', she said, 'only one person who can fill this role. Our friend, our inspiration, our saviour: Jeremy Corbyn.' The Labour Party headquarters, renamed 'Jeremy Corbyn House', issued a framed portrait of the new party President for Life to each Constituency Labour Party. This, however, was not enough for some of his most fervent supporters. The way in which a true Corbyn superfan could be identified was by a new tattoo that thousands had on their inner arms: the number '17', to commemorate Corbyn's great success at the 'game-changer' general election of 2017.

Long-Bailey was swift to appoint a new shadow Cabinet. Her approach was to reward loyalty, to promote talent and to pass the torch to a new generation of left-wing MPs. Naturally, there was no place for her opponents and critics. Keir Starmer, Jonathon Ashworth and Emily Thornberry returned to the back benches. Diane Abbott voluntarily stepped down. Long-Bailey knew it would be four or five years until an election, and so her new team would have time to learn on the job. When the appointments came, they were eye-catching and bold: Ian Lavery to shadow Chancellor; John McDonnell to shadow Foreign Secretary; Claudia Webbe to shadow Home Secretary; Sam Tarry to shadow Justice; Apsana Begum to shadow Housing Minister; and frontbench roles for Tahir Ali, Dan Carden, Mary Foy, Kim Johnson, Nav Mishra and Zarah Sultana.

In a surprise move, the new Labour leader announced a new policy and a new shadow department: the next Labour government would establish a new Department for Space, with a view to boosting the UK government space programme.

Richard Burgon, as deputy leader of the party, became shadow Chancellor of the Duchy of Lancaster and chair of the party. After a month on the road, and with sixty seats under his belt, he drafted a report for the NEC on what he had learned. Fortunately, it was hugely reassuring to the new leadership. Unlike some newspaper reports and so-called 'opinion polls', the Burgon Report showed that support for Jeremy Corbyn was strong among working-class communities, and that Labour's manifesto in 2019 had been a popular vote-winner – it was just that the voters had chosen, this time, to vote Conservative. What had caused Labour to lose 2.6 million votes between 2017 and 2019, it turned out, was two-fold: the Brexit policy of Keir Starmer, and the legacy of Tony Blair's leadership of the Labour Party, especially the Iraq War. From the former pit villages in Bolsover to the former steel town of Consett, to the docks of Grimsby, the Iraq War was seldom far from voters' minds.

The Burgon Report boiled down to a simple truth: Starmer and Blair were to blame – Starmer for failing to support Brexit and Blair for winning. This thinking shaped Labour's approach over the next five years; the lingering vestiges of Starmerism and Blairism would be expunged. Keir Starmer himself was elected chair of the Justice Select Committee in 2020 and carved out a distinguished role for himself.

The first Labour NEC meeting, in June 2020, went on for seventy-two hours straight; there was plenty of business to occupy the time. First, there was the timetable for parliamentary selections. In line with the leader's and deputy leader's pledges, all constituencies would select their candidate from a fresh shortlist, regardless of whether there was a sitting Labour MP or not. The sitting MP could put their name forward alongside any other hopefuls but without any special privileges. The aim was to select all candidates by 2022, to allow those in seats Labour hoped to win plenty of time to campaign. Priority was given to the so-called 'Red Wall', and among the first candidates to be selected were Laura Pidcock, Emma Dent Coad, Karen Lee, Thelma Walker and the octogenarian veteran left-winger Dennis Skinner. Despite bitter deselection campaigns directed at those MPs considered 'centrist', generating damaging publicity and deep fissures inside Constituency Labour Parties, no sitting MP was deselected.

The NEC had to consider the application for affiliation from Jewish Voice for Labour, a group established in 2017 to defend the former leader against the smears that he was, in some way, antisemitic. We know, via leaks on Twitter, that Rebecca Long-Bailey spoke up in favour of the affiliation. 'The Labour Jewish community is obviously split down the middle, and all sides of the argument must be given due prominence,' she told the meeting. Jewish Voice for Labour, an organisation less than five years old, was thus affiliated alongside the Jewish Labour Movement, which marked a century of affiliation in 2022. The news was greeted with great joy by the members of Jewish Voice for Labour, especially those who had only recently discovered that they were Jewish.

But the centrepiece of the NEC meeting was discussion of a new constitution for the Labour Party. For the second time in the party's history, a new Clause IV, Part IV was adopted, first by the NEC and later by a special conference conducted on Zoom. Out went the Blairite wording agreed by the membership in 1995, which had read:

> The Labour Party is a democratic socialist party. It believes that by the strength of our common endeavour we achieve more than we achieve alone, so as to create for each of us the means to realise our true potential and for all of us a community in which power, wealth and opportunity are in the hands of the many, not the few, where the rights we enjoy reflect the duties we owe, and where we live together, freely, in a spirit of solidarity, tolerance and respect.

In came a new credo, reflecting true Corbynism:

> The Labour Party is a socialist movement. It believes in a transformation in the social and economic relations between humans, and between humanity and the natural world. It believes that under socialism there will be no property, no work, no ownership of people or things, only an abundance of food, clothes, healthcare, technology and shelter distributed on the basis of need. Parliament remains an important forum in the battle of ideas, but social change comes outside Parliament, from the grassroots, not from parliamentary elites. Therefore Labour, as a social movement, is dedicated to social change outside the so-called representative assemblies, parliaments and

council chambers, and our success cannot be measured by outmoded twentieth-century notions of 'winning elections' and tallies of 'votes' and 'elected representatives'. Instead, we struggle for social progress with every tool at our disposal: social media, speeches, demonstrations and rallies.

This new Clause IV, Part IV was the result of hours of late-night online deliberations by Labour's intellectuals.

Alongside the new Clause IV, the NEC agreed a new policy statement; a kind of permanent manifesto based on the success of the 2019 document. It enshrined as Labour policy the key pledges in that document, not for this election or that but for all time. The perma-manifesto included the following: state corporations running the railways, electricity, gas, water, the Royal Mail and telecoms, thus doubling the number of jobs provided by the government overnight; and an end to all private-sector involvement in public services, including the NHS. From now on, government-run factories would produce the drugs and equipment, such as ambulances, bandages and beds, needed for the nation's healthcare, and government officials would form committees to plan their manufacture and distribution.

There would be an end to religious schools, private schools and schools free from local authority control; instead, a national education service would provide the same education to every child, regardless of who they were or what their parents wanted. Nursery education would be free, provided by thousands of new state-employed nursery staff. A 'green industrial revolution' would create thousands of new jobs in every UK region, with government factories manufacturing wind and wave turbines. Private landlords would be abolished and their properties purchased compulsorily by the government. University education would be free for all for life. There would be free dentistry. Social care would be provided free. The government would establish a new system of free broadband for everyone. And all of this would be delivered with people working no more than a four-day week.

Labour first adopted Clause IV in 1918, with the following policy:

> To secure for the workers by hand or by brain the full fruits of their
> industry and the most equitable distribution thereof that may be
> possible upon the basis of the common ownership of the means of
> production, distribution and exchange, and the best obtainable system
> of popular administration and control of each industry or service.

Sidney and Beatrice Webb, the authors, had left the wording vague
enough to encompass many forms of organisation, including municipal
and co-operative.

The 1995 version had as Labour's goal: 'A dynamic economy,
serving the public interest, in which the enterprise of the market and
the rigour of competition are joined with the forces of partnership and
co-operation to produce the wealth the nation needs.' This was designed
to acknowledge the existence of the market, but also to open the door
to forms of ownership such as co-operatives and community interest
companies, and to better controls, regulations, environmental standards
and interventions, such as windfall taxes.

But the 2020 statement had none of the nuance of 1918 or the social
market realism of 1995: it was a bald statement that the state should own
and run as much as possible, from sewage farms to British Airways;
that the government should manufacture everything from aspirin to
cars; and that the majority of people should work for the government,
live in government homes, travel on government transport and use the
private sector only as a last resort. This new policy statement represented
the end game of an ideological battle that had bedevilled the Labour
Party for over a century. The Marxists had triumphed, and the liberals,
co-operators, municipalists, social democrats and pragmatists had been
vanquished. The Labour Party finally owed more to Marx than to
Methodism. 'Labour', as one historian later wrote, 'was no longer a party
with socialists in it but at last a socialist party.'

The next challenge for Rebecca Long-Bailey was to choose a general
secretary of the Labour Party. The person to succeed Jennie Formby
would need to be an RLB loyalist; someone steeped in left-wing politics, with experience of running a large organisation and a track record

of winning elections. In the end, the person anointed by the NEC as Long-Bailey's chosen candidate made perfect sense. He had served as a councillor, an MP and a member of the NEC, he had run a major municipal authority, and he had won a major election against the odds, not once but twice. Labour's new general secretary was announced: Ken Livingstone.

Livingstone entered Jeremy Corbyn House like General MacArthur wading ashore on the Philippines. He stood under the newly cast bronze statue of Jeremy Corbyn at the front of the building and announced: 'I am back.' He got down to work immediately, restructuring the entire party machine, creating dozens of new 'community organiser' posts, soon filled with energetic young loyalists, and sacking the 'plotters' and 'traitors' who had let Jeremy down so badly. The new regional directors and senior managers were drawn from the ranks of the only places guaranteed to be loyal to the Labour leadership: Unite, Momentum and the Communist Party. The new general secretary announced an amnesty for all Labour members who had been expelled or suspended, and a new Head of Compliance, 'someone with a real understanding of Labour's disciplinary process', Livingstone said before revealing the name: Chris Williamson.

Next, Livingstone removed the requirement for Labour members not to have nominated other parties' candidates nor stood against Labour candidates, nor been members of another political party. 'Marxism', said Livingstone 'has always been a part of the Labour Party. We welcome those from the Marxist tradition back into our ranks. No one on the left is our enemy.' Within weeks, George Galloway, Ken Loach, Derek Hatton, Tariq Ali, Peter Taaffe and Piers Corbyn were admitted as members, alongside hundreds of people previously excluded or expelled. Jackie Walker, chair of Labour Against the Witchhunt, issued a statement winding up her group and proclaimed: 'Justice is done.'

Under Jeremy Corbyn's leadership, there had been a growing number of complaints about antisemitism in the party. The atmosphere of fear and intimidation felt by many Jewish members had culminated in the statutory equalities watchdog, the Equalities and Human Rights

Commission (EHRC), launching an investigation. When the EHRC reported in late 2020, it showed that Labour had broken the law in three ways and advised that the party must institute a plan to deal with the racism in its ranks.

However, in the lead-up to the announcement, Labour's communications machine went into overdrive to undermine the EHRC and to dismiss its report. First, backbenchers and media outriders co-ordinated their messages that the EHRC was influenced by 'Zionists'; that it was a tool of the Conservative government; and that it was part of a plot to 'smear Jeremy'. Second, the party commissioned its own report, which showed that the number of complaints was tiny; that antisemitism was much worse in the Conservative Party; and that attempts to deal with complaints were deliberately delayed to make Jeremy look bad. Third, the party rejected the methodology and findings of the report, claiming significant factual errors.

In a Zoom broadcast, Long-Bailey announced that the next Labour government would abolish the EHRC. She also announced that Labour would introduce a new definition of antisemitism, even better than that agreed by the International Holocaust Remembrance Alliance. A working group including Jon Lansman, Baroness Chakrabarti and David Feldman from the Birkbeck Institute for the Study of Antisemitism was established to come up with a new set of words. The party's new general secretary would institute a new programme of anti-semitism training for all party members, including certain previously overlooked historical facts. The next day, Margaret Hodge MP resigned the Labour whip in protest, and the Jewish Labour Movement started a consultation among its members, which would eventually lead to it disaffiliating from the Labour Party.

One area of policy continued to dog and divide Rebecca Long-Bailey's Labour: Europe. Where once Labour leaders had managed to square the circle of a pro-Europe party membership and a (mostly) anti-Europe electorate, Long-Bailey failed. The back benches of the Parliamentary Labour Party (PLP) were overwhelmingly pro-EU, representing middle-class, urban, university-educated electorates. The voices of the Eurosceptic post-industrial towns, the left-behind lacunae of modern Britain, were largely silent within the PLP because those constituencies were now represented by Conservatives. Labour conferences in 2021 and 2022 voted to rejoin the EU 'at the earliest opportunity', leaving Long-Bailey in a near-impossible position. Her strategists told her that the only way to rebuild the Red Wall was to offer a post-Brexit vision for Britain. But her party pulled in the opposite direction. The Tories, once they identified Labour's weakness, lost no time in mercilessly punching the bruise. In the 2020s, it was Labour that was irreconcilably divided over Europe, just as the Conservatives had been in the 1990s and beyond.

In the parliament elected in 2019, just seventeen Labour MPs had also been elected in the 1997 landslide. Most Labour MPs had little or no experience of their party in power, running departments, taking decisions and instituting change. With each passing decade, the Labour Party had moved further from governing, not just electorally but politically, philosophically and in terms of instinct. It had lost the governing gene and metamorphosed into a permanent opposition, happier with a placard than a Red Box. The moderate wing disintegrated. Some moderate Labour MPs left Parliament to take jobs as the heads of trade associations or industry bodies; others settled into an easy routine of select committees, speeches and parliamentary questions. In the constituencies, moderate Labour members stopped attending meetings because of the toxic atmosphere, and votes on policies and for local office holders, delegates to conference and council candidates were solidly pro-leadership. A few fought a courageous rearguard action. But the political force that had once declared itself the 'political wing of the British people', that had won 418 seats and 13 million votes and that had represented places from Braintree to Castle Point, from Dartford to Romford and from Stevenage to Shrewsbury, was as dead as Ernie Bevin.

In December 2020, as the country reeled from the second wave of the pandemic, Parliament, with little comment or fanfare, passed the Parliamentary Constituencies Act. This provided the government with the green light to redraw constituency boundaries, based on 650 seats but with more equal numbers of voters. Psephologists later calculated that the boundary review, presented to Parliament on 1 July 2023, gifted ten extra seats to the Conservatives before a single vote was cast. The Act also raised the national campaign spending cap at the 2023 election from £19.5 million to £33 million, which the Conservatives spent in full but Labour's fundraising efforts failed to come close to. Even millions in donations from Unite, presented to Long-Bailey in person by the union's general secretary, Howard Beckett, could not match the Tories' groaning war chest.

The strategic move which cemented the Tories' likelihood of another majority was an old favourite: swap one leader for another. It had worked in 1992 and in 2019, and this time, ditching Boris Johnson and replacing him with Rishi Sunak gave the Conservatives an immediate poll bounce. Sunak seemed to ooze energy, modernity and success, and he attracted global attention as the UK's first BAME Prime Minister. In spring 2022, as Boris Johnson left Downing Street with Carrie Symonds at his side, he seemed to take the bad memories of Covid-19 with him.

With the vaccine rollout fully delivered, the Covid-19 pandemic seemed to many like a distant nightmare. The economic impact was still felt by hundreds of thousands of people who had lost their businesses, jobs or homes, and thousands of families remained deep in grief. But the removal of restrictions on travel, leisure and work created a kind of collective euphoria, not unlike the Roaring Twenties that had followed the First World War. Unveiling the new Portland stone memorial on Whitehall to the 160,000 who lost their lives to the virus, the new Prime Minister told the nation: 'The darkness is over. Now light is spread upon the land. Better days lie ahead.'

The British people took him at his word. The Roaring Twenties were reborn, with a lively revival of restaurants, cafes, clubs, pubs, cinemas, theatres, spa weekends, mini-breaks and even the British seaside holiday, as people sought to avoid the day-long queues at the UK's borders. Hoteliers from Eastbourne to Blackpool to Bridlington saw their bookings soar. Businesses in the retail, travel and entertainment industries reported healthy trade. The economy, claimed Chancellor of the Exchequer Kwasi Kwarteng MP, in his third Budget speech, was on the upward climb of a V-shaped recovery. From a peak in 2022, unemployment was falling. Millions of office staff were now working the majority of their weeks from home, commuting only when necessary on trains and Tubes no longer packed at peak times. There was a spike in sales of home office furnishings and remote working tech – the 'Zoom boom'. New business start-ups were growing. The Prime Minister, Rishi Sunak, entered his first general election campaign in 2023 against a backdrop of tentative but steady economic growth and a swelling sense of optimism.

The Conservative pitch was simple – 'Keep Brexit Done' – with the warning that a vote for anyone but them risked reopening the divisions of Brexit and undermining the new trading relationships Britain had forged with the economic powerhouses of Japan, New Zealand and Peru. As ever, the old 'don't change a horse midstream' message worked. Throughout the campaign, Rishi Sunak led Rebecca Long-Bailey – and 'don't know' – on the question of who would make a better Prime Minister.

Labour's campaign managers hoped to recapture the success of 2017, when Labour had come within a whisker of winning, just a trifling 758,224 votes and a mere fifty-five seats short of the Conservatives. They ran a series of rallies in major towns and cities with leading Labour figures such as Diane Abbott, Lord McCluskey and even the President for Life himself. These rallies attracted crowds of thousands, but as usual the mainstream media failed to report them on the news, as though 5,000 people in a park in Salford chanting 'Oh, Jeremy Corbyn' was not newsworthy.

Livingstone, like his predecessor as general secretary, abandoned any notion of 'target' or 'key' seats; instead, every seat was a target, and Momentum activists piled into places with four-figure Tory majorities in the fervent hope of unseating Cabinet ministers. Key social media figures encouraged busloads of young activists to travel to seats like Welwyn Hatfield, Great Yarmouth, Cannock Chase, Sherwood, and Reading West, once held by Tony Blair's Labour Party but now represented by Conservative Cabinet ministers. Despite hundreds of students and young people descending upon them, armed with their talking points and guides to doorstep conversations, these local communities remained unpersuaded and returned their Conservative MPs with increased majorities.

All talk of opinion polls was banned at Jeremy Corbyn House. It was decreed that polls got it wrong on purpose and that the polling companies were run by Tories. The Labour campaign focused on the character and ideas of the party leader, Rebecca Long-Bailey, positioned as the British Jacinda Ardern with a dash of Sanna Marin. They produced 'RLB' merchandise, from beanie hats and T-shirts to knitted dolls – later discovered in large quantities in a landfill site in Pitsea, Essex.

The pro-RLB social media 'outriders' pumped out endless memes and videos, poking fun at Jacob Rees-Mogg or calling Priti Patel a 'fascist'. Each message was co-ordinated by Labour's campaign managers and circulated via WhatsApp. One day it was an attack on fat-cat footballers and pop stars and on another the threat that the Conservatives would eventually get round to privatising the NHS. One meme showed RLB as Che Guevara; another as Lenin. RLB's fans on Twitter, with their red rose emojis and followers in the tens of thousands, took time out from their personal fundraising efforts to support the Labour leader with Twitterstorms and hashtags. #RLB4PM trended day after day. Celebrity endorsers from Alexei Sayle to Clean Bandit expressed their support online. And yet somehow the opinion polls, which showed steady Conservative leads, refused to budge. It was almost as though the public was not listening to 'The Canary' blog and 'Rachel from Swindon'.

As historians would later show, the Labour campaign pledges to seize billions-of-pounds-worth of privately held assets and to pass control to committees of government employees and trade-union-appointed workers failed to excite many voters. Indeed, many – especially the three quarters of the 33-million-strong workforce who did not belong to a trade union – saw them as threats to their freedoms. Polling suggested that voters quite liked their smartphones, electric cars, Amazon deliveries, Starbucks and Sainsbury's and would prefer it if government officials did not grind their coffee or cut their hair. Even Labour's big pledges on state investment in green jobs and industries looked somewhat modest compared to the actual record of state intervention that the Tories could point to from 2020/21. Public spending had ceased to be an ideological dividing line in the minds of most voters. The Labour Party's focus on the politics of the Middle East; its seeming admiration for South American dictatorships; its disdain for the Union Jack; and some unfortunate remarks about the police and armed services added up to a sense that the party and the public were on utterly different pages. The debacle at the coronation, when the Leader of the Opposition was filmed yawning as the Archbishop of Canterbury anointed the new King, was the last straw.

By the final week of the campaign, the Conservatives were micro-targeting millions of voters via social media with videos of 'RLB' making speeches while crowds waved Palestinian and Syrian flags and wore Jeremy Corbyn T-shirts, faded with so many washes. Opinion polls suggested that the Red Wall switchers, far from showing any buyers' remorse, were doubling down on their decision in 2019 and preparing to vote Conservative for a second time. As one Red Wall voter, on the eve of poll, told BBC *Newsnight*: 'We were right last time, and we'll be right next time too.' Like their grandparents, who had switched from Labour to Conservative in 1979 and voted Conservative again four years later, they found that once the tribal bonds were severed, it was easier the second time around.

The result, when it came, was no great surprise. In order for Labour to win a majority at the 2023 general election, the party had required a swing bigger than in 1945 or 1997; Rebecca Long-Bailey's Labour needed to perform better than the party under Attlee or Blair. Labour needed at least 124 gains to form a government.

Long-Bailey had hoped for a repeat of 2017, with Labour gaining seats and hitting 41 per cent of the vote. But instead, it was closer to 2019, the worst result for Labour since 1935. Out of the fifty-four seats that had gone from Labour to Conservative in 2019, just a handful flipped back, like Kensington. But simultaneously, the same deep-seated political, demographic and social factors that had created the collapse of the Red Wall in 2019 caused another bank of seats to turn from red to blue. The legacy of the 2019 election was a slew of Labour seats with minuscule majorities, and these the Tories took in 2023: Bedford (majority 145), Coventry North West (208), Alyn & Deeside (213), Dagenham & Rainham (293), Coventry South (401), Weaver Vale (562). In Wansbeck, the shadow Chancellor of the Exchequer saw his 814-vote majority overturned by the Conservative candidate Jack Gebhard, with a winning margin of 3,500.

The Conservatives won a majority of ninety-seven seats. Rishi Sunak walked back into No. 10 and began to appoint his Cabinet. The Labour Party had lost the fifth general election in a row. The defeat raised the serious prospect that the UK would become a polity where one party governed on a semi-permanent basis, with the dynamics of opposition, conflict and renewal contained within the boundaries of a single party, rather than between parties contesting against each other for power. This dominant-party system of government has been seen down the decades in Canada, Turkey, Hungary, Russia and Japan, as well as across Africa. By the time of the 2027 general election, the Labour Party had not won an election for twenty-two years, with little prospect of power on the horizon. The UK was in effect a one-party state.

Rebecca Long-Bailey resigned as leader of the Labour Party on Friday 5 May 2023, along with her deputy, triggering a leadership election between Wes Streeting and Zarah Sultana, which, as history records and after all the lessons of the previous thirty years, could surely only end one way.

Chapter 22

What if President Trump had died of Covid-19?

Simon Marks

The true genius of Mike Pence is that by the time he was sworn into office as America's forty-sixth President, no one really knew very much about him. Nearly four years into the Trump presidency, he remained the Charles Pooter of American politics: a nobody in the minds of most Americans.

Sure, he had spearheaded the Trump administration's response to Covid-19, filling the vacuum left when his boss refused to recognise the threat the pandemic posed to American society. And of course he had also served as the Republican Governor of Indiana and as a six-term member of Congress from his home state.

But by the time Mike Pence had presided over President Trump's funeral and begun to settle into the Oval Office himself, most Americans knew only one principal aspect of his biography: he had once described himself as 'a Christian, a conservative and a Republican... in that order'.[1]

Many Republicans privately believed that Donald Trump evinced none of those qualities and viewed Mr Pence as the polar opposite of the President he had loyally served. They had no idea, at the time, that he would become the party's most significant figure on the national stage since the late Ronald Reagan. Like Moses, Pence would lead the party out of the dead-end political desert to which President Trump had delivered it.

Mike Pence's faith was a centrepiece of his life from the moment that he abandoned his family's embrace of Roman Catholicism and became a born-again evangelical during his years studying at Hanover College, a small liberal arts university in his home state. His break with Catholicism wasn't the only decision he made that greatly disappointed his mother;[2] he also walked away from the family's traditional support of the Democratic Party, and as he engaged in his own evangelical exploration, he found himself galvanised by modern American conservatism.

So, when Vice-President Mike Pence received the call from President Trump's chief of staff, Mark Meadows, on the sunny autumn afternoon of Sunday 4 October 2020 and heard that the President had succumbed to Covid-19 while being treated on a ventilator at Bethesda's Walter Reed National Military Medical Center, his first response was to pray.

He offered prayers first for the President's salvation – prayers that his wife, Karen, had long argued the entire Pence family should be including in their nightly devotions, but only after she had overcome her initial fury at the revelations, during the 2016 presidential campaign, of Donald Trump's sordid extra-marital affairs and hush-money payments to strippers and porn stars. The 9 October 2016 release of the infamous *Access Hollywood* audio recording, in which Mr Trump had boasted of grabbing women 'by the pussy', seemed to most contemporary observers to represent a body blow to the New York mogul's presidential hopes;[3] it had led Mrs Pence initially to insist that her husband drop out of the Trump campaign. But after several days behind closed doors – many of them spent in prayer – calmer heads prevailed in the Pence family home.[4] And also, seemingly, in homes all over the country, as Donald Trump remained not just in the 2016 race but of course went on to win it.

The second set of prayers Mike Pence offered was for himself. His evangelicalism led him to believe that the news imparted by the weeping White House chief of staff was – whatever one thought of it – God's will. And therefore it was God's will that he should prepare himself for the biggest challenge of his life: not just leading the Republican Party into the presidential election a mere month away but winning it and using the victory as an opportunity to reanimate the Republican movement and remould it in his own image.

President Trump's last public appearance was on the afternoon of

Friday 2 October 2020. His final tweet had been published shortly before 1 a.m. 'Tonight', he wrote, '@FLOTUS and I tested positive for Covid-19. We will begin our quarantine and recovery process immediately. We will get through this TOGETHER!'[5] To this day, there remains speculation that the President did not author the message himself.

At lunchtime on Saturday 3 October, the press corps at the White House was hastily informed that Trump's physician, Dr Sean Conley – an osteopath, not an infectious disease specialist – had concluded that it was time to transport the President to the Walter Reed Medical Center, a state-of-the-art-treatment facility with a suite and medical staff on permanent standby to accept a presidential patient. Unbeknownst to the photographers who had captured the President's slow walk to Marine One (the presidential helicopter that landed on the south lawn of the White House to convey him to hospital), he would never be seen in public again.

That final image – so famous now – of the masked President walking on the arm of a uniformed and masked protective US Marine, was designed to project presidential strength. We now know that the moment was choreographed as carefully as the images, eighty years earlier, of President Franklin Delano Roosevelt. Then, the public was never permitted to know that America's thirty-second President had contracted polio at the age of thirty-nine and was unable to stand unaided. A raft of visual tricks, coupled with the tacit agreement of the reporters who covered the White House at the time never to disclose the President's true state of health, had allowed Roosevelt and his press secretary, Stephen Early, to hoodwink the public into believing that FDR was a man of steel.[6]

Eight minutes after departing the White House, President Trump's helicopter landed in Bethesda. Large privacy screens erected around the medical centre's helipad earlier in the day served as the first indication that the crisis was deeper than the public had been told. Behind them, the ultimate showman was stretchered into an ambulance and conveyed across the centre's grounds to its entrance.

President Trump had a well-known fear and loathing of hospitals, once telling the Washington correspondent for Britain's ITV News that he was 'a germaphobe'. (He was responding at the time to questions about whether he had ever engaged in the kind of hotel-room activities described in a dossier detailing scatological conduct with prostitutes in Moscow.)[7]

In hospital, the President's decline was precipitous. Overweight and with pre-existing health conditions that were never disclosed to the American public, he was placed on a ventilator in the early hours of Sunday morning, 4 October. A President who had, on numerous occasions, described himself as the 'King of Ventilators' was now relying for breath on medical machinery whose production he had ramped up during the early stages of the Covid-19 pandemic.[8] In keeping with the four-year tradition of the Trump White House, the President's physician and the White House press secretary issued a series of entirely false statements about the President's condition.

Network anchors and White House correspondents received off-the-record reports from inside the hospital indicating the situation was far more serious than was being publicly disclosed. Quiet but hasty efforts began in newsrooms across the city to ensure that presidential obituaries, always pre-produced and filed away in advance, were fully up to date and ready for publication.

By dawn on Sunday, the President's condition was worsening by the hour. Vice-President Mike Pence was warned of the possibility that soon the President would be unable to perform his duties in any meaningful sense. But the twenty-fifth amendment to America's constitution, allowing for a temporary transfer of power, was never formally invoked. By the time the President took his final breath, the necessary paperwork had still not been despatched to the Vice-President's home in the grounds of the US Naval Observatory. In the early evening of Saturday 3 October, the President's daughter, Ivanka Trump, eager to continue projecting a sense of her father's invincibility, had inserted herself into the constitutional process. At that point, only dreaming of the Senate career upon which she would later embark, she demanded to inspect the formal papers 'for accuracy'. Her husband, Jared Kushner – his father-in-law's senior adviser – privately told White House chief of staff Mark Meadows and White House legal counsel Pat Cipollone that the family would not tolerate the transfer of power to the Vice-President even for a few hours.

The death of the President changed all that. When Donald Trump took his last breath at 3.17 on Sunday afternoon, Mike Pence received the news in the private quarters of his residence on Washington's grandest of boulevards, Massachusetts Avenue. Once his prayers were completed, a whirlwind of activity began. His motorcade conveyed him and America's new First Lady at high speed along Washington's Embassy Row. They swept past the mansions where the world's diplomats were only just learning of the President's death and hastily communicating with their own governments back at home.

At the White House, Mr Pence offered condolences via video-conference to First Lady Melania Trump, herself isolated with Covid-19 in the residence. The virus had spread through the West Wing like wildfire since the 26 September outdoor event in the Rose Garden to honour the President's Supreme Court nominee Amy Coney Barrett.[9] Washington's Republican elite had gathered mask-less for what days later had become a 'super-spreader event', in the parlance of the pandemic.

Minutes later, Mr Pence was greeted by Chief Justice John Roberts in an executive residence anteroom. They moved together into the East Room, with only Karen Pence, the Vice-President's chief of staff, Marc Short, and the official White House photographer on hand for the swearing-in.

President Mike Pence swore the oath of office on the same bible he had used when he became Vice-President in January 2017. Once owned by Ronald Reagan, the bible was used by the champion of America's conservative movement when he became President on 20 January 1981. It was, President Pence understood, a vivid symbol, conveying his commitment to the conservative agenda and his determination to save the Republican Party from the brink of ruin to which Donald Trump had led it. In a further act of symbolism, choreographed by Pence himself, everyone in attendance wore facemasks for the swearing-in.

That the Republican Party was facing catastrophe at the presidential election four weeks later was clear to President Pence. Since January 2020, over their weekly lunches at the White House – painful events he had privately come to dread – the Vice-President had consistently urged the President to take the threat of Covid-19 seriously. Tasked in the earliest days of the crisis with leading the President's Coronavirus Task Force, Pence understood that Trump had no time for the detail, nor the hard work, involved in responding to a pandemic. But even Pence did not fully anticipate the President's determination to undercut the efforts the task force members were making and the recommendations they sent to the Oval Office desk.

Pence, along with other members of the President's inner circle, did his best to persuade Trump that his decision to deny the threat posed by the global pandemic ran counter to the traditions of Republican philosophy. The presidential oath of office, after all, required Trump to protect the nation 'from all enemies, foreign and domestic'. The Vice-President had explained that Covid-19 was in every sense an 'enemy', and he urged robust and forthright communication with the public about the measures needed to protect the country from the virus, coupled with urgent action to inspire a wartime effort to tough it out.

The President would not hear of it.

His relentless refusal to wear facemasks in public; his insistence that, 'like a miracle', the pandemic would 'just go away'; and his determination to reopen the economy as rapidly as possible put the United States on the perilous path to Covid-19 disaster.

It also propelled the country on the road to potential political disaster by emboldening conspiracy theorists who challenged the very existence of the virus and actively rebelled against the government's public health guidelines. Race-baited by a President who regularly referred to the virus as 'the China plague' and 'Kung flu', some of them even broke into hospitals with video cameras in a bid to prove that the pandemic was a hoax.[10]

By President Pence's first day in office, the country had lost 210,000 souls to the virus. There had been more than 7.5 million cases of infection. More than 30 million Americans were out of work. Small businesses were closing at the fastest rate since the Great Depression. Towns and cities of all sizes were bracing for a cash crunch as tax revenues dried up. Internal White House polls showed that Joe Biden, the Democratic Party presidential candidate, was on course for an easy victory in the 3 November election. Republican pollsters anticipated not just a loss of the presidency but possibly also of the party's majority in the Senate.

President Pence understood the need for urgent action simultaneously on multiple fronts. His visceral knowledge of the American heartland came not from policy papers, weekend political retreats or conversations with the party's elite funders. Rather, it was rooted in his earlier experience as a radio talk show host in his native Indiana following two early, failed attempts to win election to Congress.

The Mike Pence Show ran from 1992 to 1999, at its peak being broadcast by eighteen radio stations across Indiana every morning from 9 a.m. until noon.[11] The experience had persuaded Pence that Americans in the rural heartlands were not predisposed to believing that the pandemic was a hoax. Pence hoped that real leadership could persuade them to join a national effort to beat the virus or, at the very least, to concede – based on the President's own death – its dangers.

In short order, Pence invited the former Governor of South Carolina, Nikki Haley, to serve alongside him as Vice-President. Trump's US ambassador to the United Nations, she had departed the administration in December 2018. Her decision surprised Washington, but, uniquely among former Trump officials, she had navigated her departure without losing the President's admiration or support and had never incurred a single presidential tweet criticising her.[12]

Haley understood more than most Republicans that the mobilisation of President Trump's base in the 2016 election was not just a passing fancy. Despite his own lavish lifestyle and wealth, Trump had persuaded working-class Americans that he would champion their interests. As President, he had sought to mobilise supporters of extremist viewpoints as well, bringing them into the Republican fold. For the first time, a Republican leader had actively courted support from voters who – for decades – had been considered off-limits by most mainstream politicians.

The 'basket of deplorables' identified by Hillary Clinton in 2016 was now a substantial Republican voting bloc, both inspired by and activated by Donald Trump. Haley herself was a veteran of the Tea Party – a right-wing grassroots movement that, as early as 2009, had undermined Republican unity by campaigning aggressively for smaller government, draconian restrictions on immigration and an end to deficit spending.

But before Pence and Haley could focus on the imminent election, there was a funeral to oversee: a massive effort to honour a President whose record in office had divided Americans down the middle, and who was loathed as much as he was loved.

There was fury among Democrats when President Pence communicated the Trump family's request for the late President – impeached by the House of Representatives in December 2019 – to lie in state in the Rotunda of the US Capitol building. Since President John F. Kennedy's assassination in 1963, Congress has always acceded to the wishes of a fallen President's family, and the Speaker of the House of Representatives, Nancy Pelosi, quickly abandoned her initial impulse to fight it.

She then watched as hundreds of thousands of Americans from all over the country and from all walks of life travelled to Washington in the late President's honour. Queues of them snaked through the US Congressional building, the cradle of American democracy, in scenes that startled not only Democratic Party leaders and Biden's campaign managers but also the city's residents. Living in a Democratic bastion, the people of Washington DC were unable to conceive that so many Americans were grieving a President whose presence in their city – even in death – was unwelcome. Such was the partisan chasm in which Donald Trump had left his nation.

In the midst of the Covid-19 pandemic, the authorities in Congress imposed facemask requirements for entrance into the building. Many in the crowd refused to observe them. Some challenged the Capitol Police to arrest them; others simply donned masks to make their way past security, then – in a moment of tribute – removed them and dropped them in a neat pile on the floor of the Rotunda as they paid their final respects before the President's casket. By the time the third and final day of mourning ended and the President's coffin was removed from the building, the Congressional authorities had swept up more than 80,000 facemasks deposited in tribute.

On Saturday 10 October 2020, the funeral took place at Washington's National Cathedral – an institution that itself had made no secret of its animus to the late President. 'Have we no decency?' asked an article written by Reverend Mariann Edgar Budde, the Bishop of the Episcopal Diocese in Washington, published on the cathedral's website on 30 July 2019.[13] She and other church leaders had accused the President of 'a steady stream of language and accusations … that plays to racist elements in society'. Just over a year later, none of those phrases was to be articulated during the funeral service itself.

The service posed a challenge to Democrats too, and while Joe Biden and his wife Jill attended and conveyed their condolences to the First Lady and the Trump children, the Clintons, the Obamas and the Carters all stayed away. President Pence used his eulogy to appeal to Americans to overcome society's divisions, without noting that those divisions were in large measure due to the character and actions of the man he was in the throes of honouring.

Once the service ended, the President's flag-draped casket was conveyed to Bedminster, New Jersey, where work had already been under way on the creation of a family mausoleum on the grounds of his golf club. Legal wrangling with the local authorities had delayed its construction, but the President's final resting place was settled: he was buried in a private family service, within glancing distance of the first tee of the Trump National golf course.[14]

Later, the mausoleum would be built around his grave and decorated with 19ft-tall stone obelisks that the former President had personally commissioned for the site. Nearby, 284 other burial plots were made available for sale – the President and his family correctly surmising that some of his wealthy supporters would agree to part with large sums in exchange for the chance to spend eternity in his immediate midst.

With three weeks left until election day, Pence knew that taking the presidential oath of office had been easy; formally becoming the

Republican Party's presidential candidate would be more problematic. Two connected problems loomed: the electoral calendar, and the rules.

Republican Party regulations offered Pence (and any other candidates interested in throwing their hats into the ring) two options for succeeding Donald Trump as the party's presidential candidate.

The first possibility was to reconvene the Republican Convention that had met – albeit virtually – earlier in the summer. The 2,500 delegates would be officially brought back into session and, a minimum of ten days later, would – after considered conversation and debate – determine who would fill the party's election ticket.[15]

Pence, along with other Republican grandees, rapidly concluded that the available time was too short and the polls too grim to waste at least ten days – and under the party's rules, possibly as many as twenty – engaged in heated discussions. He strenuously argued that 'election day' itself in America was, by the year 2020, a misnomer. In some parts of the country, people had been 'early voting' since two weeks before President Trump's demise. Hundreds of thousands of people had already cast their ballots for a candidate who was now deceased. In no state was there any legal option for them to vote again. The party, he argued, needed an immediate decision, and he proposed using an alternative party rule to secure one: under the Republican National Committee's Governing Rule 9, all that Pence and Haley needed was the immediate support of a majority of the 168 members of the RNC – in essence, the governing board of the party.[16] The move would be in keeping with party rules and would also satisfy the electoral laws of America's disparate fifty states.

By acclamation, and facing no challenges, on Monday 12 October 2020, Mike Pence and Nikki Haley became the party's 'ticket' after an emergency videoconference of the RNC's members.

The next piece of the puzzle was more complex: the ballot papers in all fifty states would still continue to bear Trump's name, since all official filing deadlines had already passed. Under America's archaic election laws – the jealous preserve of each independent state – the names appearing on voting papers, and even voting machines, were considered immutable at this late stage of the race. So, while casting votes for Trump and Pence, Americans would in reality be backing Pence and Haley. Once the election was over, delegates to the electoral college – the institutional middleman that sits between the voters in US presidential elections and the final result – would be instructed by legislators in states won by the Republicans to transfer their support from 'Trump/Pence' to 'Pence/Haley'. In short, for the first time in American history, a President would be re-elected but would never take office because he was, in fact, dead.

Workable though it was, the process created fresh difficulty for President Pence. He understood that some voters would not entirely fathom why 'Pence/Haley' was not an option for them to back in the country's voting booths. Others would fret that they were being asked to put a dead man in the White House. Amidst the need to rebrand the entire campaign around Pence's name and image, the Republicans poured money into a TV and social media advertising campaign that blanketed the all-important battleground states, explaining the name change in simple, easy-to-understand terms.

Pence knew that it was an unprecedented long shot, but he was equally aware that the Republican victory in 2016 had been razor thin. Independent analyses had showed that Donald Trump had won the White House thanks to a mere 107,000 votes in the critical swing states. Those specific votes put Trump 'over the top' in the country's electoral college, and Pence firmly believed that similar maths could work in the party's favour once again.

His campaign focused like a laser beam on three key, specific communities where polling showed that the Republicans were adrift: the suburbs of Philadelphia, where female voters had deserted President Trump in droves;[17] the dairy farms of Wisconsin, long considered a vulnerability for Trump's re-election hopes due to his unfulfilled promises of economic support to help them weather the pandemic;[18] and the oil-and-gas-producing communities of Michigan, where Pence believed – and polling confirmed – that Biden's commitment to developing alternative energy sources was anathema.[19]

In the remaining days of the election, while the campaign focused on turning out the Republican vote across the country and conveying a sense of opportunity for voters eager to help forge Trump's legacy, Pence personally focused like a surgeon on those three communities. He was disciplined where Trump had lacked focus. He was empathetic where Trump had been cold. He was demonstrably conservative and Christian in communities where those qualities galvanised voters who had previously fretted about Trump's commitment to the central tenets of their religious and political faith.

Mike Pence was also uniquely positive, both in style and in message. Harkening back to a simpler, less stressful time, the Republicans tore a page out of Dwight D. Eisenhower's presidential playbook. 'I Like Ike', the three-word slogan that propelled Eisenhower to the White House in the 1952 election, was hastily modernised. Pence supporters started sporting badges, car stickers and yard signs that read simply: 'I Like Mike'.

Much earlier in his career, Pence had learned of the dangers of 'going negative'. In 1990, his failed bid for an Indiana seat in the House of Representatives is still remembered as one of the dirtiest races in the political history of the Hoosier state.[20] The following year, he wrote an essay – 'Confessions of a Negative Campaigner' – that served as an apology for his conduct and a pledge never to engage in the negative campaigning championed by Republican strategists, including the principal architect of Trump's victory, political adviser Steve Bannon.[21]

In the final days of the 2020 campaign, he completely overturned the Trump playbook. No more mask-free mass rallies dominated by the late President's stream-of-consciousness rants. No more lies about the Bidens being an 'organised crime family'. No more claims that the presidential election was being 'rigged'. No more hesitation to excoriate Russian President Vladimir Putin for outrages like the placing of financial bounties on the heads of US troops. No more raging tweets reflecting whatever was on the presidential mind at any moment of the day or night. And most importantly of all, no more denial about the threat the pandemic posed to America and its way of life.

Pence privately told advisers that the constant dystopian frenzy orchestrated by President Trump had whipped Americans up into such a state of psychosis that he feared the country's core values and governing arrangements could soon be threatened. There would be no more 'alternative facts', as White House adviser Kellyanne Conway had once characterised the President's lies. Pence was convinced they had been leading the country to the edge of a very dangerous abyss.

It is often said that American Presidents 'campaign in poetry, govern in prose'. Pence had a rare opportunity to do both simultaneously. On the campaign trail, he sought to head off electoral disaster by presenting a simple, largely positive message: Covid-19 was real and it required patriotic resolve to combat it. Vaccines were coming and would help. But so would common sense.

He entreated voters to honour President Trump's memory by restoring the country to the greatness the late President had pledged. The way to do that, he insisted, was to respect the threat posed by coronavirus but to combat it using the power Americans had within their own hands, homes and families. Wherever he went, he wore a facemask. He instilled strict new health control measures at the White House and all federal government buildings across the country. The government, he insisted, must lead by example and should consider itself engaged in a wartime effort, both for public health and for truth.

In governing the country, he put massive personal focus on the efforts to develop a vaccine, insisting that daily updates about research should be included in his PDB – the presidential daily briefing presented by the country's intelligence agencies. He made extensive use of the Defense Production Act – legislation allowing a US President to force companies to divert resources into the production of goods needed in the national interest. President Trump had prevaricated over its use, grumbling that hospitals were demanding too much personal protective equipment and failing adequately to recycle used materials.[22] Pence instead ordered the production of millions of additional facemasks, gloves and gowns, then had them shipped to hospitals and nursing homes nationwide. Although it would be weeks before the first vaccine was authorised for use, he ordered the Pentagon, the Department of Homeland Security and the

Department of Health and Human Services to begin joint planning for vaccine distribution.

He immediately pressed for a fresh economic stimulus, telling Republican leaders in Congress that not only the future of the country but also the outcome of the election depended on it. He prioritised fresh funding for the smallest of American businesses, ensuring that any enterprise with fewer than fifty employees could secure renewed economic help from the government just in time for election day.

He also put Beijing on notice: when elected, he would demand billions of dollars in financial compensation from China for the damage the pandemic had inflicted on the American economy. While Pence privately conceded that this was a non-starter, the mere idea proved popular with voters nonetheless.

When the results of the election poured in on the night of 3 November 2020, Mike Pence and his family watched from the residence of the White House. Nikki Haley and her husband, Michael (America's first 'Second Gentleman') joined them.

Former First Lady Melania Trump watched from her temporary residence at Mar-a-Lago, the Trump golf club in Florida where she was seeking sanctuary while battling with other family members over her husband's last will and testament.

Ivanka Trump and Jared Kushner watched from their home in the upscale Kalorama district of Washington DC, unaware that within weeks they would be heading to London at the new President's direction. The President's daughter would take up her position as the country's new ambassador to the Court of St James's – a role President Pence correctly surmised would neutralise any immediate plans she might have to forge her own political career and challenge his leadership of America's Grand Old Party.

Joe Biden and his family watched from their home in Wilmington, Delaware. 'We had a sense of foreboding,' he would later say of that night. For two weeks, Democrats had watched a wave of sympathy votes moving away from them in the key counties of Pennsylvania, Wisconsin and Michigan. Biden's age – seventy-seven – his decision to spend months locked down in Delaware instead of hitting the campaign trail and his ongoing verbal gaffes had taken on a new life of their own once the more vigorous Pence – sixty-one – was atop the Republican ticket.

By 11.42 p.m., the country's television networks and the Associated Press news agency had seen enough. Having earlier called Georgia and Michigan for Pence, the twin states of Wisconsin and Pennsylvania decided the election in the Republican's favour. ABC News was the first to declare President Pence's victory, with the other broadcasters and the Associated Press moments behind. Pence was projected to win 294 delegates in the electoral college to Biden's 244: a narrower win than Trump had secured in 2016, but Biden's victory in the popular vote was also narrower than Hillary Clinton's had been four years earlier.

The phone rang fifteen minutes later in the White House residence. Joe Biden offered his congratulations to the President – the final act in his own 47-year political career.

President Pence did not know it that night, but his victory would set the stage for an era now known as the 'Republican Revival'. Two presidential terms later, he had not only reinvigorated the party but secured it to Christian, conservative and Republican moorings... in that order. He had also succeeded in forcing China to pay financial compensation to countries around the world to mitigate some of the damage caused by Beijing's failure to control Covid-19 from day one.

The Democrats found themselves split asunder. Furious younger party members chastised the older generation, outraged that first Hillary Clinton, then Joe Biden had put themselves before the need to pass the torch to the next generation. The party would spend eight years in the political wilderness, resolving its internal crisis. By 2028, the party's progressive left wing, initially championed by the legendary socialist Senator Bernie Sanders from Vermont, was the dominant force in Democratic politics. Alexandria Ocasio-Cortez, the firebrand senator from New York, used Hillary Clinton's old office on Capitol Hill as the launching pad for her bid to become America's first female President. In the election of 2028, she would face off against Vice-President Nikki Haley.

Pence personally credited his success to one moment in his election battle with Joe Biden that went viral on social media and throughout society. On 22 October 2020, the two men participated in the only televised debate of that year's election. Midway through it, as the topic shifted to the policing of America's troubled cities, a large fly swooped down from the arena's rafters and landed on Pence's hair.

Pence sensed its presence. As millions watched live on television, he flicked the insect out of his hair, smiled at the camera and said: 'See? No flies on me.'

The election was over. The Republican Party was about to be reborn.

Notes

1 'God's plan for Mike Pence', *The Atlantic*, January/February 2018.
2 'Mike Pence's journey: Catholic Democrat to evangelical Republican', *New York Times*, 20 July 2016.
3 'What Donald Trump's "Access Hollywood" weekend says about 2020', *New York Times*, 12 July 2020.
4 'Mike Pence and the tale of the tape', *Indianapolis Monthly*, 6 September 2019.
5 @RealDonaldTrump, tweet, 12.54 a.m., 2 October 2020, thetrumparchive.com
6 'FDR's hidden handicap', *Wilson Quarterly* (2005).
7 'Shaking hands is "barbaric": Donald Trump, the germaphobe in chief', *Washington Post*, 12 January 2017.
8 'Becoming "King of Ventilators" may result in unexpected glut', AP News, 10 May 2020.
9 'Fauci calls Amy Coney Barrett ceremony in Rose Garden "superspreader event"', NBC News, 9 October 2020.
10 'Covid-19 and the "film your hospital" conspiracy theory: social network analysis of Twitter data', US National Library of Medicine, National Institutes of Health, 5 October 2010.
11 'The old cassettes that explain Mike Pence', *Politico*, 20 July 2016.
12 'Nikki Haley's resignation blindsides Washington, but surprises no one', *Vanity Fair*, 9 October 2018.
13 'Have we no decency? A response to President Trump', 30 July 2019, www.cathedral.org
14 'The mystery of Donald Trump and the New Jersey cemetery', *Washington Post*, 10 March 2017.
15 'Who is the Republican nominee if Trump dies before the election?', *Quartz*, 2 October 2020.
16 'Filling vacancies in nominations', RNC Rule No. 9, Ballotpedia.org
17 'White women are ditching Trump, and it could cost him Pennsylvania', *Philadephia Inquirer*, 19 October 2020.

18 'How suffering farmers may determine Trump's fate', *New Yorker*, 10 August 2020.
19 'Biden calls for "transition" from oil, GOP sees opening', AP News, 23 October 2020.
20 'The danger of President Pence', *New Yorker*, 16 October 2017.
21 'Confessions of a negative campaigner', *Indiana Policy Review*, October 1991.
22 'Trump suggests some hospitals are using too many masks', *Modern Healthcare*, 29 March 2020.

Chapter 23

What if Priti Patel became Prime Minister?

Iain Dale

It was snowing outside. The Chequers lawn was hidden by a covering of snow so deep that the crocuses couldn't penetrate it. The Prime Minister sat back in his high-backed chair in a contemplative mood. It's funny how things turn out, he thought to himself. He had come to office full of boosterish enthusiasm, optimism and energy. Three and a half years later, he was knackered. His hair was falling out, and that damned dog was driving him to distraction. The job may have taken an enormous physical toll on him, but, God damn it, he'd seen it through and come out the other side. Inquiry after inquiry. Investigation after investigation. He'd seen them all off.

He knew what some people thought of him. He was old enough to know his own frailties and failings and had eventually come to realise that his craving to be liked by everyone couldn't possibly be achieved. For a moment, he thought back to the leadership hustings in Nottingham in June 2019. It seemed a lifetime ago, yet it still rankled. He grimaced as he remembered the words of the eighteen-year-old British Asian lad: 'Mr Johnson, you're a racist, aren't you?'[1]

At first, he thought he must have misheard and looked plaintively at the moderator for reassurance. Back came there none. How could anyone possibly think that about him? Well, he'd proved them wrong, hadn't he? More ethnic minority Cabinet members than at any time in history. Two of the top three offices of state held by British Asians at the same time at one point. He'd led by example. He hoped the lad in Nottingham had taken note.

Mind you, it hadn't all been plain sailing. He'd lost his Chancellor, Sajid Javid, after only seven months, and his successor had been a constant thorn in his side. It wasn't exactly on the TB–GB scale of conflict between No. 10 and No. 11 two decades earlier, but Rishi Sunak's response to the Covid crisis had made him a contender. But as with all political reputations, they could fall as quickly as they rose. And the past six months had rather taken the polish off the Chancellorial political suit of armour.

And then there was the party chairman. Priti. The Pritster. He remembered her first party conference speech as Home Secretary back in October 2019. God, that seemed an age ago, but his recollection of the speech was as clear as the moment he'd witnessed it in his Manchester hotel suite. 'Jesus, Dom, is she actually having an orgasm on stage?' the PM queried to Dominic Cummings, who had been quietly working on the PM's own speech.

He looked up and remarked: 'I don't know, but whatever it is, I'll have what she's having.'

Boris Johnson had often wondered what he was thinking when he appointed Priti Patel as Home Secretary. She was one of a number of core 'Vote Leavers' whom he'd felt obliged to reward when he first became Prime Minister, but bringing back a colleague who had been sacked in such weird circumstances by Theresa May in 2017, and then giving her one of the top jobs in government, left most commentators scratching their heads in bewilderment. But Boris had been adamant when many of his advisers urged him to give her a more junior job instead. 'No, not having it. She stood by me when the going got tough, and she's sound.' It was a sign of things to come.

His Cabinet marked a total break. To 'get Brexit done' he needed a team of Brexiters and true believers. He'd seen how Remainers had wreaked havoc in Theresa May's Cabinet and tried to wreck Brexit at every turn, and he wasn't going to enable history to be repeated. He knew he'd have to keep a sprinkling of Remainers, but he ousted anyone who hadn't signed up to his leadership campaign, with the exception of the former party chairman, Brandon Lewis, who was kept on as Security Minister, with a seat attending Cabinet. Or, as one wag put it: 'To pick up the pieces after Priti.'

And there proved to be plenty of pieces to pick up. But however dire things looked, and however much trouble the Home Secretary got herself into, the Prime Minister was determined to stand by her, even when it meant expending his own political capital. 'I'm not going to let the bastards get her,' he told one of his advisers, who'd reckoned she ought to be sacked over the Cabinet Office's report on her alleged bullying of civil servants. However, having given her two years in the job, it was maybe time for a change, and in the post-Covid, post-local-elections reshuffle of the summer of 2021, Priti's time was up. Making public the fact that she had advised the PM to shut the borders right at the start of the pandemic, but had been overruled, had been almost the last straw. So, a plan was hatched.

She would be the new party chairman. The PM knew how popular she was among party members. Her speeches not only found her own G-spot but that of the collective party membership. They may not have been the blood-curdling flog-and-birch-'em brigade of party conferences past, but party members appreciated a bit of red meat to chew on, and Priti Patel knew they liked it rare. Boris well remembered a letter he had been sent from twenty-year-old construction worker Harry, from Manchester. He knew that Priti could reach parts of the Conservative base that he could not. Whenever an adviser would start to criticise the Home Secretary, Boris would reach into his man bag and pull out Harry's letter and quote from it:

> When I was on my college course, I soon realised I was the only working-class Tory among a sea of Body Shop-bathed champagne socialists. During this time, I would use YouTube to watch debates, and I accidentally fell down the rabbit hole of Conservative supporters posting clips of Members of Parliament or Andrew Neil 'DESTROYING' Owen Jones. It was a thirty-second clip of Priti

Patel on *Question Time* making the case for capital punishment. I laughed and thought it was fantastic. Here was a Conservative Asian woman on the BBC saying the things that 'people like me' say. By the phrase people like me, what I really mean is working-class people.

On the morning of 23 May 2017, our community woke up to the news that Salman Abedi bombed our local arena. In the following weeks in our local boozer, I remember the talk. 'He and his brother should have been strung up!' To connect the dots between this incident and Priti Patel: it related to us; she was saying what we thought. Something other Conservative grandees would never say!

I was still in school when the European Union referendum happened. I wasn't old enough to vote, and at that time I couldn't care less what the decision was. I will never forget a moment that captivated me more than the BBC's *The Great Debate*. During the programme, there was a section where Priti was talking in a makeshift dugout for political experts. 'They take our money, they spend our money, they don't account to themselves fiscally,' said Patel. Quite persuasive to people who don't have much of it. She was incredibly convincing and looked strong. She has numerous nicknames in our household varying from the Pritt-Stick, the Pritster and some less generous given from my mother. The men in our house love her, and the women despise her. She does have support from working-class plebs like me.[2]

The falling snow was entrancing the Prime Minister. Even though he'd been PM for more than three years, he still had the same sense of wonderment he'd felt the first time he walked through the door of Chequers as PM in late July 2019. But he knew he wouldn't have many weekends to enjoy the comparative tranquillity offered by the house Sir Arthur Lee had donated to the nation in 1917. He might still be enjoying the job, but it was time to plan his succession – something few Prime Ministers ever got to do. Most left office after an election defeat or at a time not of their choosing. He had already served for longer than James Callaghan, Gordon Brown and – most importantly – Theresa May.

He flipped open his laptop and googled 'Prime+Minister+Length+Tenure'.

Eight Prime Ministers had served for between three and four years, but not a single one had served for between four and five years. That's settled, he thought to himself. 24 July 2023 it is. Four years. A good run. Out of Britain's fifty-five PMs, he'd be the twenty-sixth longest serving. Mid-table mediocrity, some would say. But any longer and Carrie would have a seizure.

Suddenly there was that sound again. Squirt. Squirt. Squirt.

He looked up. 'Bloody dog. Shoo, shoo,' were the words emanating from the prime ministerial mouth. Yet again Dilyn had cocked his leg against the bottom row of bookshelves. If anything settled his decision to plan his departure, it was Dilyn's dog piss.

There was a big part of him that imagined being an ex-Prime Minister might be considerably more fun than it had been actually being Prime Minister. It would certainly be more lucrative.

~

Boris kept his decision to himself for several weeks. He knew that the wider the circle of people in the know became, the more likely it was to leak. And sure enough, at the beginning of March, Tim Shipman splashed the story in the *Sunday Times* under the headline: 'Boris: I've had enough.' Shipman quoted several sources close to Boris who had told him of the plan to quit on the fourth anniversary of his coming to power. But he had laid his plans well. Apart from Carrie, he had only told four people. He'd said something different to each of them. At long last, he was able to identify the 'Chatty Rat' who had, over the previous two years, leaked various confidential stories to the papers.

A week later, he held a press conference and announced his imminent departure, triggering a three-and-a-half-month leadership contest. Seven candidates came forward initially, somewhat cruelly nicknamed 'the seven dwarves' by *The Sun*. The two leading candidates to start with were certainly the most vertically challenged – Priti Patel and Rishi Sunak. They were joined on the hustings by Michael Gove, who was clearly hoping it would be third time lucky. The hope was quickly extinguished when he struggled to get enough MPs to nominate him. Matt

Hancock, who had been summarily sacked by Johnson the previous year, pitched himself as the post-Johnson candidate; someone who would restore 'rigour' to government. Jeremy Hunt had long pondered another tilt but decided that he quite liked his work–life balance and announced that he would not be standing. Johnny Mercer, sacked by Boris Johnson in April 2021, was the first to throw his hat into the ring. He was, however the last to hand in his nomination papers, having struggled to get the requisite eight nominations.

Liz Truss became a media darling and portrayed herself as the reincarnation of Margaret Thatcher – but the new Iron Lady was found to be rather porous when it came to her policy platform. When Priti Patel launched a deliberate dig at her, saying, 'If you want another Thatcher, vote for the real thing, but beware of pale imitations…' it was like a dagger through the heart of the Truss campaign.

Gillian Keegan, who had joined the Cabinet the previous year as Education Secretary, was seen as the plucky outsider putting down a marker for the future. She knew she wouldn't win, but she raised her profile, and whoever won was certain to promote her. Job done.

In the first round of voting among MPs, it became clear who would be progressing to the final round, where Tory members would have their say. Rishi Sunak was ahead of Priti Patel but not by as much as the commentators had predicted. Priti knew that if she were within thirty or so votes of him, it was perfectly possible that she would triumph in the end. And she was: Sunak 133; Patel 102; Hancock 42; Truss 31; Keegan 30; Gove 22; Mercer 6.

There was no second round. All five bottom candidates dropped out, leaving Rishi Sunak and Priti Patel to go forward to the party's membership. They would have to duke it out all round the country before members started voting in the middle of June. There were ten regional hustings, in which Priti Patel found a new spontaneity and charm which had been largely absent in her media performances over the years.

She knew her party in a way that Rishi didn't. He hadn't had to work his way up the way she had. If the party had a G-spot, she knew where to find it. She knew Rishi would appeal to the party matriarchy. He'd want to come across as the perfect son-in-law they'd never had. But she could trump that. She had beliefs – lots of them – whereas no one really knew what Rishi believed in beyond self-promotion. He was bloody good at it, but he was a technocrat. There was no passion, no blood or thunder. And that was something Priti knew she could deliver to order.

All leadership campaigns have moments which define them. Cameron doing his 'look, no notes' act in 2005 was probably the most memorable, and Priti tasked her campaign team to come up with ideas for one of her own. And so it was that on the weekend ballot papers were sent out to members, Priti Patel fired her Exocet missile. She and Rishi had given the same seven-minute opening speech at each of the hustings so far; so much so that they could each recite each other's anecdotes word for word. This time, it would be different. The venue couldn't have been better. The Basildon Sporting Village had played host to David Amess's famous victory in 1992, which had set John Major on his way to his surprise victory – and these were Priti's people.

Rishi went on first and made his usual pitch – more houses, a green revolution, cuts in red tape, stand up to China, cut taxes. All very worthy but lacking a little excitement. The audience applauded more out of a sense of duty than of excitement. But he was the front-runner. Why take a risk? What a shame he hadn't consulted David Davis, to learn from his 'safety first' approach in 2005.

And then up stepped Priti. Literally. The organisers had thoughtfully put a box behind the lectern for the use of the two vertically challenged leadership contenders. Rishi's macho pride had led him to dispense with it, with the effect that the TV cameras could only make out the top of his head; his face was masked by the big black microphone muff. Priti didn't make the same mistake. Up she stepped and delivered her bombshell speech. She made the campaign promise which sent an electric surge through the men and women of south Essex in the audience. As she delivered the pledge, the audience rose to its feet, almost as one, and started cheering and fist-pumping. No one noticed the dozen or so party members who walked out. But the deed was done. The pledge was made. The detail could come later. Couldn't it?

~

She woke with a start. The bedside clock told her it was 5.59 a.m. Could it really have happened, or was it just a cruel dream? One way to find out. She reached for the remote control and zapped the TV on the wall at the end of the bed. 'You're watching GB News, the fair and balanced way to start your day,' intoned the voice of Andrew Neil, overlaid on a remix of 'Land of Hope and Glory'.

And then it hit her, as she took in the newsreader's first headline. 'The new Prime Minister, Priti Patel, is about to announce her first Cabinet appointments...' The new Prime Minister... So it was real.

She kicked off the duvet, walked into the bathroom and ran a bath. As she lay in the piping hot water, she began to think about the day ahead. She knew that her Cabinet appointments would set the tone for her premiership. Throughout her career she had been underestimated; now was the time to show them she meant business. She carefully picked up her mobile from the side of the bath, dialled Switch, the nickname in the building for the No. 10 switchboard. 'Get me John Redwood,' she said. 'That'll show them,' she thought. She smiled as she slipped back under the water.

It wasn't long before Redwood's appointment as the new Chancellor of the Exchequer began to slip out. *Tribune*'s Grace Blakeley took to her bed following the onset of a fit of the vapours; Owen Jones bashed out a furious column for the *Morning Star*, where he had eventually found a perch following his acrimonious departure from *The Guardian*; while a perplexed Robert Peston told the *ITV Lunchtime News* anchor, Stacey Dooley: 'I thought I'd seen it all.' Meanwhile, GB News decided it was time to play the national anthem for the third time that day.

On Sky News, the new political editor, Joe Pike, was struggling to cope with doing live reports on the *Breakfast* programme while simultaneously reading texts from those within government who purported to know what was in the mind of the Prime Minister. The truth was that there were only three people who did: the PM herself, her new Chief Whip, Gavin Williamson (restored to government for a fifth time), and her chief of staff, Darren Grimes.

The Fixed-Term Parliaments Act had been abolished in the autumn of 2021, with the support of the Labour Party. The Prime Minister knew she could call an election any time she wanted. Her dilemma was whether to do it very quickly or whether to let the parliament run to its natural end. Her priority was to signal to the electorate what they would be getting if they re-elected PM Priti, as the tabloids had dubbed her.

She wanted to signal the continuation of her 'tough on crime' agenda. Who better could there be to enforce that than the hardline, outspoken Leicestershire MP, Andrew Bridgen? Who better to build on the American alliance than the Washington-o-phile Dr Liam Fox as Foreign Secretary?

It really was out with the old and in with the new. Few survived the cull. And all the outgoing ministers were made to do the perp walk up Downing Street. There was no hiding place. Michael Gove emerged into the morning sunlight having had a particularly brutal interview without coffee. Wiping the tears from his eyes, he ignored the cameras and got into his ministerial car for the last time, only to be told by his driver that he'd been told not to take him home, and that he could walk. The humiliation was complete. 'That was for Boris,' the Prime Minister thought to herself.

Throughout the day, more and more appointments dripped out. Steve Baker as Business Secretary. Andrea Jenkyns as Education Secretary. Mark Francois at Health. Suella Braverman at Defence. 'It's the Return of Proper Conservatives', screamed a *Daily Telegraph* headline. 'The Return of the Living Dead', bleated *The Guardian*. 'Priti Woman Gets Into Gere', chirped *The Sun*, in a headline that had anyone under the age of fifty scratching their heads in bemusement.

Later that day it was time for the new Prime Minister to face her first Prime Minister's Questions. She knew that the whole country would be watching, and she also knew exactly what the Leader of the Opposition would be asking. She hadn't been in the job long but was slowly finding her feet after a difficult start to her leadership.

Although Jess Phillips had, uniquely, found ways of rattling Boris Johnson's nerve, she hadn't been able to impose her will on a party which was riven by factional infighting. The demise of Keir Starmer had been inevitable following Labour's disastrous performance in the 2022 elections and the revelation in *The Guardian* that he had been secretly meeting EU leaders to discuss how Britain might re-enter the union. The final straw was the replacement of Lisa Nandy as shadow Foreign Secretary with Lord Mandelson. 'Namby Pamby Replaces Nandy with Mandy' was the memorable headline in *The Sun*. The trade unions revolted; Unite announced they wouldn't be giving any more money to the Labour Party as long as Sir Keir remained leader, and several of the other big unions followed suit. The party teetered on the edge of bankruptcy.

Jess Phillips had emerged from the pack with a series of speeches and interview performances which had surprised not only party members but herself. Outwardly gobby and self-confident, Phillips had always suffered from imposter syndrome. But she was among the few to understand that the party needed to take a risk. Slowly and surely, Labour MPs, members and trade unions came to the same realisation. Even the right-of-centre media came to have a sneaking regard for the 'Brummie Mummy' who called a spade a shovel. Or sometimes a JCB.

As Phillips rose to ask her first question, the House fell silent. 'The Leader of the Opposition, Ms Jess Phillips,' roared Speaker Bryant.

'Mr Speaker, Sir, can I first of all congratulate the Right Honourable Lady on becoming Britain's third woman Prime Minister?' At that moment, she realised her mistake, as the Tory benches started chanting '3–0 to the Tory boys', highlighting the fact that there had yet to be a female Labour Prime Minister. Eventually, the barrage of noise dissipated. Phillips regained her composuure and rose again.

Mr Speaker, the Prime Minister bullied her way into No. 10. She sacked anyone in the previous Cabinet who had any semblance of competence – and, to be fair, there weren't many of those. She made promises to her party which she must have known she can't keep. And she insulted every immigrant who has come to this country and helped make it is what it is today – and yes, that includes her own parents. If I was her mam, I'd disown her. She's looking for one word. It's 'sorry'.